P9-APJ-105

Rural Planning of One County

WORCESTER COUNTY
MASSACHUSETTS

Rural Planning of One County

WORCESTER COUNTY MASSACHUSETTS

John Donald Black
Henry Lee Professor of Economics, Emeritus
Harvard University

and

George William Westcott
Professor of Agricultural Economics
University of Massachusetts

and Others

HARVARD UNIVERSITY PRESS
Cambridge · Massachusetts
1959

Distributed in Great Britain by
Oxford University Press • London

Library of Congress Catalog Card Number 59–11508

Printed in the United States of America

Preface

Twenty-two years ago, several of us at Harvard conceived the idea of conducting an experiment in the planning of the land use of a county. This was just at the time that a group in the United States Department of Agriculture who had been concerned with the administration of several of the new action programs — those of the Agricultural Adjustment Administration, the Soil Conservation Service, and the Farm Security Administration — and those administering the already established agencies concerned with agriculture, forestry, and land use generally, out in the states even more than in Washington, were coming to feel strongly the need for a better on-the-land integrating and unifying of their activities. Out of this situation in Washington and in the states presently evolved the Mount Weather Agreement between the Federal agencies and the states and the County Land-use Planning Program explained in Chapter 8 of this book. What the Harvard group finally did was to join in with a group at what is now the University of Massachusetts and set up an independent undertaking in county planning. This book is the report on this undertaking from 1936–37 when it was begun until the last Federal Census in 1954.

Worcester County in Massachusetts was chosen for this undertaking because of its location and because it is about median for southern New England in land types, in agriculture and forestry, in balance of systems of farming, and in balance of rural and urban.

Although the major responsibility for this undertaking has been that of the two persons accredited with this report and the institutions engaging their services, other agencies have contributed importantly to it and several other persons have shared in the writing, as will be indicated chapter by chapter, and many others in the research and analysis. The most help from Federal sources was received from the Forest Service, the Soil Survey (now in the Soil Conservation Service), the Soil Conservation Service, and the Farm Management and Farm Population and Rural Life branches of what was then the Bureau of Agricultural Economics.

The staff of the Harvard Forest at Petersham were prime movers in the initiation of this project and all of the early forestry or woodland analysis was done by its staff, under the direction of Allan Cline, now of the United States

Forest Service. Dr. Ernest Gould of the Harvard Forest has reviewed and adapted this early analysis as necessary and contributed much to its later stages.

Almost from the beginning, this undertaking has been affiliated closely with the Seminar in Land-use Planning and Conservation of Harvard's Graduate School of Public Administration. It was the original intention to include in this undertaking a review and revision of the planning analysis of most of the towns in meetings with groups of officials and citizens of the towns. The nearest that it was possible to come to this, because of the pressure of other duties on the leaders of this undertaking and on the Massachusetts Extension Service, was the series of meetings, reported in Chapter 20, in the six Sections into which Worcester County is divided in this report. These were arranged jointly with the Worcester County Extension Service and members of the Seminar under the leadership of Dr. Ayers Brinser, a member of the Seminar Staff, and now its director. Dr. Brinser has in addition contributed much to the guidance of the undertaking and revision of this report.

Harvard University's part in this undertaking other than much of the Harvard Forest's part of it has been financed over the years as follows:

The Rockefeller Foundation through its grant to the Harvard University Committee on Research in the Social Sciences;

The Carnegie Corporation through its grant to the Seminar in Land Use and Conservation;

The Graduate School of Public Administration through its support of the Seminar.

Although of the final writing of this report George Westcott did only Chapters 7, 8, 21 and 22, he and his collaborators and the staff of the University of Massachusetts had a large hand in the field work and its detailed supervision and in the assembly of the planning data and its analysis.

The Conservation Foundation of New York City and the Ford Foundation contributed to the support of the Seminar in the three years ending in 1953, and Resources for the Future of the Ford Foundation has been contributing to it since. But these were not contributions directly to this project. A more nearly accurate statement is that the project furnished case material for use in the Seminar.

This set of acknowledgments would be grossly incomplete if it did not report the enthusiastic cooperation which the workers on this project have at all times received from the Extension Service staff of Worcester County. It is our earnest hope that they will feel this report rewards them in part for their effort and helps them toward the goals they are nobly seeking.

John D. Black
George W. Westcott

June, 1959

CONTENTS

LIST OF TABLES

LIST OF FIGURES

Rural Planning of One County

WORCESTER COUNTY
MASSACHUSETTS

CHAPTER 1

The Undertaking

This book is the report of an effort to develop a plan for future land use. Although it is restricted to the study of a particular county — Worcester — the authors believe it may be of interest to a wider public because groups in counties throughout the country are concerning themselves more and more with such planning as a guide to future action.

The idea of the plan for Worcester County was conceived twenty years ago and the task was at least half completed before the war. Since that time the work on this project has been interrupted by other activities. Also, land use and related circumstances have changed greatly during the twenty years. What follows is in considerable measure a running account of the planning activities in the county of the groups concerned; the original objectives, although they have not been lost sight of, have not been altogether realized as yet. It has seemed best to those concerned to report at this time on the progress made and let the final objectives come to fruition in the next decade or so; reporting the results to date should assist importantly to this end.

OBJECTIVES

This is a planning project, but its purpose has not been simply to make a plan. Instead, it has been to help the people of Worcester County to use its land and related resources in such a way as to live more abundantly from them. This means not only helping the people directly, but also helping public servants, ranging all the way from the town selectmen (so-called in New England) and other town officials and public servants, to the county extension service staff, the local soil conservation district staff, and the like, to the Secretary of Agriculture and department heads in Washington, in such a way that their services will be more helpful to the people of Worcester

County. Plans are useful only as they make the efforts of those using them more effective.

At the beginning of this undertaking in 1936–37, and ever since, however, the groups working upon it have had in mind a second and broader objective than helping the people of Worcester County. They have hoped that by testing certain planning procedures that to them seemed fitted to the needs of county farm and land-use planning they might determine wherein they were and were not so fitted, and thus furnish valuable guidance to future planning. This report is written with the broader implications constantly in mind.

APPROACH AND METHOD

It is true, of course, that the plans or programs that have evolved from this planning analysis, and even the alternatives for operating-unit organization and land use that have been tested here, are probably not the ones that would be tested for most other counties or comparable area units. Instead, the value for other areas is that this analysis may suggest ways of going about the task of assembling the data needed for resource planning, and of choosing alternative courses of action. Perhaps its most effective use will be to provide an example of how public officials, specialists in land-use management, technicians, and the people of a county can work together.

In no sense is a particular plan or program developed for Worcester County or some part of it proposed as a "model" for other counties. Not even the analysis is intended to serve as a model. It is instead a case study and trial of particular analytical procedures.

It is true that in general some one plan is finally chosen to be carried out in the particular unit analyzed, whether it be a farm, a forest holding, a section of a town called an "area" in this report, a town (called township, precinct, and so forth in other parts of the United States), a conservation district, or the county as a whole. But this particular plan is chosen only by general agreement after a process of analyzing various other promising plans, and after discussion of these by the family or group most concerned. As will become clear later, moreover, this final stage of general agreement was not carried through to the end in the case of the county, nor even of most of the towns. This is the major uncompleted part of the undertaking.

It will be apparent from what has been said that the planning analysis is limited very largely to the rural areas of Worcester County. The cities and their role in the economy of Worcester County are by no means ignored, but they are mostly taken as given and no planning is done for them. They are not, however, assumed to be static. Instead, their future growth and development has been projected and the rural land use of the county is fitted in with them as they are expected to be in the future. If this limitation had not been placed on the scope of this study, a planning analysis like the one worked out for dairy farming, for example, would have been needed for each of the several score of manufacturing industries in the county, and similarly for the various urban lines of trade as well as for each urban community as a whole.

Even for some of the rural land uses, such as recreation, water supply, and highways, it has not been possible to analyze alternatives in the way it has been done for agricultural and forestry uses.

This undertaking makes the county the unit of planning. It is the fourth in a series of four analyses of rural New England. The first encompassed the whole of New England as a region and its results were published in *The Rural Economy of New England, A Regional Study,* by John D. Black.[1] The second is limited to a single town and is published under the title, *Planning One Town — Petersham, A Hill Town in Massachusetts,* by John D. Black and Ayers Brinser.[2] Another town, Hardwick, is analyzed in almost equal detail in Chapter 11 of this book. The first book is so comprehensive that only the broad outlines of alternatives could be analyzed. Detailed analysis had to be limited to representative samples. The second book analyzes such details as the boundaries of land-use areas or zones, zoning ordinances, and roads, schools, and other public services. The third, *Planning for Successful Dairying in New England,* by Richard G. Wheeler and John D. Black, deals with the economy of the use of land in New England as a whole by its major agricultural industry, dairy farming.[3] The present, fourth, analysis is intermediate in detail between the first and second. Closely related to these four analyses is a fifth, *Economic Analysis of Farm Forest Operating Units,* by Solon L. Barraclough and Ernest M. Gould, Jr., in which a selection of nine woodland-dairy farms in the farm-forest margin of New England are analyzed and data are assembled for use in woodland management analysis.[4]

Something needs to be said at the outset about the county as a planning unit. In the United States generally, the county is more likely than any other governmental unit to be the unit around which planning can be effectively organized. First of all, most of the national programs for agri-

[1] Cambridge, Mass., Harvard University Press, 1950, 796 pages.
[2] Cambridge, Mass., Harvard University Press, 1952, 96 pages.
[3] Cambridge, Mass., Harvard University Press, 1955, 329 pages.
[4] Harvard Forest Bulletin No. 26, 1955, 145 pages.

culture take the county as the unit in which to carry out their actual operations. Most of the state acts providing for soil conservation districts make the county the actual administrative unit. The agricultural extension service does likewise. Except in much of New England, local governmental functions are performed mainly either by counties or by municipalities.

It is not by chance that the county has become the key unit for major public functions. In an area about the size of an average county in the United States the public servants are near enough to the problems being met and to the people to see them and deal with them at first hand without having more concerns than they can attend to adequately nor too few to keep them busy. It is also about the size of territory within which a sufficient community of interest for unified local action is likely to exist. The truth of this statement is made apparent in the occasional counties that are overlarge, and in the many more counties in the South that are too small for economical administration, especially since modern transportation and highways have been developed.

For these same reasons as well as because of governmental organization, the county proves to be a good unit for any planning analysis that gets down to dealing with actual problems and people. Local leaders from about this large an area can be brought together for conferences and common action. It is interesting in this connection that Worcester County, which is twice the size of most New England counties, is organized into three soil conservation districts.

The reader may wonder why the town has tended to remain a more important political unit than the county in much of New England. A major reason is that the villages and small cities are usually not separately incorporated in New England, so that both the urban and rural governmental activities are performed by one administration, and the urban activities may be much the larger. Even in New England, however, the county has been gaining rapidly in importance since organization of the agricultural extension work on this basis and, later, the AAA and other national programs.

The actual area planning in Chapter 11 and following chapters begins with the town as a unit and continues to use the town as a means of local identification. But Chapters 12 to 17 group the sixty towns in the Worcester County into six blocks or "Sections" designated as A to F.

The reader must not gather from the foregoing that the planning analysis in this undertaking is mainly from the standpoint of the public activities relating to land use. On the contrary, the key principle of the analysis is that *all land is utilized in some form of operating unit,* either private or public, and much more often the former. Accordingly the farm is made the basic unit of analysis for all land in agricultural use, and the forest holding for all land in forest use. Chapters 9 and 10 lay the foundations for the subsequent analysis in these terms.

A corollary of the foregoing is that *no task of land-use planning is complete until all the land can be fitted into some kind of an operating unit,* either private or public.

The project planners started out with the objective of dividing an area or political unit like a town into area sub-units, each of which would include the parts of the town *for which a common set of major adjustments was agreed upon as needed.* Thus, such an area sub-unit might include the rough stony largely timbered area in the northwest corner of a certain town. Or another sub-unit might consist of dairy farms with small blocks of rough stony woodland interspersed, for which the needed adjustments are mainly pasture and forage improvement, raising of more of the herd replacements, fencing to keep the cattle out of some promising young woodland stands, and a limited amount of improvement cutting. Soils and topography and other physical features usually determine the boundaries of these areas, but other factors such as location, access to markets, and ownership of the land may also be important. In the planning analysis for the town of Petersham this objective was carried to the stage of dividing the town into seven zones as follows:[5]

> areas already in public forest, water supply, or similar uses;
> areas now in full-scale farms and to remain so;
> areas now in part-time farms capable of being made into full-scale farms;
> areas in part-time farms and to remain so;
> areas to go into new part-time farms;
> areas in residential farms and to remain so;
> areas to go into new residential farms.

This objective has thus far been attained, however, only in part in most of the County. There has been substituted for it in large measure an area grouping of the land according to its topography, stoniness, soils, cover and the like, and combinations of these.

Finally in this book a distinction is made between a *plan* and a *program,* the latter referring to the precedures followed in implementing and carrying out the plan.

[5] See Figure 33 in Chapter 12 of this book.

HISTORY OF THE PROJECT

The Worcester County project in county land-use planning was initiated under the following circumstance. Mr. Ward Shepard, at that time acting as Director of the Harvard Forest, felt strongly the need for integrating the types of woodland management that the Harvard Forest had been developing on hardwood stands following old-field pine, and on mixed stands on land that had never been cleared, into the general pattern of land use in the surrounding area. He therefore began discussing with the senior author of this book, as Chairman of the Committee on Research in the Social Sciences of Harvard University, and with the Massachusetts Agricultural Extension Service and Experiment Station, the Soil Conservation Service, and the Forest Service, the possibilities of a joint county-wide undertaking in land-use planning. The United States Department of Agriculture had become very conscious by this time that the activities of the several federal agencies that had been set up since 1933 were overlapping each other more or less and also some of the work of the state agencies. Furthermore the relations between the United States Department of Agriculture agencies and some of the state agencies had become somewhat strained as a result of dismissing the state agricultural extension directors as state AAA administrators in the summer of 1937. Mr. M. L. Wilson, then Under-Secretary of Agriculture, asked the senior author of this book in June 1937 to work with an interagency committee that he had created and to help draft a plan for coordinating the activities of the different agencies relating to land use.

What followed immediately was the establishment in the United States Department of Agriculture of an Office of Land-Use Coordination under Mr. Milton Eisenhower. This Office was then asked by the Massachusetts-Harvard group to join forces with it in a Worcester County project that would test out different procedures and develop methodology for county land-use planning. This request was refused, but the different agencies and departments in the USDA approached separately all agreed to furnish personnel to assist with the project, or to direct their county staffs to provide needed information. These included the Soil Conservation Service, the Agricultural Adjustment Administration, the Forest Service, and the Bureau of Agricultural Economics.

The reason Mr. Eisenhower refused to cooperate was that his Office was in the midst of formulating what came to be known as the Mount Weather Agreement (July 1938) with the states under which a general nationwide program of federal-state collaboration in land-use planning was authorized.

Eventually all the states but Pennsylvania and California signed a contract in line with this Agreement. As outlined in Chapter 8, following the Mount Weather Agreement the USDA proceeded to develop a comprehensive nationwide program of county land-use planning under the leadership of the Bureau of Agricultural Economics.

There was a major difference between what Secretary Wilson's special committee recommended as procedure for the Office of Land-Use Coordination and what was actually developed. The special committee proposed beginning by organizing several "planning teams." Each would be composed of staff members from the different federal agencies or departments and each would go out first into a single county and join forces with a similar team from the state, and learn by actually doing how to plan for land use within a county. These federal teams would then move into other states and the state teams into other counties in their own states. The Massachusetts-Harvard group thought of Worcester County as fitting into this program. The USDA, however, called for beginning work in all the states at once according to procedures spelled out in "Work Outline No. 1." Chapter 8 relates what happened to this program while it lasted, from 1938 to 1942, and indicates the lessons to be learned from this experience.

In the country at large, the committees set up in the counties to function under the Mount Weather Agreement were called County Land-Use Planning Committees. They were absorbed into the County War Boards during World War II, and, in Massachusetts, were called Rural War Action Committees. In 1946 the committees were reconstituted under various names in the different counties of Massachusetts, all functioning under a Massachusetts Agricultural Program Board, on which were represented all the federal and state agencies concerned. The county committees were moderately active at the start but by 1949 only four or five of them were functioning. Subsequently, with the outbreak of the Korean War, the state committee and the county committees became the state and county Agricultural Mobilization Committees.

When the actual field work on the Massachusetts-Harvard project was begun in the summer of 1937, it was decided to operate at three levels of intensity in the county. The most intensive work was to be in the town of Hardwick, and less intensive work in nine other towns distributed over the County to represent different land-use situations. The planning for the remaining fifty towns was to be based in part on what was learned from analysis of individual farms and forest holdings in the ten towns. The group was greatly assisted in this field work and analysis by extensive mapping of roads, farm locations, land use, and vegetative cover that had already been done by the Massachusetts State Planning Board and by Clark University at Worcester, Massachusetts. In the fall of 1939, the Planning Board devoted one issue of its *A Planning Forum* to Worcester County. At that time nineteen towns in Worcester County had planning boards, eight of these having been set up under Chapter 211 of the Massachusetts Act providing for planning boards.

The field work was largely completed in December 1938, and the analysis for all sixty towns was well under way when the war came in 1941, and it was decided that other activities were of more immediate importance to the war effort. In 1942–43, however, the detailed analysis of the farms in the ten towns was used in a study that was published as *Farm Adjustments for Maximum Wartime Production in Worcester County, Massachusetts,* by Francis J. Schadegg, then on the staff of the Bureau of Agricultural Economics, with the assistance of Richard G. Wheeler, then also on the BAE staff.

The nationwide county land-use planning program initiated under the Mount Weather Agreement between the USDA and the State Land-Grant Colleges had led to the organization of what were called "Rural Policy Committees" in the counties of Massachusetts. In addition, "Rural Policy" or "Country Life Committees" were formed in many of the towns. A total of thirteen of these in Worcester County prepared and published in 1940 and 1941 mimeographed reports of their findings with supporting materials. Another four prepared and released brief preliminary first drafts consisting largely of descriptive materials. Figure 1 shows the towns for which the first draft (X^1) and second draft (X^2) of the Country Life Committee reports were prepared. Those that were analyzed intensively in this project are marked by a circle (○). Eight of them are the same towns. Figure 1 groups the sixty towns into the six Sections A to F which will be the subjects of Chapters 12 to 17.

In 1947–48, a group of 25 dairy farms were selected from those analyzed in the ten towns and included in the 241 New England dairy farms in the Harvard Dairy Farming Project supported by the Charles H. Hood Dairy Foundation. It was possible in this way to check the progress made on these farms and to revise the analysis to fit changes in technology, in family plans, in milk-feed ratios, and the like.

It was also decided at that time to prepare the New England-wide study for publication first, and to wait until the 1950 census data became available by towns before completing the Worcester County study. In the meantime.

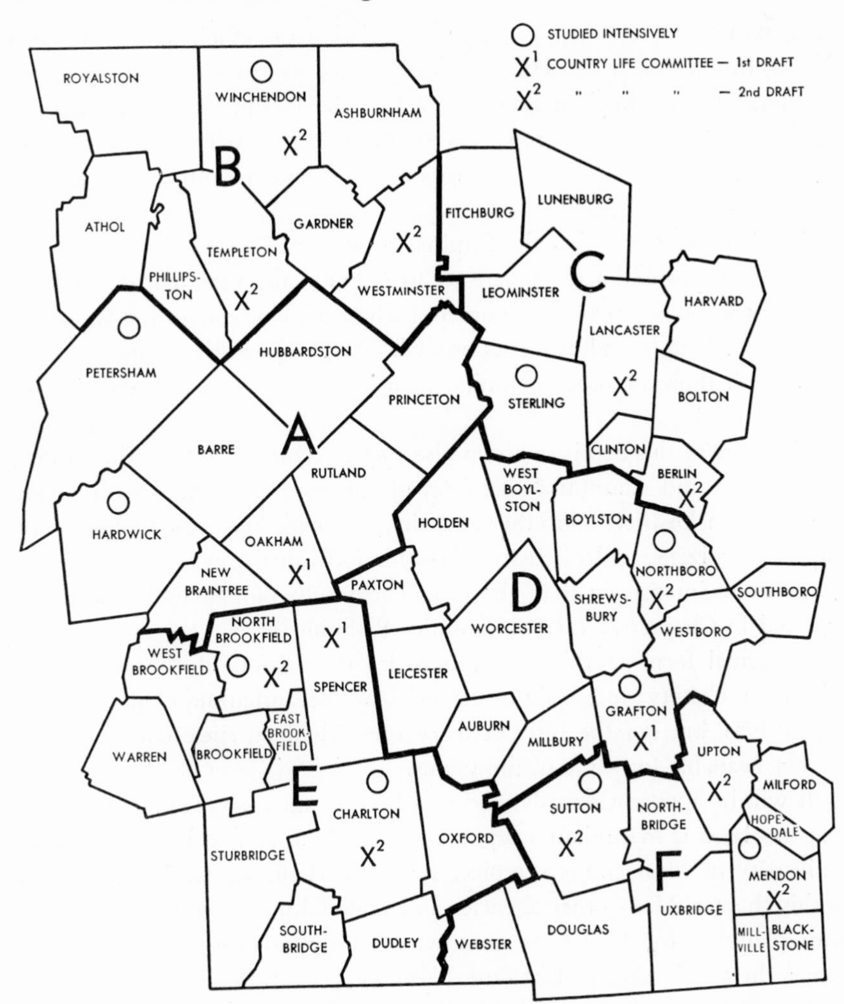

Figure 1. ***The sixty towns in Worcester County, the sixteen for which Country Life Committee Reports were prepared, and the ten studied intensively in this project; also the boundaries of Sections A to F.***

the Seminar in Land Use and Conservation in the Graduate School of Public Administration, beginning first in the fall of 1952, has devoted considerable attention to Worcester County's land-use problems as case study analyses. One outcome of this was the report on the town of Petersham already mentioned. Members of the Seminar from the Department of Regional Planning in the School of Design of Harvard University found Petersham of special interest because of its problems in public finance and the impact upon it of the industrial population of Athol. The Petersham Village Improvement Society specifically requested that a study be made in Petersham and made a small grant to assist in the study. This Society presented one copy of this report to each family in the Town, and a series of meetings was arranged at which its findings and recommendations were fully discussed.

Another result was that the Seminar group in 1953 organized itself into six small groups and each undertook to map out the sub-area units in one of the six sections shown in Figure 1, analyze the alternatives for each, and indicate the land-use adjustments needed. The results of this work are combined with those of other planning analyses in Chapters 12 to 17 in this book.

Members of this Seminar group also met at central points in the County with officers and committee members of the local Extension Service, Soil Conservation Districts and other agencies, and with local town officials and interested citizens, and discussed plans for individual towns, for six of the towns more intensively than the rest. The results of this undertaking are reported in Chapter 20 on "Community Planning."

The final form of this report includes recognition of the changes in Worcester County since 1950 as reported by the agricultural census in the fall of 1954, but not the full details of these changes, since data by towns are not available for some of the towns.

It will be apparent already, and will become more so as we go forward, that this book is more than a report of the specific Harvard University and University of Massachusetts project in county land-use planning outlined in this chapter. Many other agencies and undertakings have been concerned with planning for Worcester County. Most outstanding of these was of course the whole County Land-use Planning Program of the United States Department of Agriculture collaborating with the states from 1938 to 1941, as outlined in Chapter 8. The Country Life Committees (Rural Policy) set up in many of the towns were part of the Massachusetts contribution to the movement. But before these got under way the Massachusetts State Planning Board in a Works Progress Administration project had mapped the land use and cover in detail for all the towns in Worcester County and classified the land according to its suitability for agriculture. Professor David Rozman of the Massachusetts State College played a major role in the execution of this project. The maps resulting provided the basis for the maps in Chapters 11 to 17. First, the Wheeler-Schadegg wartime project and then in 1948–49 the further analysis of twenty-six of the dairy farms by Dr. Herbert Brown in connection with the Hood Dairy Foundation project, provided follow-up for the original farm planning in 1937–38. The results of these other undertakings are used freely in this final report. This book therefore is a report of much planning experience besides that immediately a part of this project. It should be read as a report of the whole planning experience as well as of the particular project outlined in this chapter.

CHAPTER 2

The County

Worcester County makes up the central fifth of Massachusetts. It stretches all of the forty-seven miles from the New Hampshire to the Connecticut–Rhode Island boundaries, and is forty-one miles wide at its maximum width. Figure 2 shows its geographic relationships to its surrounding area. Its boundaries include 970,240 acres of land. Its largest city, Worcester, had a population of 203,490 in 1950, and Fitchburg, Leominster, and Gardner had populations of 42,690, 24,075, and 19,580, respectively. The 1950 Census of Occupations reported only 2.3 percent of its workers as having agriculture as their major occupation, as compared with 50.4 percent for manufacturing, 15.8 percent for wholesale and retail trades, 15.4 percent for private and public services combined, and 4.5 percent for construction. Worcester County is therefore very much an industrial county.

In several respects, Worcester County represents pretty well the three southern New England states. Its density of population is 360 per square mile compared with 535 for the three states; and its 2.3 percent employed in agriculture compares with their 2.1 percent. Its land surface is also about average as to roughness and stoniness. Like the rest of southern New England, it has limited areas of relatively level land.

THE LAND

The nearest approach to a mountain in Worcester County is Mount Wachusett. It rises a mere 2,015 feet, in the town of Princeton; but this peak towers above its surroundings. The western two thirds of the County is part of the Eastern Highland of southern New England, with much of the land over 1,000 feet above sea level. The eastern edge is mostly less than 300 feet above sea level. Running down through the County north to south from Fitchburg through Worcester to Douglas is a considerably smoothed and

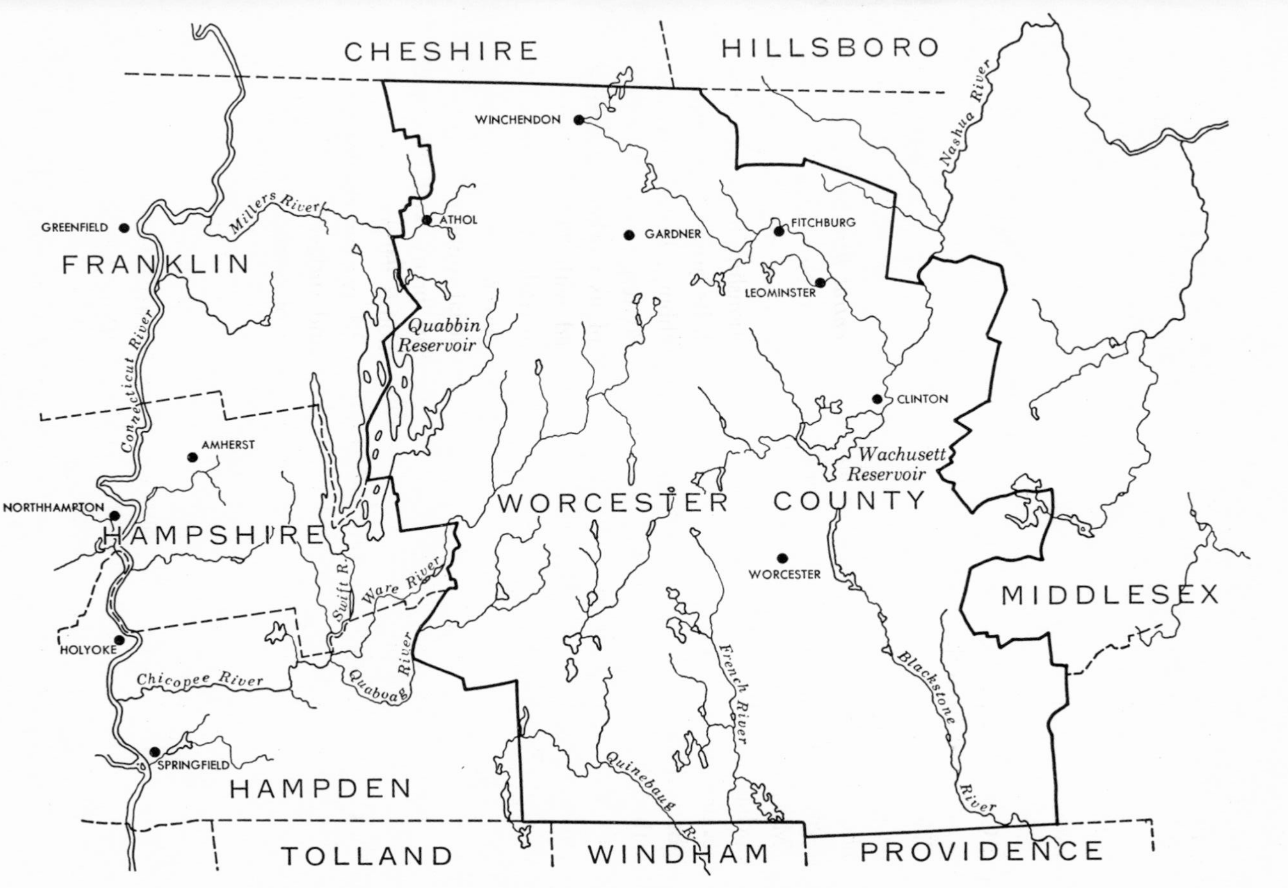

Figure 2. *Worcester County and its immediate geographic environment.*

broken-down escarpment facing eastward. The land surface also slopes generally to the south, the difference in elevation between Ashburnham on the north and Dudley on the south being around 500 feet. The western two tiers of towns generally slope gently westward, with drainage into the Connecticut River. The southeast towns drain through the Blackstone River into Narragansett Bay, and northeast towns through the Nashua River northeastwardly into the Merrimack River. The general topographic effect, therefore, is that of a rounded-off ridge somewhat east of the north-south axis of the County that slopes gently southward, with slopes and drainage to the east and west from this ridge.

The 1950 Census reported 38.9 percent of the land of the County in farms. The parallel figure for 1940 was 42.1 percent. The rest of the land is in timber, except as it is used for cities and villages, for highways, airports, and railways, and for rural residences and recreation.

Much of the reported decline in land in farms from 1940 to 1950 was due to a change in the census definition of a farm. From 1925 to 1940, any three acres or more of land under one management was called a farm if only very slight agricultural operations were conducted upon it, and any holding of less than three acres if its value of agricultural products totaled $250 or more. In the 1945 Census the definition of a farm was tightened a little — the enumerators were told not to include places of three acres or more unless they had three acres or more of cropland or pasture and these three acres produced $150 or more of farm products. The census definition of a farm was tightened still more in 1950. A minimum value of products of $150 *exclusive of home gardens* was set for places of three acres or more, and of $150 for sales of products if less than three acres of land of any description. This had the effect of reducing the number of farms counted both above and below the three-acre division point. The enumerators were, however, told to bring in a schedule for every place with three acres or more of land whether or not it was considered a farm and for places of less than three acres if they had 100 or more of poultry, or three hives of bees, etc., and the elimination of units not meeting the standard was done in Washington rather than by the local enumerators as in earlier censuses. A total of 35,200 Massachusetts schedules returned by the enumerators were classified as nonfarm in the editing done in the offices of the Bureau of the Census, but only 4,800 of these had any farming other than home gardening.

The effect of this change in census procedure on number of farms reported was very drastic in areas like southern New England with many part-time and residential farms. For Massachusetts as a whole, the number of farms appeared to decline from 31,897 in 1940 to 22,220 in 1950, or 30 percent. For Worcester County, the decline was from 6,505 to 4,234, or 35 percent. Of this decline of 2,261 farms in actual number, 711 were in farms of under 10 acres, and 771 were in farms of from 10 to 29 acres, but all of the size groups up to 220 acres and over showed some decline. The rule of $150 exclusive of home gardens may have excluded in 1950 for the first time in New England an appreciable number of holdings of a hundred acres or more of woodland and only a few acres of pasture or hay. Part of the decrease, however, was obviously due to the combining of farms. Some of this appears in the actual increase of 54 in number of farms of 220 acres or over; more of it in the smaller decreases in the size groups above 140 acres.

The decrease in acreage of land in farms from 1940 to 1950 was, however, only 13 percent, and much of this was surely due to exclusion of places with much woodland and very little agriculture. It was the smaller farms mostly that were counted out in 1950.

The foregoing is all in terms of comparison of 1950 with 1940. What about 1945? In spite of a slight tightening of the definition of a farm in 1945, the census of that year reported 671, or 11 percent, more farms than in 1940. Ever since the first quinquennial farm census in 1925, these mid-decade censuses have shown an apparent increase in number of farms in southern New England and similar territory. The reason for this is that no occupation census has been taken along with the farm census in these years. If, in the regular decennial censuses, the head of the household reports a nonfarm occupation as his "principal occupation," the enumerators tend not to follow up with the questions on the farm schedule. In the five-year censuses between, there is no such check. Accordingly, the percentage of land in farms was reported as increasing from 1940 to 1945 in spite of the tightening of the census definition of a farm.

The new techniques of enumeration introduced in 1950 and continued in 1954 appear to have checked completely the over-counting of farms in the mid-decade years. They may indeed have gone somewhat too far in the other direction. The 1954 Census reported declines from 1950 and 1945 as shown in the tabulation.

	Decline from 1950	*Decline from 1945*
Number of farms	22 percent	50 percent
Land in farms	11 percent	29 percent
Cropland in farms	8 percent	6 percent

The decline in actual cropland appears to have been small, and could well have happened.

THE CLIMATE

As for climate, Worcester County, like the rest of southern New England, is warmer than the same 42° latitudes in southern Wisconsin and northern Iowa in the Midwest. But this extra warmth is all and more in the wintertime. The summers are as cool as those of northern Wisconsin and Minnesota. These differences are caused of course by the fact that Massachusetts is near the ocean and the Midwest is far inland. Worcester County averages about 4° colder than Boston in the winter months, altitude being a factor in this, but it is slightly warmer in summer.

The average date of the first killing frost in the fall in most of Worcester County is a little after October 1, but it is a week or two earlier on the highest ridges and in the valleys with poor air drainage. The companion date in the spring is May 10. This gives a growing season for a frost-sensitive crop like corn of around 160 days. Frost-resistant grasses have a growing season 40 to 50 days longer than this.

The fruits that can be grown on sites with good air drainage in Worcester County are more nearly like those of the lake-shore fruit-growing district of southwestern Michigan than like those of southern Wisconsin.

The rainfall of the County averages around 43 inches, with a little more of it in the summer than in the winter months, in contrast with that on the coast, which is heavier in the winter, and with that in the Midwest, which is much heavier in the summer. Iowa, with a third less annual rainfall, has several inches more of it in June, July, and August. Still, southern New England has fewer drought periods than Iowa, and more of the days are cloudy, with the result that pastures are greener than those in Iowa in July and August as well as in the late fall.

The other side of the coin is that curing hay is more difficult in southern New England than in the Midwest. The rain comes at more frequent intervals and is more irregular. One of the reasons for the irregularities of the weather in this section of the country is that it is at the meeting ground of two storm systems, those that cross the country from west to east and those that come up the Atlantic Coast. The latter are less frequent and do not always reach as far inland as Worcester County. The hurricane of 1938 surely did so, and also one early in the century before. The flood accompanying the 1938 hurricane, and three others since 1927, did considerable damage; but history records no other period with as frequent floods.

The winter rainfall, or more often snowfall, contributes ground water for forests and orchards even if it does not help field crops much. As we shall learn in detail later, the soils are of porous types well suited to tree growth. As a result, all of New England was covered with trees when the white man came. Birch, beech, maple, and hemlock were the dominant types in the primeval forest of the Worcester County part of New England, with a verging toward the oak and hickory of the next forest zone to the south. White pine grew on the sandier sites. The forests that followed the first logging contained much more oak, and those that developed in the old fields and pastures as they wore out were mostly pine. By 1890, the woodlands of central New England were dominantly white pine.

THE AGRICULTURE

The agriculture that is likely to be practiced under the foregoing circumstances has the following general characteristics. (1) It is devoted very largely to supplying the urban population with its fluid milk, fresh vegetables and fruits in season, fresh-killed poultry, and nearby hennery eggs. (2) It is combined with a good deal of off-farm work in urban employments. (3) It runs strongly to pasture for dairy herds and to hay and other forage. (4) It could combine a good bit of farm forestry with the dairy farming, especially if the timber stands were under good management, but at the present stage of forestry in the United States the woodland in such an area is likely to be in unusually poor condition because the young hardwoods were cut for fuel, fence posts, and the like at an early age, leaving mainly a poor growth of stump-sprout trees to follow, and the market for fuelwood and other products of such stands is now weak.

Actually, the sales of crops in Worcester County — mostly fruits and vegetables — were only 16 percent of the total farm sales in 1949. Of the sales of livestock and livestock products, 38 percent were of poultry and poultry products, and nearly all the rest were from the dairy herds. The sales of forest products from farms reported in 1949 were only $54,000 for the whole County.

Of the cropland harvested in 1949, making up only 22 percent of the land in farms, 82 percent was in hay and 5 percent in corn.

The foregoing inventory may give an impression of relatively little agriculture in Worcester County. In the census ranking of counties by sales of all agricultural products in 1945, however, Worcester County was sixty-seventh from the top. The County is large, it is true, but not much larger than an average midwestern or western county. A more important consideration is that a sizable part of the output is based on poultry and dairy feeds shipped in from outside New England. If a measure of agricultural output comparable with "value added by manufacture" in industry could be devised, Worcester County would have ranked much lower. It was not in the first hundred in the Special Report on "Ranking Agricultural Counties" of the 1950 and 1954 censuses. This is only in minor part because of the elimination of well on toward two thousand places with little agriculture and the 13-percent decrease in land in farms from 1945 to 1950. The total sales of farm products reported in Worcester County in 1949 were 12 percent higher than in 1944; in the United States, 36 percent higher. Under several other measures of production, however, Worcester County ranked down from the top only as follows in 1949 and in 1954:

	Rank	
	1949	1954
Value of dairy products sold	32	48
Milk cows on farms	86	100+
Whole milk sold	86	94
Sales of poultry and poultry products	24	34
Chickens on farms 4 months old and over	19	28
Value of chickens sold	26	48
Value of eggs sold	16	27
Apples harvested	19	34
Apple trees of all ages	27	34
Nursery and greenhouse products	56	80
Fruits and nuts sold	80	100+

It will be observed that the decline in the ranking for Worcester County was about the same in all lines of production. No doubt this decline is associated with Worcester County's very large dependence upon local market outlets, combined with a general tendency for products of other areas to invade eastern markets.

HISTORY

Settlement began in Worcester County well before 1700. As early as 1733, Petersham on the western border of the county was granted to seventy-one proprietors and settlement followed at once. Northboro on the eastern edge was split off from Marlboro, now in Middlesex County, in 1717 and made a separate town, but Marlboro had been incorporated in 1660.

The early agriculture was almost entirely self-sufficing. The families grew wheat, corn, potatoes, a little buckwheat and flax, and a scanty supply of vegetables and fruits for family use, and feed for the cattle, hogs, sheep, and poultry that produced their meat, butter and cheese, eggs, and wool. The villages had few industries in the early years and these provided a living for only a few families. A small surplus from the farms in time found a market after a slow haul by ox team to Boston to provision the ships of the growing commerce of the port of Boston and lesser seaports. Land development began on the high uplands rather than in the valleys. The valley sides were steep and stony. The early villages were all on the uplands until the factories began to move them into the valleys. The early manufacturing of New England made use of the waterpower on the streams at the fall line and farther inland. The number of textile mills increased rapidly during the first half of the nineteenth century.

The building of the railroads produced another great readjustment. Manufacturing developed rapidly in the villages along the railroads and declined slowly elsewhere. Before the railroads came, the village of Sutton in Worcester County was much larger than Worcester. It was on the main line of coach travel from Boston to New York. Still later, with the use of coal and steam power, the seaport towns had advantage in location, and cities like Fall River and New Bedford became important textile centers. The final stage was the development of hydro-electric power, which gave some advantage to location on the large rivers like the Connecticut and the Merrimack.

In spite of the lack of outside markets, however, agriculture developed rapidly in Worcester County from 1730 on. At its peak, fully 80 percent of its land must have been in farms, and all but the rough stony lands were in cropland or pasture. Indeed, much of the stony land was in rock-strewn pasture. The reason for this early development was in large part the growth of the farm population. Many farm families had two or three sons who wanted farms of their own.

In time, however, the expansion of industry gave some of the sons jobs off the farms. It also provided more of an off-farm market for farm products. Also, some of the sons early began moving on to the new frontiers, both northward into New Hampshire and Vermont and westward to New York. Some of the towns in southern New England actually began to decline in population well before 1800. Most of the Worcester County towns reached their agricultural peak between 1800 and 1830.

Another circumstance also figured in these declines. The virgin timberland soils had relatively low fertility of the kind that is needed for growing crops. Trees can grow from the minerals of the subsoil; annual crops require a topsoil with considerable humus. The forests of New England produced very little humus. Hence yields of wheat, corn, and other grains declined after several years unless manure was applied liberally and crops were rotated with grass. The manure supplies were seldom adequate, and much of the manure was wasted. Consequently the practice was followed of letting the "worn-out" fields become pasture land and clearing new fields for crops. When all of their possible cropland had been cleared and exploited, many of the families moved to new land on the frontier; or at least the young men in the family did so, leaving the parents to eke out the rest of their days on the old farm. In the meantime, the pastures deteriorated and in time began to fill in with brush and trees. This process is still under way, but at a much reduced rate.

With the growth of the villages and cities from 1800 on, southern New England had shifted considerably from subsistence farming to grain and livestock farming. With the opening of the Erie Canal, however, and especially the building of the railroads, flour and hams began coming into New England cities at prices lower than the farms of central New England could withstand. The decades of the 1840's and 1850's witnessed declining land values, a closing out of mortgages, and a rapid turnover of land. More and more of the old fields and pastures reverted to stands of white pine and more and more farms were abandoned. A counter-movement began to develop in the 1870's around Worcester and the larger cities, namely, an increase in dairy and poultry farming, with some growing of vegetables and fruit for local consumption. This did not increase the acreage of cultivated land, but it did that of hay. The reverse trend continued to the end of the century and afterwards.

The general trend in southern New England agriculture since 1900 has been toward more and more specialized production for consumption in the still growing cities of the region, of milk and cream first and most, of eggs and poultry meat, and of vegetables and fruit. Indeed Boston now has to depend on the three northern New England states for all but a little of its supply of fluid milk and cream, and cities like Worcester and Springfield get part of their supply from the north. The poultry output of southern New England even before 1900 was helping to supply the New York market, and it has continued to do so. The 1940–1950 decade saw more than a doubling in egg and poultry meat production in this region.

But nearly all of the expansion of poultry production, and well on toward a half of that in dairy output is based on feed shipped from elsewhere. The output from the land of the region itself has continued to decline. Figure 10 in Chapter 6 clearly shows this decline since 1925 in terms of land in farms in Massachusetts, and Figure 11 shows it in terms of land in farms and cropland harvested ever since 1880 for Worcester County. Some of the decrease of a third in cropland harvested in Worcester County since 1920, however, has been offset by higher yields and by shifting to alfalfa and other clovers and by pasture improvement. These improvements are general in New England. The milk supply of Boston in recent years has averaged 40 percent or more in excess of fluid milk consumption.

The specialized farm products of New England for sale in other markets — potatoes, cranberries, blueberries, tobacco — have also continued to expand with the market for them. Orchards and small fruits and fresh vegetables have not kept up with local consumption, as has been the case generally in eastern markets. The competition of fresh and frozen products from outside has been too strong.

In the aggregate, New England agricultural output has been holding its own since 1910, and expanding since 1940; but not so if deduction is made for the increasing use of feeds shipped in from elsewhere.

The history of the region would not be complete without more reference to the virgin timber stands and what became of them. In the very early days of land clearing, the trees were usually destroyed by burning as effortlessly as possible. A little later, the ashes were used as a soil supplement or in industries. Then as the farms began to spread over the countryside, and villages to grow, local sawmills using waterpower were built at intervals along the many streams. Along a brook draining westwardly from Worcester County a summer sojourner recently counted fifteen former sawmill and gristmill sites within a distance of twenty miles in an area with virtually no farming now. By 1800, the urban demand for lumber had become important, and by 1850 the loggers were reaching well into Northern New England for pine and spruce. By 1880, the stands of white pine that had grown in the old hay fields and worn-out pastures had at forty to fifty years reached diameters of 10 to 12 inches and were in strong demand for boxwood and similar uses. The decades from 1880 to 1920 saw a revival of the lumber industry of Worcester County based on these old-field stands. The hardwoods which were predominant in the original stands in this part of New England, and even more so in the second-growth after cutting these stands, had limited uses in flooring and interior finishing, in furniture, buggies, and wagons and other farm implements. Also some of it was used as fuelwood, and this became a major outlet for the inferior hardwood stands that developed following the cutting of the old-field stands of pine, and also after the virgin hardwoods had been logged on the rough stony land so common in central Massachusetts. The fuelwood demand has now shrunk to a minor fraction of its former volume and no other large use has yet risen to take its place. Southern New England greatly needs a market for the relatively poor hardwood logs that are harvested from improvement cuttings.

One other development in Worcester County is worthy of mention. When Boston needed a larger supply of water, it first reached out to what is now the Wachusett Reservoir in the towns of Clinton, Boylston, and West Boylston. Then in the 1940's, it reached all the way to what is now the Quabbin Reservoir on the western edge of Worcester County, mostly in Franklin and Hampshire Counties. The reservoir took over so much of the town of Dana in Worcester County that what was left was incorporated in the town of Petersham.

CHAPTER 3

The Land

Since it is the land resources of Worcester County with which we are primarily concerned in this book, we need to have at the outset as good a description of these as we can obtain.[1] Fortunately for such an effort the soils have been completely surveyed,[2] and the geology of this part of New England has been well determined.[3]

GEOLOGY

Standing on a fairly high elevation almost anywhere in southern New England and looking about, one is likely to be faced with a fairly uniform horizon level in all directions. Only a few peaks of hard rock are likely to stand out in bold relief. This is because the present land surface is that of a dissected plateau, and the comparatively small differences in elevation, the hills and valleys, are due to differential weathering of rock formations of different degrees of hardness. Geologists tell us that this area was at one time very mountainous, being about midway in the great Appalachian mountain system in its sweep from Newfoundland to Alabama. Later the high mountains were worn down almost to a plain and subsequently this peneplain was elevated to a considerable height and erosive forces again became active. The present surface is a result of the erosion of this peneplain.

The underlying rocks are in many cases the result of metamorphism caused by folding, compression, and heat, which is characteristic of moun-

[1] This chapter is composed largely of paragraphs excerpted from a report on the soils of Worcester County written in 1938 for this project by Dr. A. B. Beaumont, formerly Professor of soils and head of the Agronomy Department of Massachusetts State College, and Soil Conservationist, Soil Conservation Service, for Massachusetts until he retired recently.

[2] W. J. Lattimer, *et al., Soil Survey of Worcester County, Massachusetts,* Bureau of Soils, U.S.D.A., 1927.

[3] B. K. Emerson, *Geology of Massachusetts and Rhode Island,* U.S. Geological Survey Bulletin, 579 (1917).

tainous regions. Above the present land surface of Worcester County at one time were several thousand feet of rock. In the depths of this mountainous mass, folding, crushing, heat, and the various forces of metamorphism were active, and as a result various metamorphic rocks such as the Brimfield schist, Bolton gneiss, and Worcester phyllite were formed from the sedimentary and igneous rocks then present. Subsequent geological erosion removed the overlying rocks and exposed these metamorphic rocks and some unaltered igneous rocks. This explains the large total area of metamorphic rocks in the County.

The detailed physiography of Worcester County, however, is more largely the result of more recent geological forces. These were the forces of continental glaciation. A mass of ice, estimated to have been 2,700 feet thick in the vicinity of Mt. Wachusett, overrode all southern New England in a slow movement or series of movements in a slightly southeasterly direction. Mt. Wachusett, the highest point in the County, was overridden by the ice sheet and probably considerably reduced in elevation by it.

The great ice invasion of Massachusetts has been correlated with the Wisconsin stage in the Midwest. The action of the ice was severe. By pushing great masses of ground rock and soil ahead of it, rounding off angular rock projections, filling valleys, and depositing the rock and soil as ground moraine, much of it eventually in places as terminal moraine, the ice effected marked changes in local topography. In some cases pre-established river courses were changed by the deposition of glacial debris in the channels. Throughout the County, but especially in the middle portion from north to south, are hundreds of ponds and lakes from five acres to 100 acres or more in area which owe their existence to the partial obstruction of pre-existing drainage channels by glacial deposits. Lake Quinsigamond, near Worcester, and Lake Chaubunagungamaug, near Webster, are good examples of such lakes.

PHYSIOGRAPHY

As a consequence of the foregoing, most of the hills in the County are comparatively low, not more than 400 feet higher than the surrounding territory, but there are several outstanding peaks in the north-central part of the County which rise five hundred feet to one thousand feet above the general level of the area. These are called monadnocks, and owe their existence to the resistant rock, usually granite, of which they are composed. Mt. Wachusett is chief among these monadnocks in Worcester County.

Some further details as to topography and drainage are needed to understand the soil pattern. The escarpment from which the land drops off to the east is around 1,100 feet above sea level to the west of Fitchburg on the north and 800 feet above west of Oxford to the south. The drop to a level of 300 feet or even less in the eastern border towns means that the terrain is as broken in the eastern towns as to the west even though the level is lower. The drainage westward to the Connecticut River is through the Millers River in the northwestern towns, the East Branch of the Swift River in Petersham, the Ware River from Hardwick to Hubbardston, and the Quaboag River in the Brookfield Towns and Paxton, all branches of the Chicopee River. The drainage southward to Narragansett Bay in Rhode Island is from as far north as Worcester City in the center of the County. The rivers are the Quinebaug in the west, French, and Blackstone in the east. A very little of east-central Worcester County drains eastward into the Charles River and Boston Harbor. The drainage northeastwardly is mostly into the Merrimack through the Nashua River and its branches.

Another characteristic physiographic feature of the Worcesterian landscape are the low-lying, smoothly rounded elongated hills known to the geologist as drumlins, but locally called "hogbacks," or "whalebacks." The base of a typical drumlin is ovoid with the greatest width nearer the stoss end — that is, the end from which the ice moved, which in this area is always the north end. Drumlins in this county vary considerably in size. Measurements of 160 drumlins in the Quinsigamond quadrangle showed them to vary from 225 feet to 4,950 in length with an average height of 100 feet. A drumlin map published by Alden shows 355 drumlins in Worcester County.[4] They are widely but not evenly scattered over the county. There is a high concentration of them in the vicinity of the Brookfield Towns and they are numerous east of Fitchburg. Most of the drumlins of the County lie in a belt eight to ten miles wide running across the County from Dudley to Winchendon towns. There are very few of them west of a line passing through Barre and Athol.

The drumlin is a product of glaciation. Geologists do not fully understand the cause or methods of its formation. It is a type of ground moraine which was packed and smoothed down by the ice as it moved over it. A typical drumlin contains no ledge and few large boulders, and the soil (Paxton series) is retentive of moisture. It is valuable for agricultural purposes, desirable for building sites, and, with its graceful curves and slopes, an object of beauty on the natural landscape.

[4] W. C. Alden, *The Physical Features of Central Massachusetts,* U.S. Geological Survey Bulletin, 760 (1925).

Other land forms in Worcester County which owe their origin to the receding melting glacier are the high terraces or branches formed along the shore lines of glacial lakes or by streams active during the period of recession. In case of drainage to the north or northeast, water was impounded by the ice acting as a dam, and the lake disappeared with the complete melting of the ice. Such was the case in the valley of the Nashua River. The present large Wachusett Reservoir coincides almost exactly with the glacial Lake Nashua. The better of these glacial lake and river terraces make valuable land (Merrimac soil series) for agricultural purposes, especially for intensive types of farming. But more or less associated with them are the more irregular land forms caused by glacial streams such as the hummocky kame-and-kettle topography and the serpentine deposits called eskers. The material in these consists mainly of coarse gravel and sand, such as would be carried only by swift streams. Such land is classified in the Hinckley soil series and has little or no agricultural value.

SOILS

Fully as important as the effect of the glaciation on topography was its effect on soil formation. The advancing ice sheet tore loose large quantities of fresh rocks, ground and pulverized them, mixed them with preglacial soils and transported the whole mass more or less. But although the glaciation was severe, the drift was not carried very far. Notwithstanding the fact that certain boulder trains have been traced greater distances, geologists have estimated that most of the drift is to be found within fifteen to twenty miles from its starting point. Despite this, the materials were pretty thoroughly mixed. This had an effect not only on the rare elements such as boron and copper, but on the more common elements of magnesium, phosphorus, and potassium. The granites and gneisses, which together comprise something more than 50 percent of the rock formations of the County, contain considerable quartz. It is only natural that the resulting soils should contain a large proportion of quartz sand particles and that the soils of the County are on the whole sandy, with sandy loams predominating. The extensive Brimfield schist was formed from a calcareous sandstone and a mass of shale. The Paxton quartz schist is a micaceous whetstone. Only in a few places and in very limited quantities are carbonates found. The soils are generally deficient in lime.

Soils are first of all classified into *series* according to origin as indicated by parent material, profile, drainage, related chemical composition, and color. Worcester County soils are classified into ten series, plus Rough Stony,

Meadow, and Muck. The series name is usually that of the town in the vicinity where the soil was first recognized and studied as a distinct series. A *soil type* is a combination of series thus defined and of texture; thus Gloucester sandy loam. The soil map of Worcester County maps twenty-four such types, and various phases of these, such as *stony, heavy, slaty, dark,* and *brown,* in addition to Meadow, Muck, and Rough Stony land, which are not considered soil types in the strict sense of the word, but are commonly used in soil mapping in the United States. Meadow is overflow land of variable texture and is usually poorly drained. Muck as mapped includes both peat and muck. Rough Stony land includes all steep and stony areas that are practically nonagricultural.

Following are the names of the ten principal soil series[5] in Worcester County, grouped according to origin.

1. Glacial till (unassorted drift)
   Bernardston, Brookfield, Charlton, Gloucester,
   Paxton, Sutton, Whitman, Rough Stony.
2. Water-worked outwash (kames, terraces, etc.)
   Hinckley, Merrimac.
3. Recent alluvium (subject to overflow)
   Ondawa, Meadow (poorly drained).
4. Cumulose (mainly organic, poorly drained)
   Muck.

Figure 3 is included here in order to show that these soils do have a general geographic pattern of distribution, with the two Gloucester and Rough Stony associations both on the west and on the east, the Brookfields next on the west, and the Charlton, Paxton, and Sutton in between, and three smaller areas with Paxton, Sutton, Bernardston and a good deal of

[5] In this chapter, only the soil series mapped by W. J. Latimer are classified. Since his report was released in 1938, the mapping of the soils of the County has been refined somewhat in connection with the work of the Soil Conservation Service. Some of the older series have been broken down and new ones added. These refinements do not affect materially the conclusions of this chapter.

Several series will be named, however, in the six chapters (12 to 17) on the six sections into which Worcester County is divided for analysis purposes, which are not included in the soil series listed or named in this chapter, and a few words about them are needed:

Agawam is a water-laid soil, brown to dark brown, on level to undulating land in the Connecticut River Valley and immediately adjoining tributary valleys.

Hadley is like Ondawa except darker in color with greenish subsoil, with the same good internal drainage.

Scarboro is another lowland soil, but with poor drainage.

Suffield has a heavy topsoil and clayey subsoil on level to undulating land.

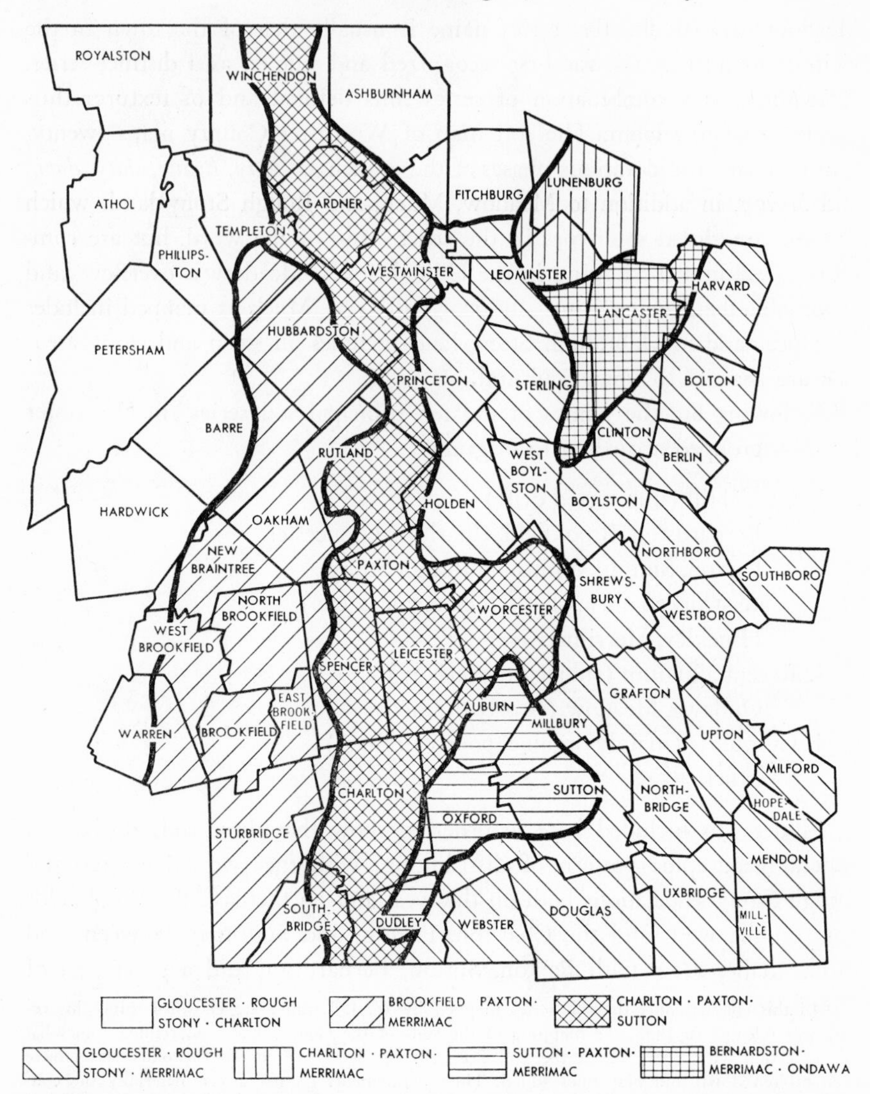

Figure 3. ***Worcester County generalized soil map with the soils grouped into associations.***

Merrimac along the stream channels. As we explore the situation section by section in Chapters 12 to 17, we shall discover that the more agricultural towns are not all in the best soil areas. This is particularly true in the Southwest Section. Warren Town, for example, has much more agriculture than adjacent Brookfield, and Sterling in the Northeast Section has more than Lancaster.

Soils derived directly from glacial till cover 73 per cent of the County. The remainder of the soils are from glacial material reworked by streams, and muck. Most of the streams and rivers have sufficient fall to guarantee a fairly rapid to swift current, but the Nashua for some ten miles between Clinton and the point of exit from the County, and the Quaboag and its tributary the East Brookfield and Warren, are rather sluggish, and their valleys are the location of large acreages of poorly drained Meadow and Muck. Also, there are considerable acreages of wet, mucky land in the valleys of the Assabet and Sudbury Rivers in the town of Westboro. There is more or less poorly drained land along all the major streams. Worcester County has 12 percent of its land area mapped as Muck, Meadow, and Whitman soils.

A small fraction of the wet lands have been artificially drained. Some of them cannot be drained economically for agricultural purposes, but there are still many that can be. There are small poorly drained areas on many farms whose drainage would increase the net returns of the farm.

The Gloucester series of soils occupies 29 percent of the land area of this County, and because of its extent and the generally good quality where it is not too stony it may be considered the most important series of the County. Still, its most common use is in forests. Its stony fine sandy loam is the most extensive member of this series and occupies 11 percent of the County. This type and the other stony members of the series are of particular interest in land-use studies because of the competition between their use for forests and their use for pasture. The Gloucester stony fine sandy loam will be discussed later in the section on land types.

The Brookfield series is also derived from a shallow till. It has uses similar to those of the Gloucester soils, but the corresponding types are not quite as productive as those of the Gloucester. The Brookfield soils have a rusty-brown color caused by the weathering of iron pyrite which is present in the parent material. The Charlton soils derive from a deep till, and because of their greater depth have better water-holding capacity. They also are freer of stones and are considered to be a little better than the Gloucester soils. The Paxton series is limited mainly to drumlins, is retentive of moisture, is comparatively free from stones, and is considered one of the best soil series for orcharding and general farming. Sutton soils are good but tend to be poorly drained. The Bernardston soils are the heaviest in the county and are often poorly drained. They are best suited to hay and pasture. The Whitman series consists of poorly drained dark to black upland soils.

The Merrimac soils find their best use for intensive farming, but can be used for general farming. The Hinckley soils are mostly too subject to drought for any but forest use. Ondawa soils are well drained but subject to occasional overflow. Meadow is usually poorly drained and subject to overflow, and its best use is for pasture. Drainage is necessary for the Whitman soils and muck, both of which are potentially very productive for certain vegetable crops and forage. Rough Stony land is best suited to forests.

Rough Stony land is more definitely associated with Gloucester soils than with any other series. This is due to the fact that granites and gneisses, among the hardest and most resistant rocks of the County, are the principal parent rock materials of the Gloucester series.

The Gloucester-Rough Stony-Charlton group is the most extensive in the County. More Gloucester stony sandy loam and sandy loam is found in the northwest corner, in the towns of Royalston and Phillipston, than in any other section; and more loam in Barre and Hardwick. Most of the Gloucester stony fine sandy loam is found in the eastern group, and this type and Rough Stony land are especially prevalent in the towns of Northbridge, Uxbridge, Mendon, and Douglas.

The Charlton-Paxton-Sutton group is the next most extensive group in the County and extends in comparatively narrow strips across the middle of the County in a north-south direction. This group has the highest percentage of good soils and improved land in the county. The Brookfield-Paxton-Merrimac group is the next most extensive group. Owing to the high percentage of Brookfield stony loam in this group, especially in the southern part of the area, it has only a medium percentage of good farm land. In the vicinity of the Brookfields there is a high percentage of good farm land mapped as Paxton and Brookfield loams.

The Bernardston group is fairly well localized. Some scattered small areas of Bernardston soils are also found as far south as Worcester. The large amount of terrace (Merrimac) and alluvial (Ondawa) soils in this group is due to the generally low elevation of the area. The Sutton soils are found in Leicester as well as in the area dominated by this series. In Leicester the drainage of the Sutton soils is poorer than in the larger area farther south.

The soils of Worcester County belong to the gray-brown group of forest soils of northeastern United States. Only at the highest elevations is any podsol effect apparent. The soils are generally some shade of brown in the surface, with a yellowish subsoil. The prevailing brown color is correlated with the parent material, the open structure, the rainfall, and the resulting vegetation. Local modifications in color are due mainly to differences in parent material and drainage. The rusty brown color of the Brookfield and Paxton soils is traceable to the pyritic schists which are present in the parent material. The gray color of the Bernardston series is due to the slate-like phyllite from which the soils are derived. Soils in perennially moist or wet situations accumulate partly decomposed organic matter which darkens the color, as, for example, in the case of the Whitman series. The black color of muck shows the extreme effect of this.

Generally speaking, glaciated soils are more productive of the crops suited to them than are nonglaciated soils. This superiority has generally been attributed to greater fertility induced by the rejuvenating process of glaciation. From these statements it should not be concluded that glaciated soils on the whole, and those of Worcester County in particular, need no supplemental fertilization. The reverse is true.

One of the principal assets of such soils is their physical condition. With few exceptions they are sufficiently light and sandy to work easily through a wide range of moisture conditions. They are permeable to water, but (except Hinckley and the lighter phases of Merrimac) retain it fairly well. Except for the Paxton series they have little or no hardpan within a profile of three feet deep. Owing to their youth, they have not developed through the process of eluviation that undesirable, tight, clay-pan subsoil which is found in some of the southern and midwestern soils of the United States.

Also of importance is the fact that the structure of the soils of Worcester County is primarily single-grained, due to the relatively large percentage of sand. This is the nearest approach to a "fool-proof" structure known. Consequently, there is no need for the complicated methods of handling required by the much heavier soils found elsewhere. Because of these physical conditions and the usually favorable rainfall, the soils of the County give good response to commercial fertilizers and other supplements. The group least needing plant food supplements is that comprising recent alluvium and mucks, the least extensive group of the County. The group requiring the most supplements is intermediate topographically and consists of the reworked sands and gravels found in kames, terraces, and outwash plains of old second or higher bottoms. The group intermediate in its fertilizer requirements is the extensive group of upland soils derived directly from unassorted glacial drift.

LAND TYPES

Illuminating as a classification by soil groups may be, it does not closely fit the needs of analysis from the standpoint of land-use adjustment. For this purpose, a classification by *natural land types* has proved more useful. A natural land type may be defined as a body of land having uniform physical characteristics within the limits demanded by the objective of the classification. A land type may be coincident with a soil type, but more often it includes two or more closely related soil types. It may even cut across soil types. In Worcester County 37 soil types or phases of soil types have been mapped. For the purpose of land-use adjustment studies in this County, it appears feasible to reduce these 37 units to 12 land types under 4 principal groups, a workable number, as follows:

A. Uplands derived from glacial till; topography rolling to hilly.

1. Soils of medium texture, good drainage, and few stones; best soils of A group; suitable for general farming, dairying, and orcharding.

   Brookfield loam (Bl)
   " " heavy phase (Bl)
   Charlton fine sandy loam (Cf)
   " loam (L)
   Gloucester fine sandy loam (Gf)
   " loam (Gl)
   " sandy loam (Gs)
   Paxton loam (Pl)
   Sutton loam (Sl)

2. Same as A1 except containing enough stones and ledge to interfere with cultivation; best use is pasture or woodland; considerable area cleared of stones for cultivation.

   Brookfield stony loam (Bt)
   Charlton stony fine sandy loam (Ch)
   " " loam (Cs)
   " loam, slaty phase (Cl)
   Gloucester stony fine sandy loam (Gr)
   " " loam (Gt)
   " " sandy loam (G)
   Paxton loam, stony phase (Pl)
   Sutton loam, " " (Sl)

3. Soils of heavy texture, drainage poor to good, suitable for dairying and general farming.

   Bernardston silt loam (Bs)

4. Same as A3 except containing enough stones to interfere with cultivation.

Bernardston silt loam, stony phase (Bs)

B. Land at intermediate and lower levels, derived from terraces, glacial outwash materials, and recent alluvium; topography level to hummocky; drainage good to excessive.

1. Soils of medium texture; level to undulating; free from large stones, organic matter and fertility low; subject to drought; best soils of B group; best suited to intensive farming.

   Merrimac fine sandy loam (My)
   " sandy loam (Ms)
   " " " ", brown phase (Ms)

2. Same as B1 except of coarser texture and more subject to drought.

   Merrimac loamy coarse sand (Ml)
   " gravelly sandy loam (Mg)
   " " " ", brown phase (Mg)

3. Soils of medium texture, hummocky topography, and excessive drainage; best suited to woods, but may be used for pasture.

   Hinckley stony loam (Hl)
   " " ", dark phase (Hl)

4. Recent alluvium; usually well drained, but subject to occasional overflow; fertility high; best suited to hay and pasture.

   Ondawa fine sandy loam (Of)

C. Poorly drained land requiring artificial drainage for agricultural use, texture of soils variable.

1. Soils high in organic matter; potentially valuable for general farming and truck crops.

   Whitman stony loam (W)
   Muck (Mu)

2. Soils of low to medium organic matter; subject to overflow; best use pasture or hay.

   Meadow (M)

D. Land of little or no agricultural value; best use is for woods, recreation, building sites, etc.

1. Soils of coarse texture, hummocky topography, and strongly subject to drought; low in organic matter.

   Hinckley gravelly sandy loam (Hg)
   " " " ", dark phase (Hg)

   Hinckley loamy sand (Hs)
   " " ", dark phase (Hs)

2. Land of very rough topography; very stony or ledgy.

   Rough Stony land (R)

This classification, it will be noted, is in terms of potential use, which may or may not be identical with present use. It gives a picture of the land-use possibilities of the County as accurate as the soil survey on which it is based, and it can be further refined by using a base map of larger scale and doing the field work in corresponding detail. Considerable detail is necessary for certain types of land-use planning, as already indicated for individual farms.

The list following gives the percentage distribution of the natural land types of the County. These figures do not take into consideration the land now utilized for roads and urban sites, which, in the aggregate, is considerable, but which would not seriously affect the percentage distribution of the land type.

A. Uplands from till	
1. Soils of medium texture, good drainage (best uplands)	28.7 percent
2. Same as A1 except stony	32.3
3. Soils of heavy texture	0.9
4. Same as A3 except stony	0.4
Total of A group	62.3
B. Land at intermediate levels	
1. Soils of medium texture, level to undulating (best of B group)	4.4
2. Same as B1 except coarser texture and more droughty	2.3
3. Soils of medium texture, hummocky topography	1.6
4. Recent alluvium; good but subject to overflow	0.6
Total of B group	8.9
C. Poorly drained land	
1. Soils high in organic matter; potentially good	6.8
2. Soils of low to medium organic matter; subject to frequent overflow	5.1
Total of C group	11.9

D. Land of little or no agricultural value

1. Soils of coarse texture, hummocky	7.0
2. Rough and stony land	9.9
Total of D group	16.9

VEGETATION

The soil and climate of a region find expression in the type and quality of its vegetation. The natural vegetation of a community may serve usefully as an index of its agricultural possibilities. But plant species introduced from elsewhere often prove to be equally or better adapted to a region than are the indigenous species, particularly when certain soil defects are corrected. Exotic species quite commonly become the most valuable economic crop plants. The ensuing discussion is intended merely to furnish a background for an interpretation of the agriculture of the County.

The historic vegetational cover of the uplands of Worcester County was a forest. But much of the soil of the intervales was too wet, heavy, or fertile to permit tree species to compete successfully with grass and grasslike species which abounded there and which constituted the principal source of forage for the livestock of the early settlers.

An interesting and significant factor in land use in New England is the type of forest cover that follows on degenerated pastures and haylands. L. B. Cunningham made a study of the relation of this to the major soil types of Worcester County.[6] He found that the association of gray birch and red maple comes first on all but the more shallow till soils and the excessively drained outwash formations where the red maple is represented or absent. The gray birch–red maple association is generally succeeded by the white pine association, although pitch pine are numerous on the very sandy tills, the coarser Merrimac types, and Hinckley soils.

On areas of Gloucester stony fine sandy loam that have been pastured, juniper and gray birch appear first, but white pine follows soon on many sites and pitch pine on others. This soil type generally offers a better site for white pine than for hardwoods since the pine need more moisture. Only a little white pine appears on the Gloucester stony loam but it would do exceedingly well on the fine sandy loam of this series if it were not for the competition of hardwood species. The oaks, especially white and red, thrive on this soil type. Very little hickory comes in, probably because the soil is too acid. White pine is generally common on Gloucester sandy loam, but

[6] Thesis at Clark University, 1938.

white and red oaks do not thrive on it, nor does hickory. The succession on Gloucester loam is quite similar to that on Gloucester stony loam.

In the next stage of succession, generally the oak-hickory association succeeds the white pine except on the stony fine sandy loam. In all cases the oak is far more common than the hickory. Cunningham writes that "all studies indicate that the birch-beech-maple-hemlock association will finally establish itself as the climax forest on all (Gloucester) types,"[7] although the climax "has not been attained at any place on the upland." Succession on the Charlton and Brookfield soils is similar to that on the Gloucester series, but hardwood species apparently do not thrive as well because of the greater acidity of the soil.

T. S. Brierly made a similar study on the Paxton and Sutton soil series.[8] He found a succession of trees similar to that reported by Cunningham for the Gloucester series, except that the white pine association was found only in isolated stands on either Paxton or Sutton soils. The birch-beech-maple-hemlock association was not found on Sutton soils, except for a few isolated groves of hemlock in protected areas. The oak-hickory association succeeds the gray birch–red maple association on Paxton soils in the southern part of the county, but no hickory is found on this type in the northern half of the county. On the Sutton soils the oak association follows gray birch and red maple, the drier the area the more white oaks, with black oak dominant under more moist conditions.

In the natural transition from pasture to woods or from abandoned cropland to woodland, a number of species of shrubs appear in the early stages of succession. Shrubs or "brush" mostly come first on pastured land because they thrive better under open-field conditions, are more resistant to trampling, and are less palatable to stock than are the tree species. The more common shrubs in the pastures of Worcester County are, in the approximate order of their prevalence, as follows: sweet fern, hardhack, meadowsweet, sheep laurel, low sweet blueberry, huckleberry, male berry, high or swamp blueberry, low juniper, and hawthorn.

This is not a natural "grass" region in the sense that such areas exist in the prairie lands of the West. Still, the climate of the County, while not ideal for grasses, is satisfactory for many species. In their natural condition the soils are too deficient in lime, potash, and other nutrients, and generally not retentive enough of moisture to furnish perfect edaphic conditions for grasses.

[7] This statement assumes that hurricanes or other disasters will not occur before the climax forest stage is reached. Studies at the Harvard Forest in Petersham indicate that this stage has never been attained in this part of New England since time of settlement.

[8] Thesis at Clark University, 1939.

Nevertheless, eighty-five species of true grasses have been found. In the well-drained mowings and open pastures of the county, the grasses are largely introduced species, mainly timothy, red top, Kentucky blue grass, Colonial bent, and sweet vernal — in addition to the red, alsike, ladino, and white clovers, also all introduced. These introduced grasses and clovers were the so-called "English" grasses of the colonists, and made up their "English" hay.

More numerous than the true grasses (*Gramineae*) are the grass-like plants, mainly sedges (*Cyperaceae*) and rushes (*Juncaceae*), of which eighty-four species, particularly the sedges, so closely resemble true grasses as easily to be mistaken for them. Most of these "wild" grasses are more at home on the wet and swampy areas of the intervales than on the well drained dry soils. They constituted the principal source of hay of the early colonists. In general they produce a forage of low palatability and inferior quality.

In general, as a pasture or meadow degenerates, the native and "wild" grasses replace the introduced grasses, and then the shrubs come in place of the wild grasses. Finally, the trees replace the shrubs. It is the essence of good pasture management to keep growth of these replacments to a minimum. It would be helpful always to remember in this connection that the natural cover of the upland soils of Worcester County is not grass and clover but a forest. Consequently, if pastures are to be maintained, it is necessary so to modify these soils as to make them more suitable to the growth of pasture herbage than to shrubs and trees — and this means the use of lime and fertilizers.

CROP ADAPTABILITY

During the colonial period and for some years after the Revolutionary War, when the agriculture of the County was largely of a subsistence type, a much wider range of crops was grown than in later years when the agriculture became more specialized and commercialized. Flax and hemp were grown for fiber. Corn, wheat, oats, rye, barley, and buckwheat were the grain crops for human food and animal feed. Potatoes, root crops, and a variety of vegetables were raised. Tobacco was grown in a small way for home consumption. Many tree and bush fruits, and grapes, were common. The apple was the most popular tree fruit, and it appears to have been grown primarily for cider. Nearly every farmer had one or more barrels for storing the year's supply of this popular beverage.

It is not clear from the record when the English grasses were introduced into New England, but the time was probably prior to the establishment of Worcester County as a political unit. No further additions of permanence or great significance were made to the list of forage crops until the introduction of the millets, particularly Japanese millet, and alfalfa, soybeans, and Sudan grass, all of which were introduced in the nineteenth century. Recently, ladino clover, a plant with growth habits similar to those of white clover, but larger, has been introduced. This legume has become the most popular cultivated pasture plant in the County.

On the whole, the soils of Worcester County are better suited to tilled crops than to grass crops. It is difficult to maintain a good grass stand over a long period. By proper supplementation, however, the best-adapted soils in the county can be made quite productive of grasses. Grassland should be cultivated and reseeded once every three to five years for best growth.

The best upland grass soil is Bernardston silt loam. This soil type is heavy enough and of sufficient depth to make it one of the most retentive of moisture. The best lowland grass soil in its natural conditions is Ondawa fine sandy loam; but when artificially drained, Muck, Meadow, and Whitman soils are as good or superior. The poorest soil in the County for grass is Hinckley loamy sand because of its susceptibility to drought. Intermediate between this type and the others mentioned are the various loams and sandy loams. In Table 1, all the soil types are rated according to their adaptability to crops and grasses. This rating of soils for crops assumes the use of practices common or reasonable for the County. If unusual or unusually expensive operations are necessary in order to put the soil in condition for crop use, its rating is low; for example, the rating of all stony soils is lowered considerably for crop use because of stoniness, and to a lesser degree for pasture for the same reason. Also, naturally wet types such as Whitman, Meadow, and Muck are penalized in the rating.

Grasses differ widely in their lime and nutrient needs. Therefore, in planning a crop rotation it is necessary, for best results, to select a combination of crops adapted to a given pH reaction range and general nutrient level. For example, timothy, red clover, corn, barley, and soybeans are crops which may well be grown on soils of medium reaction range and medium to high nutrient levels; whereas alfalfa, mangels, and most vegetables require both a somewhat higher soil reaction and nutrient level for best results. Red top, rye, oats, potatoes, and buckwheat will grow on soils of rather low reaction, but do better on soils of a medium reaction. Rye is one of the best "poor land" crops, but it, like the others, produces best yields on soils of medium to high fertility.

TABLE 1

Rating of Soil Types of Worcester County for Certain Uses*

Soil type	*Corn*	*Hay*	*Pasture*	*Apples*
Bernardston silt loam	85	90	90	70
Bernardston silt loam stony phase	55	70	80	55
Brookfield loam	86	85	85	84
Brookfield loam heavy phase	80	86	86	74
Brookfield stony loam	50	65	75	57
Charlton loam	90	88	88	90
Charlton loam slaty phase	65	75	83	70
Charlton stony loam	60	70	80	66
Charlton fine sandy loam	88	87	87	88
Charlton stony fine sandy loam	58	73	82	60
Gloucester loam	87	86	86	87
Gloucester stony loam	57	67	77	58
Gloucester fine sandy loam	86	85	85	85
Gloucester stone fine sandy loam	56	66	76	56
Gloucester sandy loam	83	80	80	80
Gloucester stony sandy loam	53	63	73	83
Hinckley gravelly sandy loam	49	47	45	39
Hinckley gravelly sandy loam dark phase	51	49	47	42
Hinckley stony loam	45	55	65	42
Hinckley stony loam dark phase	49	59	69	45
Hinckley loamy sand	35	33	31	36
Hinckley loamy sand dark phase	39	37	35	40
Merrimac fine sandy loam	80	75	70	64
Merrimac sandy loam	75	70	65	60
Merrimac sandy loam brown phase	76	71	66	62
Merrimac gravelly sandy loam	65	60	55	50
Merrimac gravelly sandy loam brown phase	66	61	56	52
Merrimac loamy coarse sand	49	44	39	45
Ondawa fine sandy loam	82	85	88	30
Paxton loam	86	88	88	90
Paxton loam stony phase	61	71	81	80
Sutton loam	87	88	88	82
Sutton loam wet phase	62	72	82	62
Sutton loam stony phase	57	67	77	60
Whitman stony loam**	10	30	40	19
Meadow**	0	40	50	0
Muck**	0	20	30	0
Rough stony loam	0	0	40	0

* Ratings made in consultation with Professor R. W. Donaldson, Extension Agronomist, and Professor W. H. Thies, Extension Pomologist, Massachusetts State College. Soil types rated below 50 are considered unsuitable for the crops indicated; 51 to 65 means poor adaptability; 66–80, good; 81 plus, best.

** Rating given on undrained soils.

The more common leguminous forage crops climatically adapted to the region can be grown successfully on the deeper loams, sandy loams, and silt loams of the County. Red, alsike, white, and ladino clovers and soybeans tolerate a medium degree of acidity, and can therefore be grown with small additions of lime. Being legumes, they need no supplementary nitrogen in the form of fertilizer, but they do need phosphate and potash for best results. The nodule organisms necessary for proper development of the clovers are generally present in the soil, so that artificial inoculation is unnecessary. Red and alsike clovers generally behave as biennials and consequently rarely persist longer than two years. They are at their best in short rotations. The short rotation including not more than three years of clover and grasses is especially suited to the more sandy Merrimac and Hinckley soils, and its use should be encouraged on these series. White and ladino clovers behave as perennials and stand close pasturing. They should be seeded in all pasture mixtures.

Although most attempts to grow alfalfa in Worcester County have not been marked with outstanding success, there is sufficient evidence in the experience of farmers in the County and in other parts of the State, and from experiments conducted at the Massachusetts Experiment Station, to justify the belief that the crop can be grown successfully on deep, well drained, open soils, and that on such soils winter-killing of adapted varieties rarely occurs. It should do best on the deep loams of the Gloucester, Brookfield, Charlton, and Bernardston series, and can probably be grown on the better phases of Merrimac and Hinckley sandy loams.

Oats are now grown primarily as a nurse crop for new seedlings of grass, clover, and alfalfa. Rye is grown to a small extent for a cover crop and for green manure, and its use for such purposes should be encouraged.

The first settlers of Massachusetts learned to grow maize from the Indians, and they called it "Indian corn." Corn has been an important grain and forage crop since the beginning of agriculture in Worcester County. The best upland and terrace soils, and the better drained bottom soils are well adapted to corn production. Generous use of manure and some fertilizer makes yields as great or greater than those of the Corn Belt. Most of the corn now grown in the County is for silage.

Potatoes are well adapted to about the same group of soils as is corn; however, because of the higher value of potatoes per acre and, therefore, the greater expense justified for fertilizer, they may be grown on some of the sandier soils too light for corn. Merrimac soils can be used to good advantage for potatoes. This series also is well adapted to the growing of miscellaneous vegetable and truck crops for the market. Any of the soil types of the county except those with poor drainage, such as Whitman, or of excessive drainage, such as Hinckley, are well adapted to the small home garden. The prevailing sandy texture of the soils is an asset of no mean value in connection with gardening, and the natural deficiency of plant food can be made up by the use of fertilizers.

In Worcester County there are many soil types pre-eminently suited to the growth of fruit trees. Climate more than soil limits the number of species that can be successfully grown. Apples, pears, plums, and cherries are sufficiently well adapted to both soils and climate to make them possible commercial crops. Of these, only apples are grown extensively. The principal soil criteria for a good apple orchard site are (1) sufficient depth of soil and freedom from hardpan to permit unhampered development of the root system, (2) texture and structure of soil favorable to good drainage and aeration, (3) stoniness and topography which permit the use of machinery, and (4) at least a medium level of natural fertility. Soils with these characteristics will also be sufficiently retentive of moisture in practically all years. Lime appears to be more necessary for the cover crops sometimes grown than for the apple trees themselves.

The best sites for apple orchards in the county are the tops and slopes of drumlins and other low hills, and the intermediate slopes of the high hills. Thus both good air and soil drainage are generally assured. Both topographic and soil needs are met in the deeper loams and sandy loams of the Paxton, Charlton, Gloucester, Brookfield, and Bernardston series. The well drained phase of Sutton soils is also satisfactory. Hinckley soils should be avoided because of excessive drainage, low fertility, and to some extent because of frost hazard. Merrimac soils are not quite so subject to drought but more subject to frosts.

The bush fruits and grapes have about the same soil and topographic requirements as have the apples. Also, sites for bush fruit plantations and small vineyards can frequently be found in localities generally too rough or stony for orchards.

The yield and quality of most of the agricultural products of Worcester County are fair to good, and, according to meager information available, better than they were a hundred years or more ago. According to Bidwell and Falconer's *History of Agriculture in the Northern United States,* the yield of hay in the County in 1801 was 0.82 tons per acre. These untreated pastures are probably poorer than they were one hundred years ago, and that, according to some writers of that period, was indeed poor.

PRESENT CONDITION OF THE LAND

Land-use adjustment, however, must begin with the present condition of the soils and land. Let us consider more specifically what that condition is.

First of all, much of it is as greatly in need of liming to correct its acidity as it ever was. This is evident in Table 2, which reports the reaction tests

TABLE 2

Percentage of Soil Samples in Hardwick Having the Reaction Shown

PH*	Brushy pasture	Open pasture	Cropland
Less than 5.0	16.6	7.7	3.6
5.0–5.49	76.6	80.6	45.3
5.5–5.99	6.8	10.4	35.3
6.0 and over	none	1.3	15.8
Total	100.0	100.0	100.0

* Any reaction (pH) below 5.5 is considered strongly or very strongly acid; 5.5 or above, of medium or slight acidity.

of 685 surface soil samples collected from pastures and cropland in Hardwick, which can be taken as normal in this respect. The need for lime increases progressively from *cropland* through *open pasture* to *brushy pasture*. Less than 50 percent of the cropland is strongly acid, while nearly 90 percent of the open pasture and nearly 95 percent of the brushy pasture is in this group. Any reaction below 6.0 indicates a need for lime in growing the more common crops. It is conservative to estimate that the pasture land needs at least two tons and the cropland at least one ton of ground limestone equivalent, on each acre within a period of five years. At these rates the present acreage of pasture and cropland would require 283,000 tons within the five-year period. This is probably five to six times the amount presently applied. The maintenance requirement would be somewhat less.

Second, while the productivity level of the topsoil in much of the remaining cropland of Worcester County is higher today than when it was first cleared, and probably at any time since, as evidenced by current yields per acre, the fertility level of much former cropland has been reduced to a point where only trees will grow. Also the productivity of a considerable acreage of old hay fields is still declining. Most important of all is the steadily declining fertility of most of the pasture lands.

Because of the combination of comparatively high annual rainfall and rather pronounced permeability of the soils, it is probable that the soils of this area never were very fertile, even under the cover of a primeval forest. This is a reasonable inference from numerous chemical tests and other information. Under the prevailing climatic conditions, the plant food made available by the weathering of soil minerals is leached almost as rapidly as it is produced. There is some indication from chemical tests and the growth of vegetation on exposed subsoil, as in old railroad cuts, that the parent material of Worcester County soils weathers comparatively rapidly, but that the net increase in plant food resulting is small. Only under a continuous mixed forest cover and the accumulated duff of the forest floor was there any appreciable accumulation.

It is obvious, however, that much of the cropland did in time come to be farmed in a rotation with grass, and that manure must also have been applied. Otherwise the acreage of cropland would not have increased to a peak in the early nineteenth century, and then maintained itself pretty well for several decades afterwards. With the decline in area of cropland, the tilled crops began to be rotated with hay. Also at some time in the County's agricultural history, probably when the farmers began to build larger and better barns with barn cellars for manure storage, the conservation and use of manure became common practice. The use of commercial fertilizers began about the middle of the last century.

All these practices tended to increase the productivity of the cropland, but little or nothing was done to improve pastures. The farmer's affections were lavished on his cropland, particularly his mowings. To the extent that the cropland was manured with manure produced by cows on pasture, the pastures were robbed "to pay" the cropland. The pastures of the County are still generally in a deplorable condition; the cropland is much better, but both need improvement. However, there has been a considerable change in this situation since the last war, and many pastures in the County are in better condition than the cropland.

Finally, erosion has contributed somewhat to the loss of fertility of cultivated fields. The erosion referred to here is not the slow erosion of geological time, but the *accelerated erosion* of cultivated fields on slopes. Accelerated erosion manifests itself by rapid removal of the soil more or less evenly on slopes, which is designated as *sheet* erosion, and by gullying. During the zenith period of farming in this County, a hundred years or so ago, when much more land and much steeper slopes were under the plow, erosion was undoubtedly much more active than at present. Now, not more than 12 percent of the land of the County is being cropped and much of this is in a long rotation with grass.

That erosion is not now very active in Worcester County is clear from the appearance of the streams. Rarely if ever do they run muddy, and on the rare occasions when they do it is because of bank cutting in flood time. The "Muddy Brooks" and "Muddy Ponds" of this County are not ordinarily muddy with suspended silt and clay as are those of the South and West usually, but are darkened more or less by finely divided and suspended organic matter originating in swamps. Such streams and ponds were probably so named because their banks are so soft and swampy that cattle can only with difficulty get to them to drink.

Sheet erosion with incipient gullying is the more common form now found. Sheet erosion is commonly observed on cultivated slopes of 12 percent or steeper. Some erosion is observed on grassed slopes of similar grade and with a thin vegetative cover. Little difference in erosion appears with soil series. It is a little more prevalent on the Merrimac soils, but this may be due to the fact that long slopes, which tend to concentrate run-off, are often associated with this series.

Soil erosion in Worcester County, mostly of the sheet type, does not commonly produce spectacular effects, and may therefore escape casual observation. The small gullies sometimes produced are usually plowed in from year to year. On the lighter slopes the injury from erosion is slight in any one year, and only after a period of ten to twenty years becomes clearly evident. In the majority of cases, all that is needed to control erosion in this area is a judicious use of cover crops and a suitable rotation. Cultivation needs to be on the contour on all but the gentler slopes, and strip cropping is needed if the rotations call for corn, potatoes, or other cultivated crops in half the years or more on 12 percent or steeper slopes. Only in rare cases is cropland terracing necessary or desirable. Most slopes above 25 percent should be retired from cultivation. Wind erosion appears only on loamy sands and sands of the Hinckley and Merrimac series. Such soils are totally lacking or deficient in organic matter which may serve as a binder, have low water-retentiveness, and therefore quickly dry out.

More serious than erosion is the *corrosion* or leaching of the plant nutrients. There is abundant evidence from lysimeter experiments that comparatively large quantities of nitrogen, calcium, potassium, magnesium, and other elements are removed from soils by percolating waters, and, further, that the removal of these elements is much more rapid from cultivated soils than from those protected by a vegetative cover. Cultivation particularly encourages oxidation, hydration, carbonation, and nitrification, and all these make solution and loss by leaching more rapid. High permeability of the soils, a characteristic which tends to decrease erosion, at the same time increases their susceptibility to oxidation of organic matter.

The conservation problem of Worcester County, and of most of New England, is not related closely to erosion as such, except in areas where cash crops are the main enterprises, but is concerned instead with keeping the land in crop rotations and pasture by raising its productivity level, mainly by liming and fertilization, and then with keeping it there so that it does not revert again to brush and trees. The United States with its rapidly growing population is going to need some of this land in later decades, and it is the obverse of good conservation to let it degenerate in productivity and revert to forest and then restore it to agricultural use again. This point will be developed more fully in later chapters.

SOILS ON 112 REPRESENTATIVE FARMS

When this project was started in 1937–38, it was decided to analyze in detail a small number of representative farms in representative towns distributed over the County. The information obtained for each farm was that needed to work out a plan for the most effective utilization of its land under the conditions under which it was being operated. Detailed soil maps were made of each farm, showing land use, soil type, slope, stoniness, and erosion. In the end, 112 farms were mapped and planned in this way, in the ten towns shown on Figure 1 in Chapter 1. At this stage George Westcott made a complete inventory of the land on these 112 farms and published the results in Mimeograph Release No. 1 of this project, under the title "Statistical Summary of Land Use Data." He classified all but 654 of the 13,865 acres on these farms into 65 soil types in 18 soil series. Some of the 654 acres were covered by water, or were ledge or marsh.

Of the 13,211 acres classified, 36 percent were in the Gloucester series, and 11 percent in the closely associated poorly drained Whitman series. Of the somewhat better soils, 9 per cent were in the Charlton and 8 percent in the Sutton series. Altogether, 62 percent were in Gloucester, Charlton, Sutton, Paxton, and Brookfield, and another 7 percent in Bernardston and Hollis. The remainder was of the old glacial-outwash soils, Merrimac and Hinckley mostly, 14 percent; or of Muck or other low-lying soils, 14 percent.

Of the Gloucester soils, 42 percent were classified as stony loam, and another 42 percent as stony fine sandy loam. Only 43 percent of the Charlton was classified as stony loam or stony fine sandy loam. The Sutton and Paxton were about one-third stony loam. All of the Whitman was called stony loam, and 82 percent of it was designated "too wet for tame hay." The Bernardston soils were classified as poorly drained, the Hinckley soils were only 17 percent loamy sand, the rest being gravelly sandy loam.

Again, of the 13,211 acres, only 32 percent were classified as cropland or cropland idle, compared with 14 percent in the county census classification for 1940. Well over half of the Merrimac soils were in cropland, as compared with around 40 percent for Sutton, Hinckley, and Bernardston, and with less than a fourth of the Gloucester and Charlton. Apparently the stoniness of the latter series is a major handicap. More than a fifth of the muck land was cropland. The Paxton soils on the drumlins were around 60 percent in cropland even though predominantly in the 8-to-15-percent slope class.

Of the farm land as a whole, 63 percent had a slope of less than 8 percent and only 11 percent a slope of over 15 percent. The comparable figures for cropland were 74 percent and 4 percent.

Of the land in farms, only 12 percent was classified as having more than "slight sheet erosion," and only 13 percent of the cropland.

Westcott classified 37 percent of the land on these farms as in pasture and 30 percent as in woodland. He made no separate classification for woodland pasture. These lands were only a little more sloping than the croplands; of the pasture lands, 55 percent were under 8 percent slope and 18 percent were above 15; of the woodland, 60 and 16 percent respectively. Stoniness rather than slope seems to determine what land is in pasture and woodland. The stony phase of Gloucester, Brookfield, Whitman, and Sutton are largely in pasture, or, except in the case of Whitman, in woodland.

Related to the stoniness of the land is the size of the fields. In clearing the land of stones, the stones were piled into walls that served as fences, and the smaller the fields the less the distance that the stones had to be handled or carried. Small fields were not a serious handicap when the field work was done with oxen or horses. But they are a serious handicap today. A common way of disposing of the stone fences now is to dig a trench 4 to 6 feet deep alongside the fence with a bulldozer and then push it into the trench and cover it with earth. This costs around $6.00 to $8.00 per rod today. In some cases it is cheaper to haul the stones away with a truck or steel stoneboat. Back in 1938 when the 112 representative farms were first surveyed, field sizes of a large sample of these were measured. Only 40 percent of the fields were then more than 3 acres in size, and only 20 percent over 5 acres in size. Land in these small fields tends to lie idle and go out of crop use.

CHAPTER 4

The Urban Setting

If this were a book on planning for all the resources and people of Worcester County, it would need to devote many more of its pages to its urban than to its nonurban resources and living.[1] The census of 1950 classified all but 137,766 of the county's 543,094 inhabitants as urban. Figure 4 shows the location and relative size of its cities in 1950. Three railroad lines serve the County: the New York, New Haven and Hartford, the Boston and Maine, and the Boston and Albany.[2] The population of the eleven cities and towns of over 10,000 in 1950 was as follows:

Towns and cities	Population	Towns and cities	Population
1. Athol Town	11,554	7. Northbridge Town	10,476
2. Clinton Tcwn	12,287	8. Shrewsbury Town	10,594
3. Fitchburg City	42,691	9. Southbridge Town	17,519
4. Gardner City	19,581	10. Webster	13,194
5. Leominster City	24,075	11. Worcester City	203,486
6. Milford	15,442		

The 1950 Census designates Worcester County as Metropolitan State Economic Area B, which in population is second to Area C, which includes Suffolk County (Boston) and the three adjoining counties of Norfolk, Middlesex, and Essex with a total population of 2,858,033. The increases in population between 1940 and 1950 were 7.6 percent in Area B and 7.7 in Area C, as compared with 8.1 for the state, and 14.5 for the nation.

In an area as dominantly urban as Worcester County, the use of rural

[1] This chapter makes much use of information assembled in 1939 by Dr. John E. Guthrie, and since brought up to date. Guthrie is now Professor of Economics at Washington State College.

[2] Information is as of 1955. The map is supplied by the Massachusetts Department of Public Utilities.

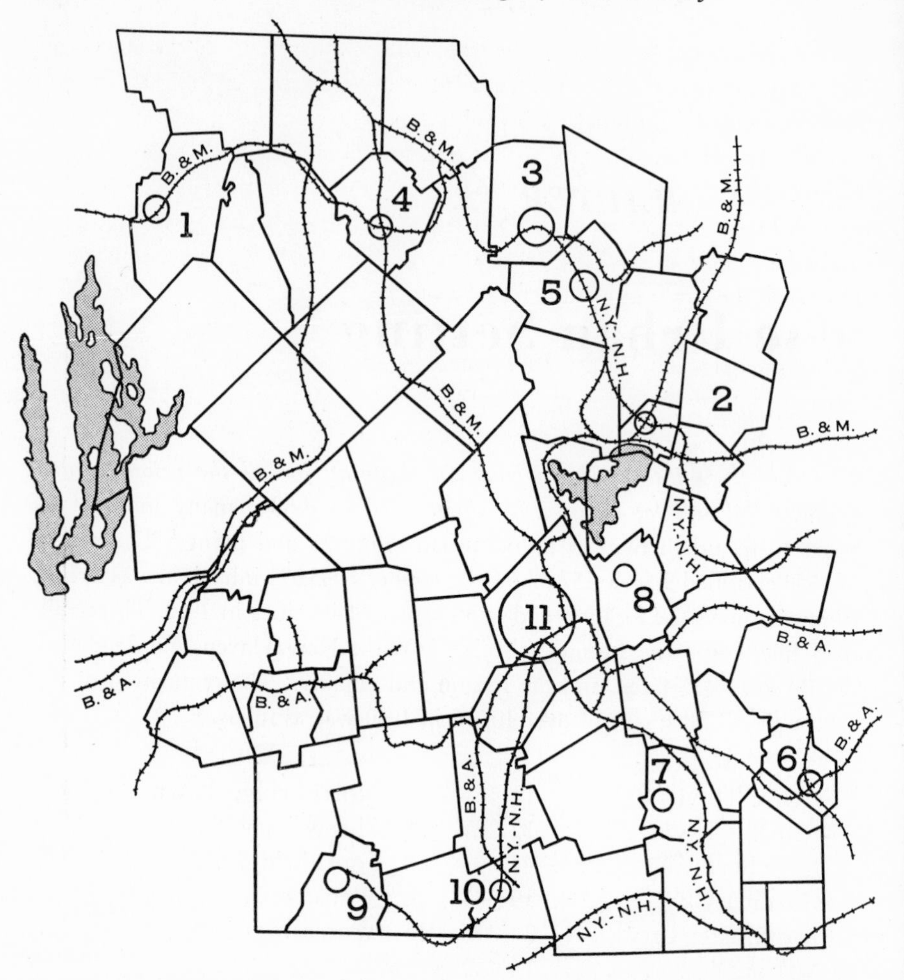

Figure 4. *Towns and cities of 10,000 or over in Worcester County, 1950, railroads, 1955, and water reservoirs. (The size of the circle indicates the relative size of the population. The towns and cities are 1, Athol; 2, Clinton; 3, Fitchburg; 4, Gardner; 5, Leominster; 6, Milford; 7, Northbridge; 8, Shrewsbury; 9, Southbridge; 10, Webster; and 11, Worcester.) The map is supplied by the Massachusetts Department of Public Utilities.*

resources is bound to be strongly conditioned by the cities. First of all, in such a situation the industries and other economic activities of any city or village are a vital part of the plans for the rural areas around it. In normal times they should (a) be vigorous enough to absorb the surplus farm population and give jobs to the part-time farm families in the "urban fringe" zone, (b) provide processing facilities for the farm and forest products of the areas, and (c) carry a proper share of the tax burden of the county and state in which they are located — in much of New England, of the town in which they are located. The decline of industry in so many New England towns has increased the tax burdens upon the rural real estate. The decline of the industries in Hardwick, Warren, and Millville, for example, has had a direct and immediate effect in raising the property tax rates in these towns, whereas in Hopedale the low rate is largely the result of the town's industrial activity.

It follows from the foregoing that the workers in the cities and villages and in the open country constitute one common pool of labor, with constant movement between the parts of it. Any planning program for either open country or city must design ways and means of getting jobs for this large mass of labor. Obviously it is more than a local problem; but its local aspects must not be neglected. If at any time the jobs are not available, public relief has to come to the rescue, at least until the population gets readjusted.

Again, the income derived from manufacturing and other urban employment determines in large measure the size of the local market for its agricultural products. The most important of these products in Worcester County are fluid milk, eggs, poultry, apples, and vegetables; and all but the apples are in large part consumed locally. The milk requirements of the County are produced largely within its borders and only a little of the local supply is shipped occasionally to Boston or other outside cities. The eggs, poultry, small fruits, and vegetables are all sold in nearby towns and cities. There is, of course, no close correlation between farm income and the size of industrial payrolls; nevertheless, the relation between them is obvious.

It follows from the foregoing that city plans need to be related to the agriculture and forestry of the surrounding area. For this, one needs a basic understanding of the economy of its agriculture and forestry. Such a question as the following becomes significant: Will the dairy farmers of the County be able to stand the competition of outside areas? And similarly for its egg and broiler producers and local growers of vegetables and fruits?

Again, a plan for either a rural or an urban area, or for both combined, needs to plan a marketing setup which will assemble and distribute effectively and economically the products of farms and forests on the one hand, and of the city industries on the other. Little of such market planning has thus far been done.

Also, recreation planning is a common need for both the open country and the city — partly because such opportunities are enjoyed mutually by the two population groups, partly because the servicing of such recreation is a source of rural income, and partly because of the conflicts of interest, overlappings and interweavings of recreational, forest, and farm uses of rural land.

A somewhat similar statement can be made for the planning of highways in rural areas and several other facilities, such as light and power, telephone, and water supply.

THE INDUSTRIES

The latest available census of the industries of the United States was taken in 1947. The one before that was taken in 1939. The changes since 1947, with some important exceptions, have been in the same general direction as those from 1939 to 1947 and earlier. The over-all situation is indicated

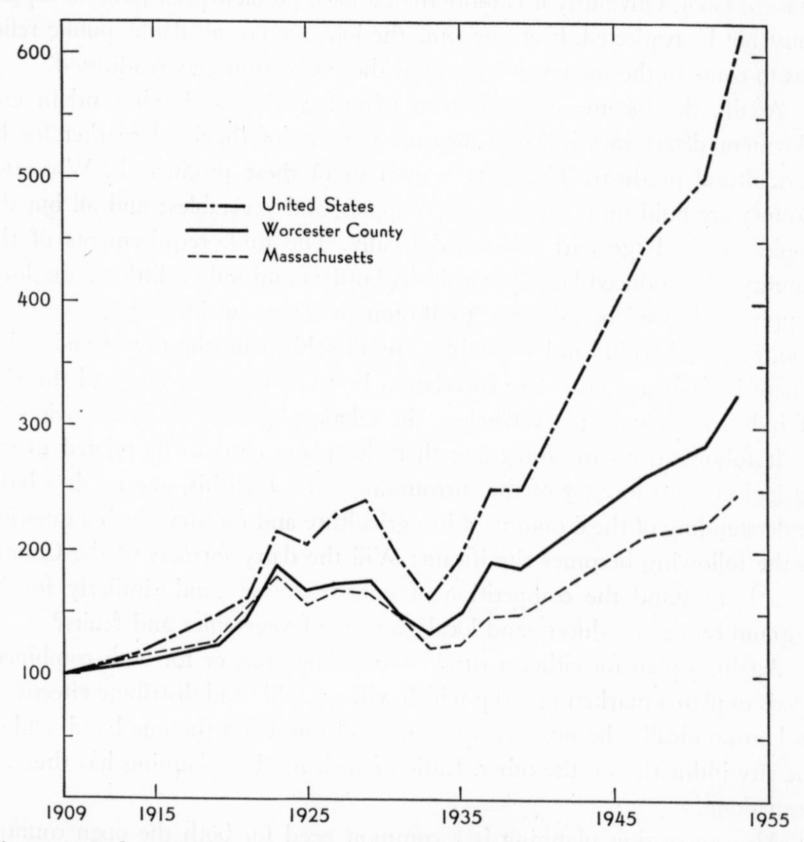

Figure 5. *Index numbers of changes in industrial payrolls, in constant dollars, the United States, Massachusetts, and Worcester County, 1909–1954 (1909 = 100).*

by Figure 5, in which the percentage change in payrolls for the years from 1909 to 1954 for Worcester County is compared with that for Massachusetts and for the United States. As one would expect, the industry of the nation has increased more than that of Massachusetts in this period — 5.8 times up to 1954 as compared with 2.5 times. In a country as young as the United States, industry will be pushing steadily out into new regions — the industrial frontier follows the agricultural frontier, but with a considerable gap between. The comparable figure for Worcester County is an increase of 3.3 times in payrolls from 1909 to 1954.

At the end of the first twenty of these forty-five years, in 1929, the relative increases were United States, 2.4, Massachusetts, 1.6, and Worcester County, 1.7. The comparable growths by 1939 were 2.5, 1.5, and 1.9, and by 1947, 4.2, 2.2, and 2.6, respectively. It is thus apparent that Worcester County has been falling behind the national rate of increase somewhat less than Massachusetts as a whole.

Other measures of manufacturing growth are number of establishments, number of wage earners, and value added by manufactures, as shown in Table 3. The number of wage earners is the best single measure. The employment during the years since World War II has been at a somewhat higher level than that of the six years following World War I. If the figures for value added by manufacture are reduced to a common wholesale price level, the 1952 value was more than twice that of 1919 and a third higher than that of 1929, at the end of that decade of large industrial expansion in the

TABLE 3

Manufacturing Industries of Worcester County, 1909–1954*

Year	Number of establishments	Wages paid during year (thousands of dollars)	Average number of wage earners	Value added by manufacture (thousands of dollars)
1909	1,408	43,146	86,011	90,090
1919	1,470	107,975	102,740	238,523
1929	1,144	105,060	83,670	243,517
1931	1,101	69,166	65,076	149,755
1939	1,106	87,466	77,783	196,685
1947	1,334	255,211	100,077	534,227
1951	1,219	328,479	99,316	748,478
1952	1,205	320,995	94,575	750,510
1954	1,209	288,261	84,041	672,125

* Data supplied by Massachusetts Department of Labor and Industries, except for 1939 and 1947, and for value added by manufacture in 1954, these being from the Federal Census of Industry.

United States. The value added by manufacture includes the effect on output of the increased ratio of capital goods to workers. This ratio would be still larger if labor were measured in hours instead of number of employees. For the United States as a whole, the number of hours of factory labor was no larger in 1947 than in 1909.

These changes can be explained only in terms of particular manufacturing lines. Table 4 compares the changes in number of wage earners employed for the seven most important manufacturing lines in Worcester County.

TABLE 4

*Numbers Employed in Principal Industry Groups in Worcester County, 1909 to 1954**

Year	Machinery, machine tools, and iron and steel products	Textile machinery	Woolen and worsted goods	Cotton goods	Boots and shoes	Paper and paper goods	Furniture
1909......	——	——	11,482	10,331	4,903	1,908	3,915
1921......	6,602	8,695	12,532	9,113	3,722	2,214	3,006
1925......	9,770	8,229	14,331	8,740	4,183	2,595	3,614
1927......	10,114	6,878	12,676	7,081	4,279	2,513	3,599
1929......	11,311	6,232	11,884	3,727	5,213	2,427	3,661
1931......	6,973	4,949	8,969	2,860	5,558	2,171	2,767
1933......	5,812	5,623	9,378	2,420	6,115	1,157	3,111
1935......	7,725	5,520	11,067	1,796	6,865	2,388	3,451
1937......	10,950	7,528	11,129	2,520	8,594	2,583	4,556
1939......	4,158	5,848	9,839	2,096	8,643	2,258	3,995
1947......	6,184	7,087	8,781	2,175	5,636	3,052	4,270
1951......	6,782	11,508	8,890	1,488	5,411	3,076	4,863
1954......	——**	6,453	5,869	924	4,800	4,532	4,463

* Source: Massachusetts Department of Labor and Industries, Boston.
** Comparable data lacking.

Cotton goods declined continuously after 1923. Worsted and woolen goods declined during the 1920's, but recovered in the later 1930's, only to suffer a sharp decline since. Boots and shoes expanded in the 1930's, but have lost much ground since. Paper and paper goods and furniture have a little more than held their own. Textile machinery slumped after 1925, but has recovered recently. The losses in several of these lines, especially after 1939, were more than made up by the growth of output of fabricated metal products and machinery other than textile.

Worcester County, and especially the city of Worcester, has long been important in the production of machinery and machine tools. A wide variety of lathes, drills, presses, grinders, boring machines, woodworking machines, and the like are manufactured in its numerous metal-working establishments. This city is also important for its output of wire and other iron and steel products. In 1947, the value added by the manufacture of machinery (other than electrical machinery) and fabricated metal products was approximately 180 million dollars, or one third of the total manufacturing output of the county, and most of this was in the city of Worcester.

New England got an early start in machinery and metal industries in the last century. The first region to industrialize in a country is likely to be the first to begin producing the machinery used in its factories. Although a large number of its other important industries have since found it advantageous to move west or south, many of the leading machinery and metal-working establishments have not done so. The reasons for this are the heavy investment in plant and equipment, the difficulty of obtaining a sufficient number of skilled machinists and metal workers in a new location, and the fact that the product differentiation arising out of long-established contacts, carefully built-up reputations, and specialized skill of particular workers is more important in this industry than in many others. Nationally known makers of lathes, drills, or boring machines do not face as severe price competition as do manufacturers of more standardized products, such as cotton goods, low-priced shoes, paper, or furniture. The relative importance of New England as a machinery-manufacturing center has declined, it is true, with the growth of the automotive industry; nevertheless, few of the New England firms appear to be at a disadvantage in their present lines and locations.

Three of the largest manufacturers of textile machinery in the United States — the Draper Corporation in Hopedale, the Whitin Machine Works in Whitinsville (Northbridge), and the Crompton and Knowles Loom Works in Worcester — are located in Worcester County. These three firms, each of which employs several thousand men, accounted almost entirely for Worcester County's production of 33 percent of the textile machinery of the United States in 1937. The development of this branch of the machinery industry is of course closely linked with the replacement and expansion policies of the textile industry. At the same time, there has been little tendency for the manufacture of textile machinery to become established in the South. In 1937, only 3.6 percent of the textile machinery was produced in the South, as against 58 percent in New England, and 19 percent in Pennsylvania.

The next most important industry in the County is the manufacture of woolen and worsted goods. At the time of the 1947 Census, it was possible to write that Massachusetts had long been the most important woolen manufacturing state in the nation and that Worcester County had steadily maintained its share of the state total. In 1909, New England was employing 63.5 percent of the workers in woolen and worsted manufactures, and in 1947 it was employing 64.5 percent of them. Unlike the machinery industry, the woolen manufacturing of Worcester County is not concentrated in one or two cities or towns, but is distributed over many towns in the southern part of the County. The economics of large-scale production up to this time had been comparatively slight in this industry. The optimum size of a plant then was one containing from 50 to 75 looms.

The woolen industry had declined in Massachusetts from 1923 to 1935, but a survey made by the state in 1935 showed that only three plants had been moved to other locations. Recovery was strong after 1939, and in 1947 the outlook for the industry was favorable. It was then being said that the skill required in weaving woolen cloth is much greater than that required in weaving cotton, and that any other area attempting to establish a woolen industry would be considerably handicapped at first for lack of skilled workers. Furthermore, Boston had long been the wool-buying center of the United States, with a well-organized wool exchange as well as excellent port and storage facilities for handling the raw product, a good deal of which is imported. Massachusetts mills were also advantageously located with respect to New York City, the principal market for woolen cloth. Rush orders are common in the clothing industry, especially among manufacturers of women's clothing; hence proximity to market is an advantage to any group of manufacturers.

How rapidly conditions in an industry may change is indicated by the following excerpts from Chapter XIV on "The Textile Industry" from the Council of Economic Advisors' report to the President, on *The New England Economy,* 1951.

> The development of new fibers, new machinery, material handling equipment, electronic controls, vacuum cleaning, air conditioning, and other innovations is increasing productivity per man-hour and reducing the number of employees required in the manufacture of textiles. These innovations are affecting New England severely. New machinery is shortening or eliminating operations required to produce yarn or fabric or to finish a piece of cloth. Synthetics are replacing natural fibers, and the form in which rayon yarn arrives at weaving mills reduces the number of employees required to prepare yarn for weaving. High labor costs as well as high prices for natural fibers are stimulating the introduction of more automatic machinery and the use of substitute fibers. As competition among fibers increases within the textile industry, substitutes such as paper and

plastic film products are also making gains as replacements for textile products.
Nevertheless, community inducements such as new plants with low rentals and no taxes in regions less intensively industrialized than New England have attracted worsted firms which have become miniature textile industries. They can process several types of fiber in their new production operations. These firms have expanded in the South and they can utilize employees trained in the cotton system of spinning. Moreover, they have available an abundant supply of new employees whom they can train and employ on the new types of worsted spinning. The importance of a cotton wage scale lower than the wage scale in the northern woolen and worsted division, and high work assignment for employees in the southern textile industry, deserve special mention. Advantages of lower power costs, fuel costs, taxes, and wage rates, and higher work assignments in the opinion of these firms seem to offset the disadvantages of employee training costs, more "seconds" of high value products, and the relatively greater distance from the raw wool market, combing plants, and principal centers of apparel manufacturing.

The paragraphs quoted apply more strongly to cotton textiles than to woolen textiles, once as important in Worcester County as woolen textiles, but employing only 2,175 workers in 1947 and 884 in 1956, compared with 5,149 in woolen in 1956. The decline began earlier with cotton textiles, differences in wage rates, power costs, and labor regulations playing a large role in the early declines. The greatest decrease occurred in Worcester County between 1927 and 1931 when several large mills in Fitchburg and Warren were closed. The mills which remain in the County have a somewhat better chance of surviving, since they have adjusted themselves to the new situation. Furthermore, competition from the South is less severe now that the differences in wage rates and hours have been reduced.

New England as a whole has for a long time been losing out in its share of the nation's shoe manufacturing, and Massachusetts in its share of New England's total. In 1919, Massachusetts was making 30.6 percent of the nation's shoes; in 1947, it was making only 18.5 percent. A little of Massachusetts' loss has been to New Hampshire and Maine, but most of it has been to the Midwest and South. Table 4 shows, however, a large expansion in Worcester County in the 1930's. This remarkable increase, at a time when production of shoes in Massachusetts was declining, can be attributed almost entirely to labor conditions in the industry. The principal shoe towns of Massachusetts, and especially those located on the north shore, where the manufacture of women's shoes is concentrated, were beset with labor troubles. Rapid changes in styles, with workers paid on a piece-work basis, gave rise to constant disputes over wage rates,[3] as a result of which firms

[3] E. M. Hoover, *Location Theory and the Shoe and Leather Industries,* Cambridge, Mass., 1937, p. 238.

moved from Haverhill, Lynn, and Brockton and other important shoe centers to Athol, Spencer, Milford, Worcester, and Webster in Worcester County, where shoe manufacturing had been established for some time. Under the prevailing system of leasing shoe machinery, it is comparatively easy for a shoe firm to move. Almost all of the Worcester County shoe towns have a large French-Canadian population, less inclined then than most other workers to join trade unions, and willing to work at relatively low wage rates. The increase in the shoe production of the County came about not so much because of an increase in the number of establishments located there as through an increase in the business of the firms already established. There has been some recession since the war years.

The manufacture of paper and paper goods in Worcester County is concentrated around the city of Fitchburg. Most of the firms manufacture book papers and Bristol board. The pulp required for these products, principally sulphite and soda pulp, is obtained from a wide variety of foreign and domestic sources, and the Worcester County manufacturers are at no great disadvantage in obtaining their raw materials. Furthermore, they are favorably located with respect to the principal markets. As shown in Table 4, the numbers employed in the paper industry in Worcester County remained stable between 1923 and 1929, and in 1937 employment was again back at the 1925 level, and it has increased somewhat since. Some of the smaller firms in the County have been forced out of business, but the larger ones appear to be holding their own.

By far the most important of the industries based on forest products is the furniture industry, centered around the city of Gardner in the northern part of the County. For more than a hundred years Gardner has been outstanding in its production of chairs and household furniture. Originally established in this locality to utilize the local native white pine, the furniture factories of Gardner now obtain most of their wood from New Hampshire, Vermont, Quebec, and New Brunswick. Yellow birch and maple are the principal species used at present. The furniture industry, like the woolen and shoe industries, has few economies of scale. One very large firm in Gardner, the Heywood-Wakefield Company, dominates the industry in that city, but a number of smaller factories are able to compete more or less successfully with it. Some of the smaller firms have been organized by groups of skilled furniture workers who have left the main factory and started in business for themselves.

The production of furniture in the County has increased steadily since 1921, and the 1937 employment was above the 1929 level. Part of this expansion, however, came because one firm closed its western plants and shifted its western business to New England. The furniture manufacturers in Gardner do not expect the furniture business in that city to expand much. Competition from the South and Midwest is very keen, and in certain lines, notably office furniture, metal is now being extensively used. Most of the large furniture manufacturing centers elsewhere in the United States are now well removed from their supply of wood. Any saving which could be effected in the transporting of wood are offset by higher transportation costs for furniture.

The manufacture of sashes, doors, window frames, interior trim, wooden tubs, pails, and boxes has also been of some importance in the County in the past. Competition from other regions where lumber is more plentiful, however, and from other products, has reduced this industry to one of minor importance. The production of wooden tubs, pails, and boxes has also declined steadily during the last two decades, due to the competition of other types of containers. Wooden candy pails, once important, are now little used. Metal pails have now supplanted wooden pails and tubs in all but a few uses. The manufacture of wooden packing boxes and barrels has also declined steadily because of the competition of paper and cardboard containers. This decline is not due to a shortage of wood, but to the competition of cheaper and better substitutes. Most manufacturers of wooden boxes and pails agree that the supply of white pine suitable for their needs is adequate.

The industries shown in Table 4 represented, in 1947, only about 60 percent of the total in terms of numbers employed. Several products such as abrasive wheels, optical goods, heating and cooking appliances, chemicals, stationery, linen goods, and shirts are very important in the County, but no census data are available for them because one large firm produces most of the output and the Census Bureau is not allowed to release the data in these circumstances.

Not included in the foregoing list is the electrical machinery industry, located in Brookfield, Clinton, and Worcester, which employed 1,739 in 1947, and 1,760 in 1951. This industry has been expanding in New England, although not at the same rate as in the nation.

On the basis of the foregoing analysis, certain general conclusions about the industrial future of Worcester County can be drawn. The predominance of the machinery, machine-tools, and metal-products industries is likely to ensure that manufacturing will not experience a rapid decline in the future. Furthermore, the wide diversity of industries will provide a greater degree of stability than would otherwise be obtained. The manufacture of some products, such as cotton goods, probably woolens and shoes, wooden boxes, carriages and sleds, will continue to decline, and of other products, such as electrical machinery and machine tools, to increase, but at less than the national rate. A group of other industries will about hold their own in absolute terms. In view of these prospects, the present market for the produce of the farms, in so far as it depends on the industrial income of the County, is fairly secure. The opportunities for farmers and their sons to earn a supplementary income by working in local factories will continue about as in the past.

These opportunities, however, are likely to be concentrated more and more in the larger towns and cities, and less in the small mill towns. The proportion of the manufacturing of the County that is carried on in small towns has been steadily declining. In 1909, 15.8 percent of the wages distributed in the County were paid in the 38 small mill towns, whereas in 1937 only 12.8 percent of the total wages were paid in these same towns. This decrease is because it is the textile and forest products industries that are generally located in the smaller towns. The expansion in the cities reflects the growth of the machinery and metal industries. These fared badly during the depression, but have since recovered considerably. Any further expansion which the County may experience is thus more likely to occur in the large towns and cities. The small mill towns, although still important to the industrial economy of the County, no longer attract as many of the new industries as formerly.

TRADE

The 1947 Census of Business reported retail, wholesale, and service trade statistics for counties and cities of 2,500 inhabitants or more and for cities with 200 stores or more. Worcester County had 6,384 retail establishments employing 27,022 paid workers and 7,596 proprietor and family workers. Of these establishments. 1,718 handled food, 1,223 were eating and drinking places, 514 sold apparel, 670 were gasoline stations, 341 sold furniture, furnishings, and household appliances, and 199 were drug stores. Of the retail establishments, 2,316 were in Worcester, 570 in Fitchburg, and 774 more in three small cities, leaving 2,724 to be scattered over the rest of the 60 towns, an average of 50 per town. The Worcester stores had average sales of $98,500 in 1947; those in the four smaller cities $72,500, and the others $48,000. By 1954, the number of retail establishments had declined 359, to 6,025, but food stores alone had declined 409, most of this occurring in the larger cities. Sales per food store had increased almost a third. Only drug stores and drinking and eating places showed an increase in numbers.

The 609 wholesale firms in Worcester County employed a total of 6,229. Of these firms, 411 were in Worcester, 53 in Fitchburg, and 36 in Gardner and Leominster. The average volume of business of the Worcester City wholesalers was $750,000. The number of wholesale firms had increased 15 percent by 1954.

The service trades include amusement houses; laundries, cleaning, pressing and garment repair shops; barber and beauty shops; shoe-repair shops; automobile repair, storage and parking establishments; hotels and tourist courts; photographic studios; funeral service establishments; and an assortment of other establishments, mostly repair shops. A total of 1,293 of these provided employment for 2,231 as proprietors and 4,197 as helpers.

All these three groups of firms combined employed 47,175 workers, or 87 per 1,000 inhabitants in Worcester County in 1950. Out of every 1,000 in the "labor force" of Worcester County in 1950, as labor force is defined by the census, 450 were employed in trade and services. This means that in general if a new industry is added somewhere in the County that employs 1,000 workers, 450 more will be needed to service them. The same effect will be produced if a present industry, or the agriculture of the County, expands to the same extent. And the 47,175 listed does not include doctors, nurses, lawyers, and especially the teachers and other public servants. Part of this extra servicing is, of course, of the families of those who are doing the servicing. The modern city grows in part because of the numbers who make a living simply by "taking in each other's washing."

OFF-FARM WORK

In many ways, however, in an area such as southern New England the closest interdependency of farm and city is in the employment of rural people in urban occupations. The structure of this employment is revealed in six of the ten towns in Worcester County that were studied intensively in 1938, and in which a classification was made of all the farm families having some employment off their home farm.[4] A total of 115 farms classified as commercial, that is, not part time or residential, reported such employment. On 66 of these, the employment was of the farmer himself, or his wife in 2 cases, or a brother or sister in 9 cases. A total of 62 sons and daughters on 44 of these 115 farms were employed off the farm.

[4] Hardwick, Sutton, Charlton, Mendon, Northboro, Grafton.

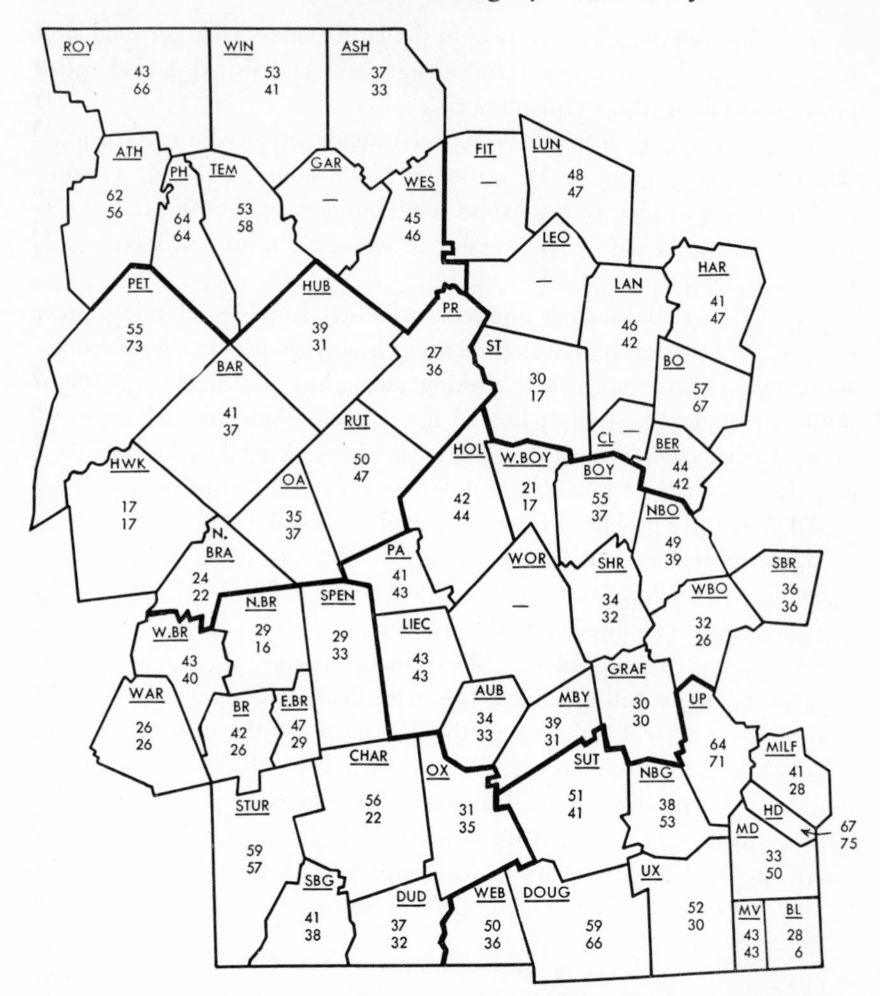

Figure 6. *Percentages of farms with operators doing 100 or more days of off-farm work (upper figure), and with larger off-farm than farm earnings (lower figure), 1949.*

What were the other types of employment of the farm operators? It will be remembered that unemployment was still general in 1938, with prices of farm products still low and jobs hard to find. Six of the 66 were on WPA payrolls. The remainder were distributed among factory work, skilled trades like carpentering and plumbing, other businesses like stores or gasoline stations, and such public services as tax assessor, town clerk, and running a mail route. A few were working on other farms or doing road work part time.

The sons and daughters were most commonly employed in factories, in stores, in offices, or in public service employments, but a few were in the professions like teaching or engineering.

In these six towns, 86 farms were classified as part time in this survey, and 365 as residential, using the census definition of these classes. Of the part-time farmers, 19 had 30 sons and daughters in urban jobs; and of the residential farmers, 66 of them had 116 sons or daughters or sons-in-law employed in urban occupations. The types of employment for the heads of families covered a wider range than for the commercial farmers, but were 40 percent factory or shop work. About a fourth of the family heads were on WPA payrolls. These families also included 8 wives with jobs outside the family and 11 with brothers and sisters holding such jobs.

About a fourth of the farms classified as residential had one acre or less of land, and another fourth had from one to five acres. About half of the part-time farmers had between 10 and 40 acres of land.

Finally, in these six towns there were 22 farmers running retail milk routes, with dairy herds ranging in size from 4 to 120 cows. Some of them bought milk from other farmers.

The pattern of distribution of the off-farm employment over the County is shown in Figure 6. The upper figure in each town measures such employment by percentage of farm operators working off the farm 100 days or more in 1949; the lower figure, by percentage of farms with larger off-farm than farm income. The second measure provides for off-farm employment for other members of the farm family. The averages for the County are 50 for the off-farm working days measure and 47 for the off-farm income measure.

The two measures run fairly close together except in certain towns like Sterling, Uxbridge, and Blackstone, where special circumstances affect the comparison. The 1950 Census does not give separate figures for largely urban towns, like Worcester, Leominster, Fitchburg, Gardner, and Clinton in Worcester County, but there is no general indication that off-farm employment in towns with cities very near to them is larger than in the more rural towns. This suggests that distance is no longer a major factor in such employment.

CHAPTER 5

The People and Their Living

This chapter will present briefly the major pertinent facts about the people of Worcester County, the kind of living they make for themselves, and how they make it, with enough historical background to indicate trends.

POPULATION HISTORY

Let us begin with an over-all review of the history of the population of the different parts of the county for the hundred years from 1850 to 1950 as presented in Figure 7, with the exception of the city of Worcester, which could not possibly be fitted to the scale of 1,000 for each small square. Worcester City's population increased from around 5,000 to 203,500 in this period. Before the railroad came to Worcester, it was smaller than Sutton, which was then on the main stage-coach route to New York.

First of all to be noted is that the population of some of the towns has declined over the whole period — Petersham, Phillipston, Princeton, Hubbardston, Royalston, and Oakham. These are towns with limited areas of good soils and topography which have never acquired any industry except of very small scale, and this has vanished in the past fifty years. Another small group have just about retained what little farming they had — New Braintree, Bolton, Berlin, and Mendon. Another group have had considerable farming throughout, but have gained very little in population — Barre, Brookfield, Charlton, Douglas, Lancaster, Northboro, Southboro. Those that have increased their population considerably have all acquired some industries — Athol, Auburn, Millbury, Northbridge, Oxford, Shrewsbury, Spencer. Then there are the towns that have become important industrial centers like Clinton, Gardner, Milford, Southbridge. A few towns have had a somewhat checkered industrial history — Hardwick, Harvard, Blackstone, Spencer.

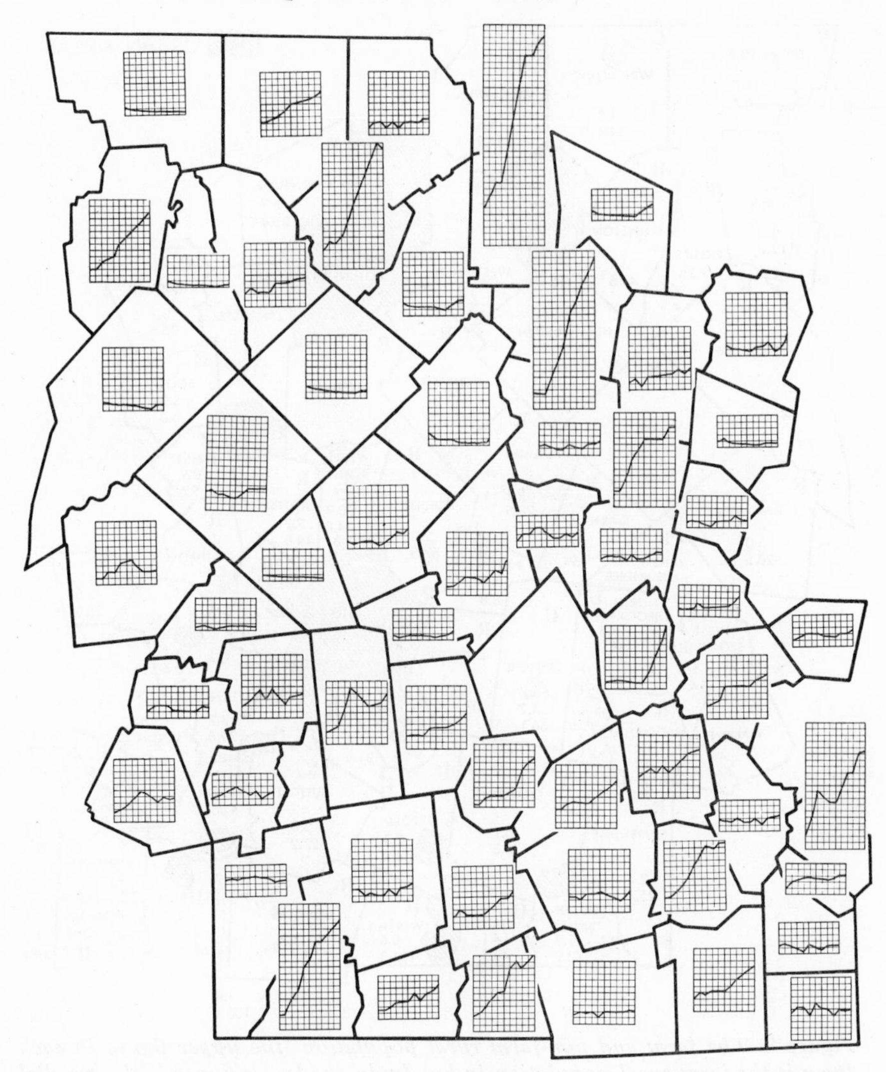

Figure 7. ***Population history of the towns and cities of Worcester County, 1850–1950 (each square = 1,000).***

URBAN VS. RURAL

As the Census Bureau classified population according to residence in 1950, Worcester County was 25.2 percent rural, with a total of 137,800 rural dwellers. This included all the territory outside the "urban" areas that are shown in black in Figure 8. This was an increase of 22.8 percent in the population of this same territory since 1940.

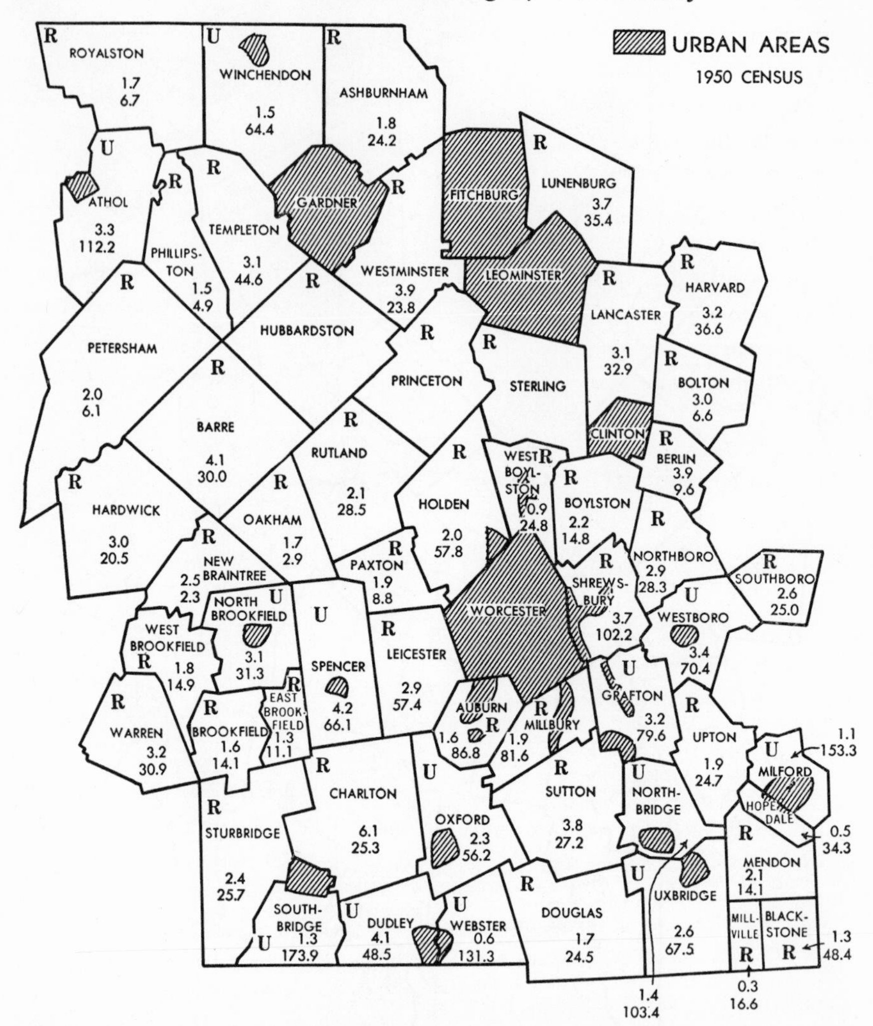

Figure 8. ***The farm and non-farm rural population (the upper figure in each town is the farm-rural population in hundreds; the lower figure is the parallel non-farm rural population), and the urban and rural areas as designated by the 1950 Census. The urban areas include all-urban Worcester plus fringe areas in adjacent towns, four other all-urban towns, and the urban areas in thirteen other towns classified as urban. Towns without urban concentrations of 2,500 or more are called rural (R).***

But the rural-urban figures actually reported by the census differ from these because of a change in the definition of rural *vs.* urban area. The Census Bureau decided, and wisely so, to include as urban the rapidly expanding "fringe" areas around cities and also any unincorporated place of

2,500 or more. For the country as a whole, this increased the urban population from the 59 percent it would have been under the old definition to 64 percent. But in Massachusetts, New Hampshire, and Rhode Island, the change in the definition increased the percentage of rural population. The reason for this is that in New England where the smaller cities are commonly not incorporated, the Census Bureau had been following the rule of calling a whole town urban if it contained one or more places with 2,500 people and half or more of the people in the town lived in such places, and calling urban *all* the population in the town. In 1950, only the people actually living within the boundaries of these urban areas were classified as urban.

The urban population of Worcester County was made up as follows in 1950:

(a) People living in the five all-urban towns and adjacent fringe area adjoining Worcester (all black in Figure 8)	297,120
(b) People living in urban areas in thirteen other towns in the county (marked "U" in Figure 8)	89,883
Total	387,003

Three of these thirteen towns were classified as rural in 1940. The urban areas of these towns added 9,275 to the urban population of 1950. But the three towns which were shifted the other way in 1950 had 16,794 people called urban in 1940. Much more important was the 31,196 of the population in the white areas shown on Figure 8 of the urban towns that was called rural in 1950 but urban in 1940.

The population of the five all-urban towns was almost stationary from 1930 to 1940 and gained only 2.9 percent from 1940 to 1950.[1] The total population of the thirteen other towns called urban in 1950 was 6.3 percent larger than it had been ten years earlier.

The rural population of Worcester County in 1950 was made up as follows:

(1) People living in 42 towns classified as all rural in 1950	106,570
(2) People living in 13 towns classified as urban in 1950	31,766
Total	137,766

[1] Even some of this gain may have been caused by adding some additional fringe areas in towns adjoining Worcester.

This total of 137,766 represents an increase of 36.0 percent over that of 1940. But most of this was due to the addition of the rural population of the sixteen towns. For the forty-two towns classified as rural in both years, the increase was 22.5 percent. This 22.5-percent gain is clearly larger than the 2.9 gain for the five all-urban towns, and only 6.3 for the thirteen towns combining rural and urban.

It thus would appear that the rural population of Worcester County gained much more than the urban in the 1940–1950 census decade. A similar comparison for the all-urban and all-rural towns in the 1930–1940 decade shows that the urban towns actually lost a little while the rural towns were gaining 13 percent.

FARM VS. NONFARM RURAL

The next step is to separate this rural population into farm and nonfarm. This is difficult because of the necessity of deciding exactly what is a farm and what is not. For the county as a whole, and according to the new census definition of rural and urban and of a farm, 89.1 percent of the rural population of Worcester County was nonfarm in 1950. Using the old rural-urban definitions and the 1940 farm definition, the percentage of nonfarm would have been 87.9. This would have been true even after adding to urban the fringe areas shown in Figure 8. In 1940, with the old definitions for both, the percentage was 79.3. How much of the shift is due only to definitional changes cannot be stated, but the spread of nonfarm living into nonurban territory was undoubtedly a large factor. The simple fact is that more and more of the people in this region are making their homes outside of cities of 2,500 and over. But we shall see presently that most of these do not qualify as part-time or residential farmers.

From Figure 8 it is apparent at once which of the towns are dominantly urban as far as occupation and residence is concerned, though they might not be so classified by the census. Holden, Leicester, Auburn, Millbury, and Shrewsbury, adjoining Worcester, have from twenty to fifty times as much nonfarm as farm rural population, even after some of the population of these towns is counted as part of the City of Worcester. But New Braintree has more farm than nonfarm, and Hubbardston and Sterling have a third as many farm as nonfarm rural people.

PART-TIME AND RESIDENTIAL FARM

The farms classified as residential in 1950 were those with sales of farm products of less than $250 that still qualified as farms under the 1950 census definition. This means that they had sales of farm products of between $150 and $250 even though they might have had less than three acres of land, or had three or more acres of land and sold or consumed in the family 150 dollars' worth, exclusive of the family garden, without exceeding the 250-dollar limit for sales. Either these families had other income or worked off the farm less than 100 days, for if they worked off-farm more than this and had sales of less than $1,200, they were classified as part-time farmers. Worcester County had 1,234 residential farms in 1950, and 557 part-time farms, compared with 2,430 commercial farms. Thus over 40 percent of the census farmers of Worcester County are mostly less than half-farmers. Figure 6, in fact, showed eleven towns in which more than half the families had larger off-farm than farm incomes in the 1950 Census. This is not a new development, but the 1940's saw an expansion of it in spite of the greater availability of urban jobs at the time. The town of Mendon, for example, had 105 residential farmers in 1930, as compared with only 30 commercial farmers, and Northboro had 77 residential and 60 commercial.

The tightening up of a definition of a farm in the 1950 Census in the manner indicated in Chapter 2, combined with a very limited amount of consolidation into larger units and some actual reduction of farming operations on the smaller-scale farms, resulted in a reduction of the number of farms in Worcester County from 5,834 in 1940 to 4,234 in 1950. The 1945 count, for reasons explained, ran up to 6,505. The decade decline was mostly in the size groups of under 10 acres and 10 to 29 acres. But even the larger size groups include some farms with nearly all woodland and very little farming that were ruled out by the new definition. The enumerators in Massachusetts actually reported over 30,000 tracts of land or "places" as farms that were ruled out as farms by the Census Bureau because they had virtually no agriculture at all.[2]

The reduction in farming operations on the smaller-scale farms in the 1940–1950 decade came about mainly because off-farm employment was unusually available. Some families gave up farming almost altogether. Others merely reduced the scale of their operations to what they and their families could or cared to handle along with a full-time job. Some full-time farmers became part-time farmers.

TENURE

A few statements will suffice concerning tenancy in Worcester County, since only 12 percent of the farmers did not own all the land they were

[2] The enumerators were instructed to fill in the schedule on land and agriculture for every place when the answer was "yes" to the question: "Is this house on a place of 3 or more acres?"

farming in 1949, and only 9 percent were renting all of it. Most of the additional rented land was a piece of pasture or hay land on a place nearby that was no longer a farm or only a part-time or residential farm. The rental was usually for cash or on some irregular arrangement that the enumerators did not classify as either share or cash. Only 45 of the farms in the whole county were operated by hired managers.

As for hired labor considered as a possible tenure stage, 923 of the farmers reported employing a total of 2,119 "regular" hired workers in 1949. This means that there was available for advancement to the operator tenure stage about two hired laborers for every three commercial and part-time farmers. In addition, there were 1,269 unpaid family workers who had worked at least fifteen hours on the farm in the week preceding enumeration. Obviously a major fraction of these will have to find some other occupation than farming, even though the average age of the farm operators of Worcester County was 53 years and an unusual rate of replacement is called for if the agriculture of this area, as in New England generally, is to do nothing more than hold its own.

A special analysis of the age distribution of the farm operators in a sample of nine of the towns in 1939 by Professor Walter McKain, now of the University of Connecticut, and Harry Norcross, now in the Agricultural Marketing Service of the U.S.D.A., showed that one fourth of the farm operators were 61 years of age and over, and half this number over 70. In Winchendon and North Brookfield, two fifths of them were 61 or more. However, a breakdown by commercial, part-time, and residential showed that less than a sixth of the commercial farmers were over 61 years old. No doubt some of the residential farmers are at least semi-retired.

NATIVITY

For Worcester County as a whole, 21.4 percent of the population 26 years old or over were foreign-born in 1950. Over a fourth of the foreign-born came from Canada, and two thirds of these from Quebec. In order of numbers, the other principal countries of origin are Italy, Poland, Eire, Sweden, Lithuania, Finland, England and Wales, and Russia. The farms of Worcester County apparently have about their proportional share of the foreign-born. In the ten towns surveyed by McKain and Norcross, 26 percent of the operators were foreign-born — over two fifths in Grafton, North Brookfield, and Mendon, but only one fifth in Sterling and Petersham.

These foreign-born farmers had mostly been farm laborers in their native lands. For the most part they took city jobs when they came to this country, and shifted to agriculture only after they had saved up a little money. Some of them, especially of certain nationalities, are part-time farmers whose families do a good part of the farming while the head of the family holds a full-time off-farm job.

A study made by Professor McKain of the farm families of the town of Hardwick in 1939 indicated, however, that more of the sons of native-born than of foreign-born farmers were planning to take over the family farm in the next generation.

Not only is the nativity of the present generation of interest, but that also of the generation before. If native-born of foreign parentage is combined with foreign-born, the percentage in 1930, according to a special study made by the Division of Farm Population and Rural Life, ran around 70 in Worcester, Fitchburg, and Gardner, and in some of the small factory towns like Milford, Blackstone, Millville, Webster, Dudley, and Southbridge. But some of the more agricultural towns like Sterling, Hardwick, the Brookfields, Spencer, and Charlton had around 50 percent or more foreign stock if thus defined. This is because they had made the transfer from city work to farming a generation before 1930 and were still farming. In only four of the towns, Petersham, Princeton, Harvard and Berlin, was this percentage below 40.

PLANE OR CONTENT OF LIVING

Surely we would like to know the kind of a living that the farm people of Worcester County are earning from their farming or farming plus other employment. To measure this directly entails taking a full inventory of everything that goes into living, not only the food, clothing, housing, and the like, but health, education, and recreation, and is almost an impossible undertaking. What rural social scientists are doing instead is to measure a selection of items that they have found by testing to be good indicators of plane or content of living.

As a measure for the United States as a whole, Dr. Margaret Hagood of the Farm Population and Rural Life branch of the U.S.D.A. is now using four items, properly weighted, as follows: (1) percentage of farms with electricity, (2) percentage of farms with telephones, (3) percentage of farms with automobiles, and (4) average value per farm of products sold or traded, the last adjusted for changes in the purchasing power of the farmers' dollars. The average of these for the whole country in 1945 is called 100. New England on this base had an index of plane of living in 1945 of 137. The only census division with a higher index was the Middle Atlantic states with

139. The indexes below 100 were all in the South, but about half of the farms in the nation are in the South. By 1950, New England's index had risen to 152 while the nation's average was rising to 122 and the South's from 65 to 92.

By states, only five in the country have higher indexes than Massachusetts, namely, Rhode Island and Connecticut in New England, New York and New Jersey, and California. It is thus apparent that nearness to large cities is a large factor in the plane of living when measured in this manner, partly because it makes electricity and telephone service more accessible, but partly because of the markets for fresh foods that make possible larger incomes. By contrast, a few counties in the remote Kentucky highlands or sandhill parts of Mississippi and Alabama have indexes down around 30.

Dr. Hagood has completed such indexes for 1940 and 1950. Massachusetts started with 120 in 1930, and the country as a whole with 75. In effect, the rest of the country has been catching up with the states near the big cities in the Northeast; that is, the people in the more distant areas are getting to live more and more like the people in the big cities or near them.

Within Massachusetts, the differences are small, from 152 in Hampshire County to 171 in adjoining Hampden, and 161 for adjoining Worcester. But Worcester County rose 45 points on the index scale from 1930 to 1950 while the state was rising only 38 points.

Within Worcester County, the range in the index numbers in 1945 as computed by Dr. Hagood's staff was as indicated in Figure 9. No clear geographic or other pattern is discernible. If one omits Winchendon with the lowest index of all, 105, the urban towns average 166, which is 11 points higher than the 1946 average of 155. The towns with relatively low ratios of nonfarm to farm-rural — like Bolton, Oakham, Petersham, and New Braintree — tend to have low indexes, but Hubbardston and Sterling in this group have high indexes. From Worcester eastward they run high, and fall off westward from Worcester. In the smaller factory towns southeastward, the indexes are about average.

No doubt nativity factors enter into the low indexes for Westminster and Winchendon. The more detailed analysis of nine of the towns by McKain and Norcross showed the foreign-born having fewer facilities and poorer housing than the native-born; this is also true for part-time and especially residential farmers as compared with commercial. These men used a more comprehensive index than Dr. Hagood's, scoring each farm from −1 to +5. The housing was graded −1, 0, +1, and so on according to its condition, and similarly for the other components. Only 1 in 8 of

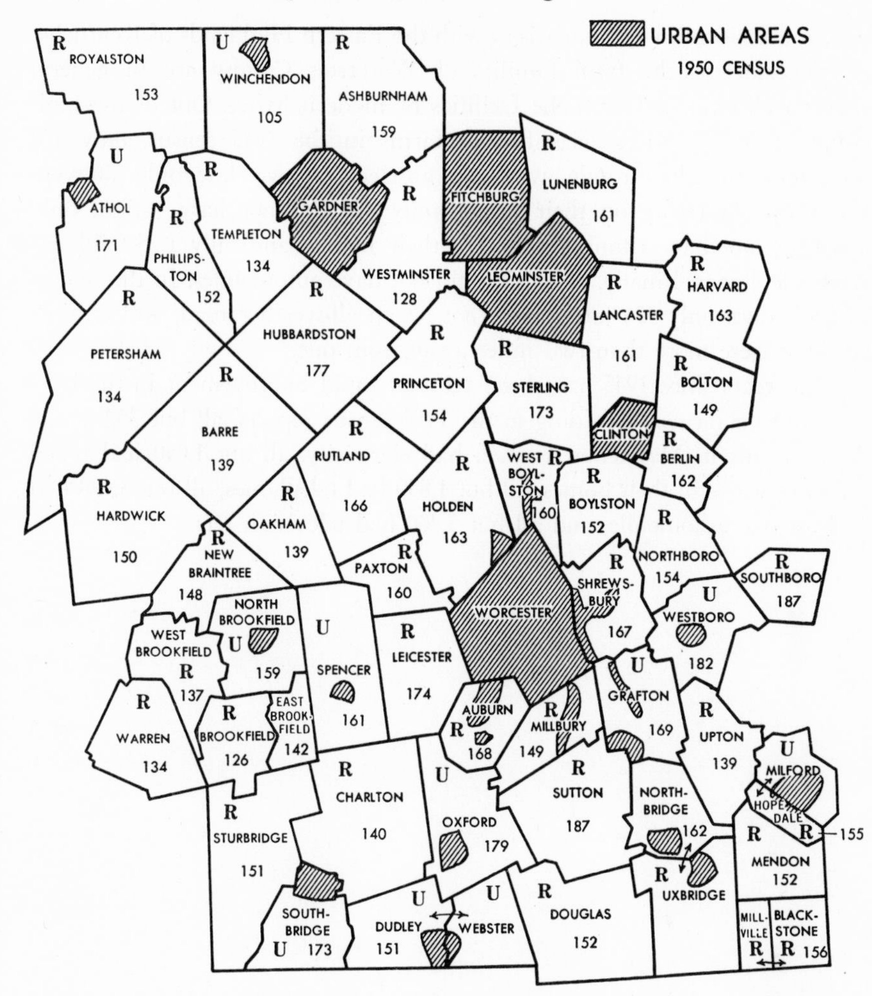

Figure 9. ***Plane of living by towns, 1945 (United States average = 100). (These index numbers by towns were supplied by Dr. Margaret Hagood of the Division then called Farm Population and Rural Life of the U.S.D.A. Two towns are combined in several cases.)***

the commercial farms in the nine towns ranked 2 or lower, compared with 1 in 4 for the part-time and 1 in 3 for the residential farms. The comparison for native-farm and foreign-farm was 1 in 6.0 and 1 in 3.6 respectively. Less than 1 in 10 of the houses were rated in strictly poor condition, and most of these were on residential farms.

It should be pointed out that even in Worcester County there are corners so remote that they are inhabited by families living near enough to a self-sufficing basis to invite comparison with the Eastern Highlands of Kentucky.

Nevertheless, the farm families of Worcester County are in general pretty well equipped with the facilities of modern living. Out of the high count of 6,505 "places" classified as farms in the 1945 census, only 436 were more than half a mile away from an electric power line, only 550 were not using electricity on their farms, only 470 did not have radios, only 1,300 did not have running water in their homes, and only 1,750 did not have telephones. Finally, only 1,580 did not have automobiles. In the matter of highways, only 924 farms were not on an all-weather road, and only 43 of these were more than two miles away from one.

The years since 1945 have been years of rapid improvement in the level of living on farms. According to the 1954 census reports, all but 352 of the 17,361 farms in Massachusetts then had electricity, all but 1,050 had piped running water in their homes, all but 1,850 had telephones, all but 3,490 had at least one automobile, and all but 5,400 had television sets.

CHAPTER 6

Land Use

This chapter will undertake to present briefly the over-all pattern of land use in Worcester County as it was in 1950, with some historical background. Detailed treatment of the town of Hardwick is reserved for Chapter 11. The six chapters following deal with the six sections into which the County has been divided for this undertaking. The best time to present details of present land use is when the plans for adjustments to new uses are outlined in these chapters.

HISTORICAL

Present land use in Worcester County and Southern New England generally can be understood only against a background of history. The census data indicate that the high point in land in farms and improved land in farms in Southern New England was reached around 1850 or 1860, but a census comparable with those from 1880 on might well have shown a peak in 1830 or 1840. Figure 10 shows for Massachusetts in solid lines the census figure changes since 1920 in number of farms and land in farms, and in broken lines what the changes would have been, as nearly as can be estimated, if the census definition of a farm and census methods in 1920 had been followed since. The 1940 census definition of a farm and enumeration procedures were similar to those of 1920. These estimated figures surely come much closer to indicating the actual changes.[1] The 1930 Census was unusually incomplete; those of 1925, 1935, and 1945, as already explained, counted more places as farms than the regular ten-year censuses; and the censuses of 1950 and 1954 are not comparable with any preceding ones. This graph in Figure 10 must not be interpreted to mean, however, that the

[1] For the method of determining these adjusted series, see Chapters 4 and 9 of John D. Black, *The Rural Economy of New England*.

present census procedures are wrong and count too few farms. As a matter of fact, they are a big improvement over those of 1920 and 1940. The graph does show that if farms had been enumerated in 1954 in the same way they were in 1920 and 1940, Massachusetts would have been reported in the 1954 Census as having around 24,000 farms instead of less than 18,000.

Census practice has affected acres of land in farms, however, much less than numbers of farms because it was mainly the small farms that were enumerated erratically after 1920. The broken lines indicate that following the 1920–1940 census procedures in 1954 would have added only 160,000 acres of farm land in all of Massachusetts, or one tenth, as compared with one fourth in number of farms.

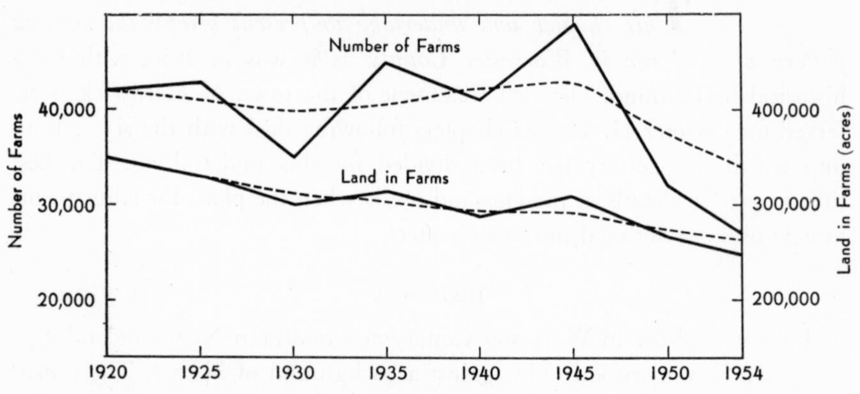

Figure 10. ***Land-use changes in number of farms and acres of land in farms, in Massachusetts, 1920 to 1954. Census series (solid line) and series as estimated in terms of census definitions and methods of 1920 and 1940 (broken line).***

Series for the rest of Southern New England would closely resemble these for Massachusetts. That they would for Worcester County alone is evident from the four series of census data shown in Figure 11. The changes in number of farms follow closely those for the state since 1920. The sharp increase in amount of improved land in 1910 was probably entirely a census irregularity; defining "improved" land so that the enumerators would all label it alike proved so impossible that the question has been omitted from the schedule since 1940. In New England, for example, when did land once in open meadow or pasture cease to be improved as it began to fill in with shrubs and then young trees? The amount of improved land shown in Figure 11 has been calculated since 1940 by combining cropland and plowable pasture. It excludes open pasture from which the stones have not been removed, this being included in agricultural land, however.

Probably at least 80 percent of the land of Worcester County was in farms in 1830 to 1850. By 1880, the census count showed 71 percent in farms; by 1910, 62 percent, by 1940, 42 percent only. A comparable figure for 1950 would be around 40 percent. The percentages of farm land in crops fell off only from 24 to 21 percent between 1880 and 1910, and had recovered to 25 percent in 1940. It was 37 percent in 1950 mainly as a result of casting out of the farm count a good many places that were almost all woodland

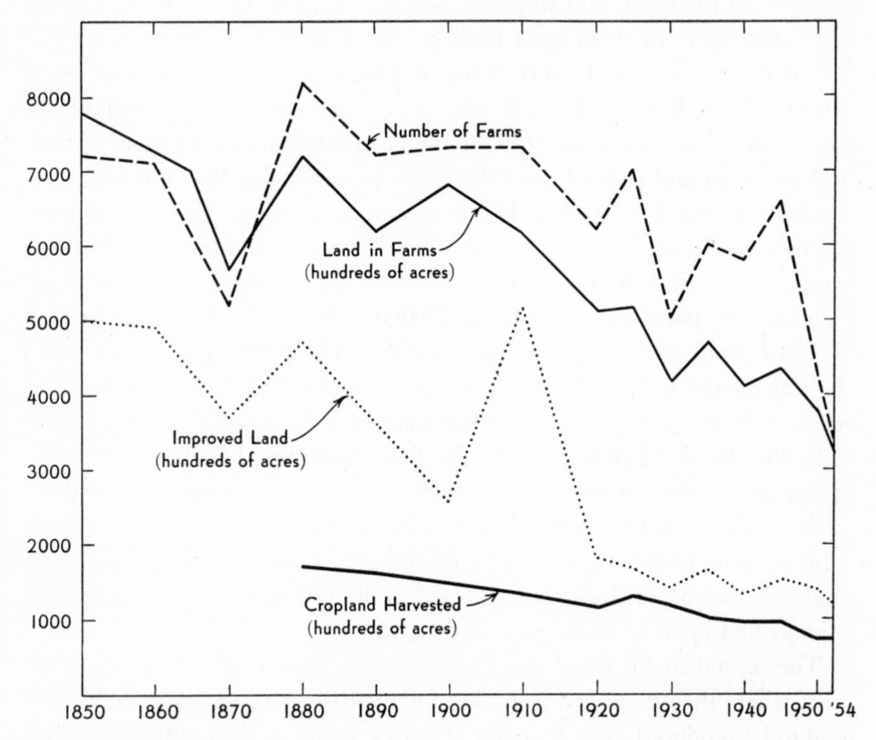

Figure 11. ***Land-use changes in Worcester County, 1850–1954 (acres in hundreds).***

or very poor pasture and that had less than $150 worth of farm output. The changes in the distribution of the rest of the land in farms among woodland, woodland pasture, and open pasture cannot be traced from the census figures for the whole period, but from 1925 to 1950 both open pasture and woodland in farms pastured fell off more than a half, and woodland not pastured increased a little. The farmers seem to be concentrating their pasture in fewer acres. They have in fact been forced to do this because, as explained in Chapter 3, pasture which is not kept productive gradually reverts to shrubs and then trees. In the last stage, the farms finally cease to be farms, which is mainly the way in which the less than 20 percent nonfarm land before 1850 became about 60 percent a hundred years later.

The decline in Worcester County agriculture which set in by 1840, if not earlier, is usually associated with the building of the Erie Canal and the railroads, which opened up the virgin Midwest to settlement and gave fertile new areas access to northeastern markets. But even before this, some young people from the farms had migrated northward, or westward to New York State. Also more of them were finding jobs in the factories that developed first along the inland streams, using waterpower, and then in the larger coastal cities and along the railroads. As the interior of New England developed in the decades from 1650 on, the farm families cleared more of their land for crops and pasture until there was little left that was not too stony, or sandy, or wet for farming. In the meantime, the land first cleared commonly tended to become acid or less fertile because it needed liming and more manure than it was getting. Some of the counties nearer the coast began to lose population as early as 1790 and 1800. Also, in the meantime, the farm population was multiplying rapidly. The simple fact is that much of rural Southern New England was overpopulated in 1830, like much of our rural South in the last eighty years at least.

In the decades following 1840, the first major trend in land use was a change from grain to hay and livestock. This reduced somewhat the drain on the land, but still the pastures and hayfields degenerated. Enough of them grew up to old-field white pine in the decades from 1850 on so that New England from Massachusetts northward to the tall mountains came by 1900 to be looked upon as white pine forest area.

The second major trend was the growth of New England's cities to the point where they furnished a market for increasing quantities of foods that need to be produced near the point of consumption — fluid milk and cream, fresh eggs, live poultry, and fresh fruits and vegetables. A few areas had special advantages in production of farm products for consumption outside New England — Cape Cod in cranberries, Aroostook County in potatoes, the Connecticut Valley in cigar-leaf tobacco, southeast Maine in blueberries, Vermont in maple sugar, and central Maine in canning crops. Together these two outlets for farm products added up to enough so that with the growth of cities by 1910 the decline in New England agriculture in the aggregate had clearly begun to level out. This leveling out continued through the 1920's and 1930's; then came an almost doubling of poultry production from 1930 on, offset somewhat by a decline in potato consumption. As will be developed in Chapter 7, however, Worcester County's agriculture is largely oriented not only to New England markets, but particularly to Worcester County markets.

The changes in woodland use of land in this area have of course been almost the reverse of those in agricultural use. It is commonly possible in Worcester County today to look over a tract of forest land, like that now in the Harvard Forest, and tell what parts of it were once cropland because the surface stones were removed and piled into stone walls (fences), what parts were open pasture since only the trees were cleared off, and what parts have always been woodland, though perhaps logged two or three times. This logging provided the lumber for farm dwellings and barns, but much more for the growing cities and wood-using industries. Fuel use was important until toward the end of the last century. The old-field white pine stands were usually logged when ten to twelve inches in diameter, much of if for use as boxwood. As explained in Chapter 3, it was usually succeeded, except in the sandier soils, by hardwoods: including oaks, ash, maple, birch, beech, but with oaks predominating. These would have made good hardwood forests under proper treatment. Instead, the trees were usually cut when they had reached cordwood size, and were then followed by a poor stand of stump-sprout trees. Much of the present woodland in Worcester County has had such a history. This is true of the major part of the land once cleared and now no longer in farms and of all the woodland still in farms except that on land which was never cleared. The kind of cutting practiced on this latter type of land has usually made the stands poorer after each cutting. The practice of letting cattle graze in the woodlands has also prevented normal regeneration down through the years on much of the woodland still on farms.

PRESENT LAND USE

The diagrams in Figure 12 show in parallel the census-data division of land use in Worcester County in 1925 and in 1954. Land not in farms in 1925 was 45 percent of the total. Part of the increase to 67 percent to 1954 was due to the more rigorous definition of a farm in 1950 and 1954 than earlier. The 377,189 acres still reported as in farms in 1950 and 323,534 in 1954 were divided as in Table 5.

The largest shift in recent years has been from woodland pasture to woodland not pastured. This means that cattle are being fenced out of more of the woodlands. Woodland pasture ordinarily carries less than a fifth as many cattle as open pasture, poor as most of this is. The "other land in farms"

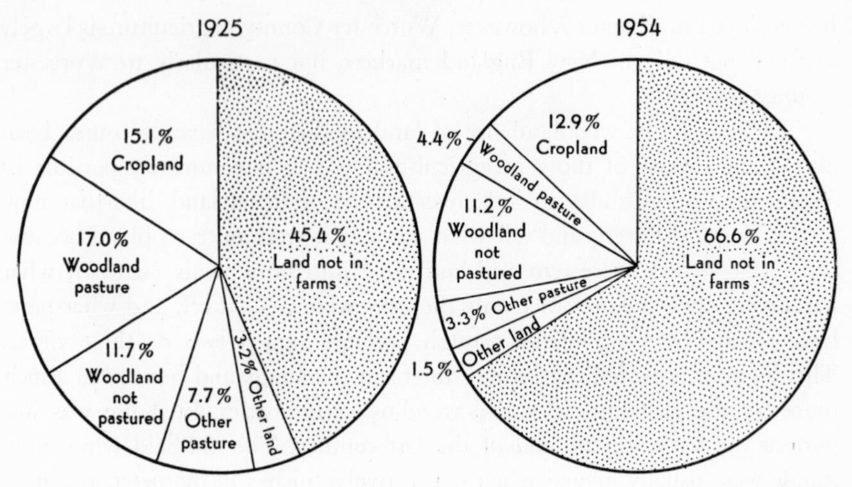

Figure 12. *Division of land in Worcester County, 1925 and 1954, according to census data.*

consists of land occupied by farmsteads, roads, and lanes, and wasteland.

Thus only about 43 percent of what land is in farms is in really productive agricultural use. This means about one acre in six of all the land of Worcester County. One driving along the roads of Worcester County will sometimes wonder where even the one acre in six can be.

For any detailed analysis of land use, one needs accurate data for smaller units than counties. That the census data for the towns of Worcester County will not serve too well for this is evident from Figure 13, in which is

TABLE 5

Divisions of Land in Farms in Worcester County among Different Uses in 1950 and 1954

Land use	1950 Acres	1950 Percentage of total	1954 Acres	1954 Percentage of total
Cropland harvested	82,083	22.4	71,155	22.0
Cropland used for pasture	36,624	9.7	37,801	11.6
Cropland idle	20,278	5.3	15,938	5.0
Other open pasture	39,581	10.8	32,326	10.0
Woodland pasture	59,594	16.2	42,974	13.3
Woodland not pastured	117,271	30.4	108,323	33.5
Other land in farms	21,768	5.7	14,844	4.6
Total	377,189	100.0	323,534	100.0

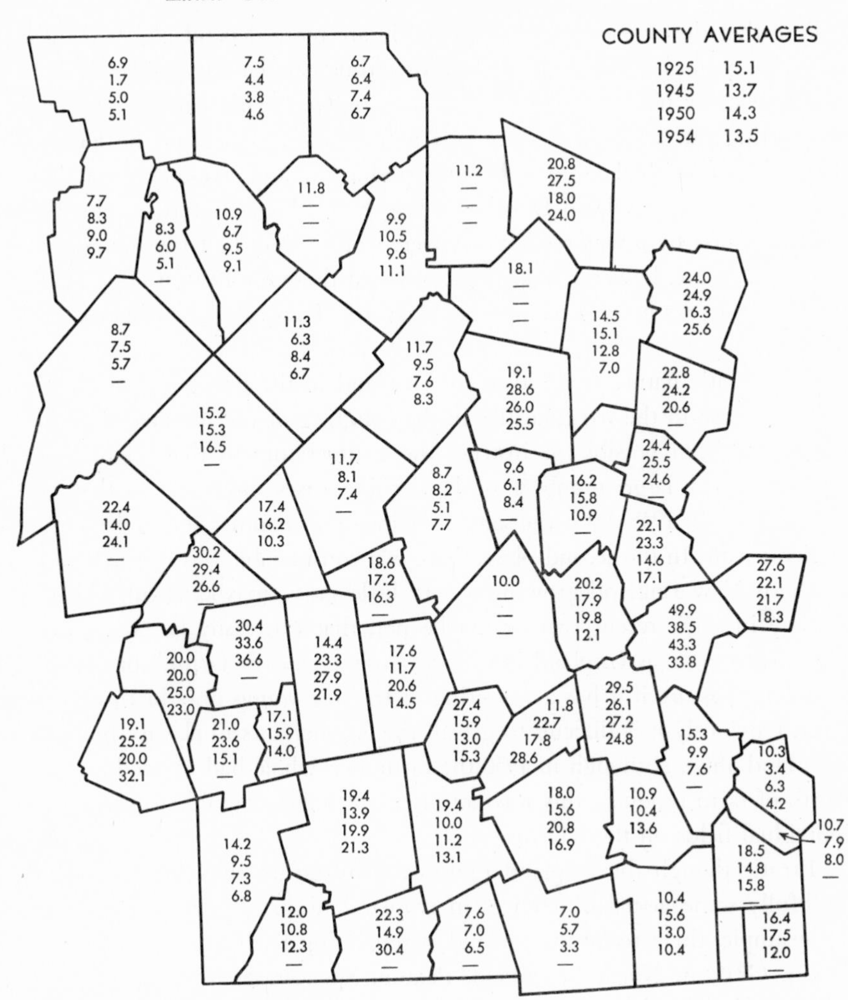

Figure 13. *Cropland by towns in Worcester County, 1925 (upper figure), 1945, 1950, and 1954 (lower figure) as reported by the Census, expressed as percentages of the total land area. (Dash signifies that the data are not available separately for that year.)*

recorded for 1925, 1945, 1950, and 1954 for each town the percentage of the total land area of the town which were reported as cropland (cropland harvested, pastured, and idle combined). The totals for all towns combined run fairly even over this period, 15.1, 13.7, 14.3, and 13.5 percents. But observe how erratic for individual towns are those of Charlton, Leicester, Lunenburg, Milford, Millbury, Sterling, Sutton, and Warren. It is reasonable to believe that the acreages reported for 1950 are more dependable than those of earlier years because then, for the first time, the enumerators were told to report every piece of land of three acres or more with a house on it and the sorting out was done afterwards in the central office on the basis of other data furnished as to sales and production and livestock kept. The analysis in Chapters 11 to 17 is based largely on this assumption. The 1954 census reports by towns separately covered only about half the towns. The 1954 returns are, however, not consistent with those for 1950 in some of the towns — for example, Lunenburg, Harvard, Lancaster, Northboro, and Warren.

The erratic nature of the data for cropland in the past has been due in the first place to the irregularities in the counting of the number of farms. It has not been possible to instruct the enumerators so that all of them have classified large numbers of border-line cases alike, or so that the enumerators in 1945 did it the same as some other enumerators did it in an earlier census. In the second place, there is a considerable acreage of land in southern New England growing a very little grass, maybe pastured or cut for hay in some recent year or maybe not, that can easily be classified as open pasture, or as cropland idle, or as "other land in farms," or even as woodland pasture if it has a scattering of trees or young gray birch clusters on it. Obviously it is difficult to get all the enumerators to classify much of such land alike. Although in 1950 the farm as a whole had to produce $150 worth of farm products, this was not always a sufficient guide to classifying individual fields on these farms.

Erratic though the cropland figures are by farms, they may point out truthfully some actual differences in cropland history by towns. Probably, for example, the acreage in cropland is remaining fairly constant in Barre, Berlin, Grafton, North Brookfield, Paxton, Spencer, Sterling, and several others, as indicated in Figure 13, but is falling off in Auburn, Blackstone, Boylston, Holden, Oakham, and others. The increases between 1945 and 1950 probably resulted mostly from adding in places missed in these towns in 1945, as in Dudley, Hardwick, Leicester, and others.

The acreage of cropland of all descriptions reported was only 5 percent less for the County as a whole in 1950 than in 1925; the more thorough reporting of land with houses on it in 1950 partly offset the cutting out of small farms. The parallel cropland harvested figures tell a different story, a decline of 42 percent. Most of this difference was surely due to changes in census procedure, but some of it reflects an increasing amount of poor hay that is no longer harvested. Most of the decrease in harvested acres reported came between 1945 and 1950, and the years from 1950 through 1954 showed a still larger decrease. Several towns, however, reported more, or almost as much, harvested acreage in 1950 as in 1945, notably Dudley, Charlton, Hardwick, Sutton, Royalston, and Templeton. The sharpest declines reported were in the Brookfields, Lunenburg, Northboro, Shrewsbury, Westminster, and Uxbridge.

The reported acreage of open pasture was almost the same in these three census years, 74,000, 80,000, and 76,000, in sequence. Nearly half of the 76,000 in 1954 was cropland used for pasture. The 1950 Census reported, however, that only 15,000 of the 80,000 had been plowed within seven years. It would appear that much of the open pasture is what is ordinarily referred to as "permanent" pasture, which in New England means that it is probably getting poorer all the time. The reported acreages of open pasture are the most irregular of all, thirteen of the towns reporting a half more in 1950 than in 1945, and seven towns a half less. Obviously census irregularities account for nearly all of these differences.

The highly erratic counting of number of farms is evident from Figure 14.[2] The general trend downward is so strong that for no town except Brookfield are more farms reported in 1950 or 1954 than in 1925, but in Dudley, New Braintree, and Berlin this almost happened. The years 1925 and 1945 are chosen for comparison partly because 1925 is the earliest year for which data by towns separately was obtained by the Massachusetts Experiment Station from the Census Bureau and partly because they are both quinquennial census years. The total counts of these two years are at least roughly comparable, and the number of farms in Worcester County probably declined something like the 8 percent indicated by the census figures for these years. The cropland in farms reported declined by 10 percent in this period, but total land in farms by 24 percent. The count for 1950 is likely to be most consistent throughout the County. If this is true, the count was probably wild in either 1925 or 1945 or both in a dozen or more other towns like Westminster, Lunenburg, Harvard, Bolton, Berlin, Northboro, Shrewsbury, Spencer, Milford, Blackstone, and Barre. Land reported in farms for the County fell off another 13 percent in 1945 to 1950 and another 14 percent in 1950 to 1954, and cropland harvested decreased by about the same amounts. It will be noted that the five all-urban towns for

[2] The 1954 Census combined the returns for pairs of adjacent towns as indicated in Figure 14; thus Paxton with Rutland at 100 (compared with 58 + 53 in 1950) (2) Berlin with Bolton, (3) Phillipston with Petersham, (4) Mendon with Blackstone, (5) Upton with Northbridge, (6) Southbridge with Dudley, (7) Douglas with Webster, (8) Boylston with West Boylston, (9) New Braintree with North Brookfield, and (10) Oakham with Barre.

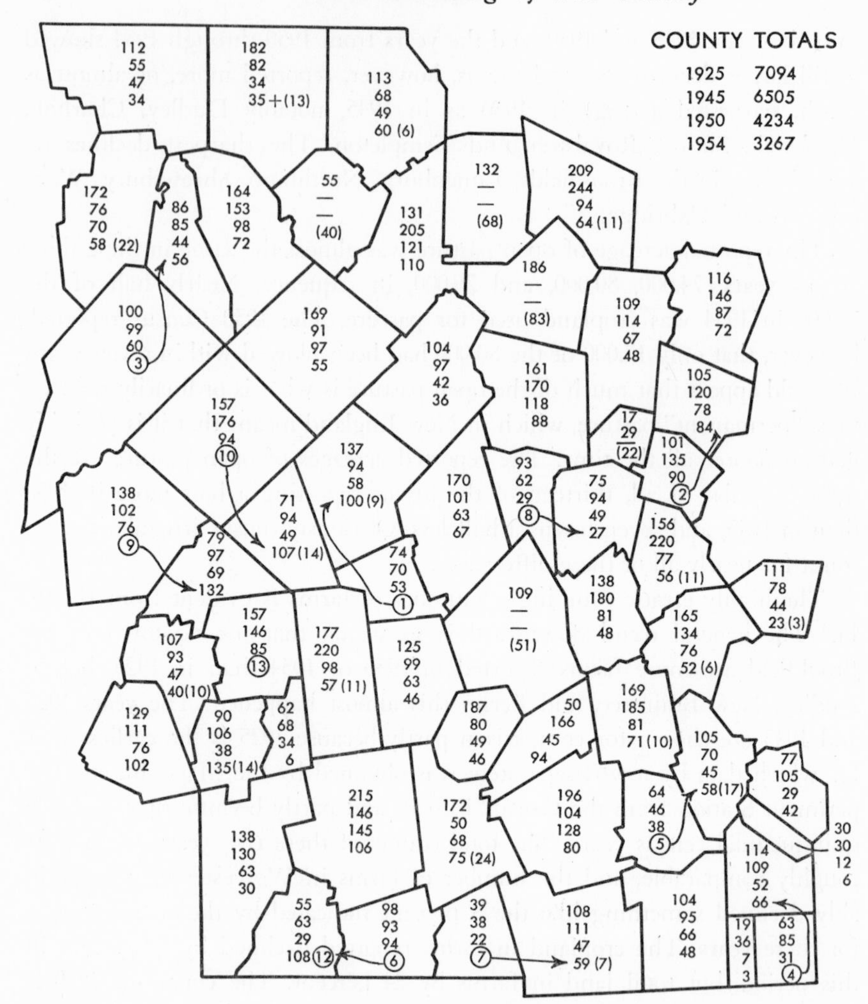

Figure 14. *Number of farms by towns as reported by the Census for 1925 (upper figure), 1945, 1950, and 1954 (lower figures). Data in parentheses are number of farms in "urban areas" within the boundaries of this, and in some cases, adjacent towns. (Dash signifies that no data are available.)*

which 728 farms were reported in 1950 were reported to have 540 farms in 1925.

AGRICULTURE

Worcester County's receipts from sale of agricultural products as reported by the United States Agricultural Census in 1949 and 1954 were distributed as shown in the accompanying tabulation.

	1949	1954
Dairy products	$ 9,490,000	$ 8,859,500
Poultry and poultry products	7,093,500	5,842,400
Other livestock and livestock products sold	2,013,400	1,572,500
Field crops	305,600	312,900
Vegetables	308,800	283,200
Fruits	1,336,800	1,533,900
Nursery and greenhouse products	1,510,500	1,230,000
Forest products	53,600	83,300
Total	$22,112,200	$19,717,700

Thus 85 percent of the sales of agricultural products in Worcester County in 1949 were of livestock products. This was a rise from 78 percent in 1944. As pointed out elsewhere, a sizable fraction of this livestock output is based on feed shipped in from other regions. Forest product sales were four times larger in 1944 than in 1949.

Adjusting for changes in the national index of prices received by farmers, Worcester County's agricultural output decreased 11 percent in the five years from 1944 to 1949 while the nation's agricultural output was increasing 4 percent. In the next five years, it just about held even while the nation's agricultural output was increasing 5 percent. The national index of farm product prices was 250 in 1949 and 249 in 1954. It is easy to see from these figures why Worcester County was no longer in the first hundred of counties in value of farm products in 1950, and still further behind in 1954.

To get a full accounting of the income from the dairy herds, there must be combined with the $9,490,000 in 1949 from the sale of dairy products most of the $1,581,000 from the sale of cattle and calves, thus making a total of at least $11,000,000 for receipts from the dairy herds. This would make the dairy receipts 47 percent of the total farm sales receipts. Poultry came next with 32 percent. Of this, 55 percent was from the sale of chicken eggs. A total of 147 farms sold turkeys, ducks, or geese for $559,000. All but 3 percent of the remainder was from farm fruits and vegetables, and this 3 percent was mostly sales of hay to other farmers near by. Worcester County grows no tobacco. Sales of potatoes amounted to only $105,000.

In terms of acreage, of the 74,134 acres reported in field crops, 90 percent was in hay crops, 6 percent in corn, and 1.3 percent in small grains. Of the hay acreage, only 7 percent was in alfalfa. The remainder was two thirds in clover and/or timothy, and the rest in "other hay," mostly more or less "wild" grasses. Only a minute fraction was in small grains cut for hay. But

130 farmers reported grass silage. All but 12 percent of the corn was used as silage.

The principal change by 1954 was an almost doubling of the alfalfa acreage and of the number of farms reporting grass silage. The corn acreage increased a little, whereas it had declined from 1939 to 1944.

The Census of 1950 reports $8,686,400 spent for feed in 1949 and $1,991,400 spent for livestock and poultry purchases (including hatching eggs). This makes a total of $10,658,000 being spent on the production of the $18,667,000 of sales of livestock and livestock products. It would appear that Worcester County farmers buy nearly half of the feed and forage consumed by their livestock. They buy nearly all of the poultry feed.

The number of cows reported in Worcester County decreased 15 percent between 1940 and 1950 and 6 percent more by 1954. In fact it has been decreasing ever since 1900. But the cows have become more and more of the dairy type. Between 1940 and 1950, milk production fell off only 10 percent, production per cow rising from 6,300 to 6,700 pounds. In 1900, the comparable figure was 5,400. The ratio of milk cows to all cattle, that is, cattle of all ages, was lower in 1950 than in 1940 or even 1900. Apparently the dairy farmers are rearing more of their heifers for replacements.

In spite of the erratic nature of the census enumerations, it seems desirable to show the distribution of the reported milk sales by farmers by towns in Figure 15. Sales of cream have been converted to whole-milk equivalents in these figures. Along with them, to serve as a guide to the dependability of the census figures, and also to indicate probable trends, are given the census-reported numbers of milk cows in 1925, 1945, and 1950. Except for a few scattered towns like Sterling, Sutton, and Mendon, the towns with more than 800 cows are all in the south and west parts of the County. In all of these towns, the number of milk cows has been increasing or holding up very well. Most of the towns near the urban centers show a decline. More than 1,000 cows were reported for Grafton in 1940 and 1945, but only 760 in 1950. The five all-urban towns had 2,512 milk cows in 1920; these, plus the fringe areas around them, plus the twelve other areas shown in black in Figure 8, had only 2,712 cows in 1950.

The number of horses has declined seven eighths since 1900, the number of sheep over a half since 1890, and the number of swine a fourth since their high point in 1920. The number of poultry has more than doubled since 1900. Egg production has trebled in this period, and likewise the number of chickens raised. Between 1950 and 1954, the number of chickens sold from

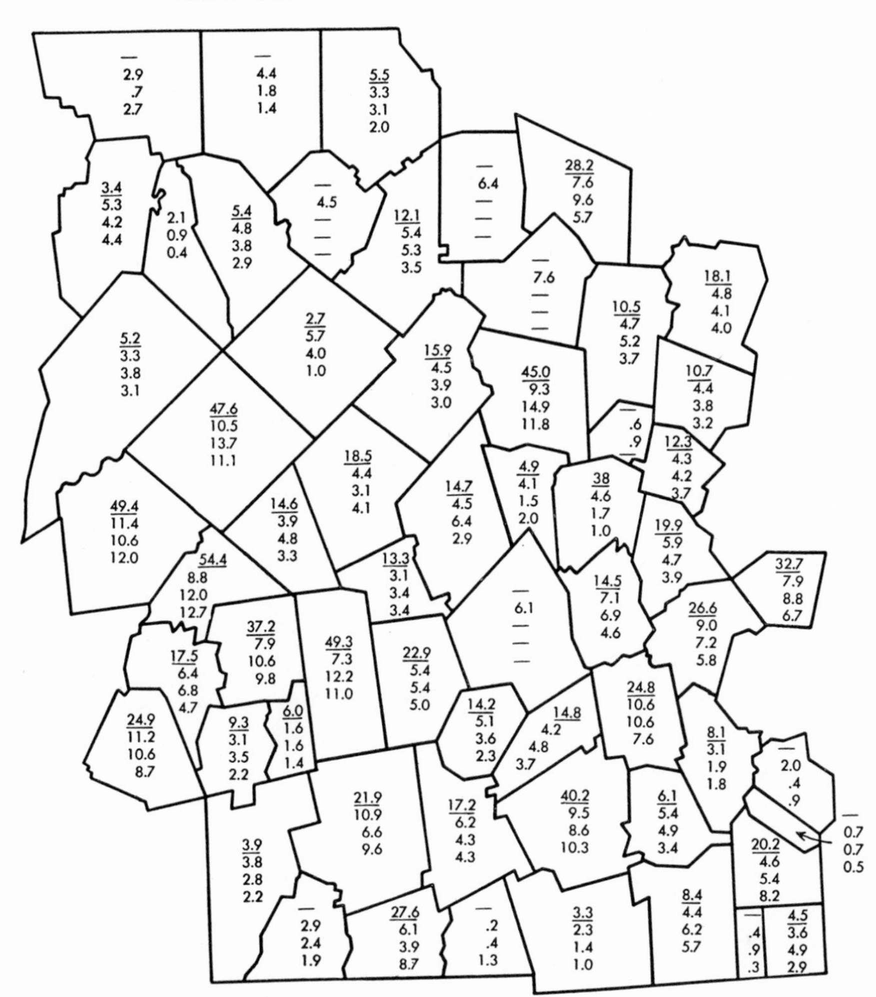

Figure 15. *Milk production by towns in 1950, and number of milk cows in 1925, 1945, and 1950, as reported by the Census in these years. Upper figure = whole milk sold (hundred thousand pounds). Second, third, and lower figures = number (hundreds) of milk cows in 1925, 1945, and 1950.*

Worcester County farms increased an eighth. The number of laying flocks reported fell off nearly a half in the same period, but the dozens of eggs sold by only a fifth.

Figure 16 shows the census-reported distribution by towns of number of chickens sold and dozens of eggs sold in 1950. The County average ratio of

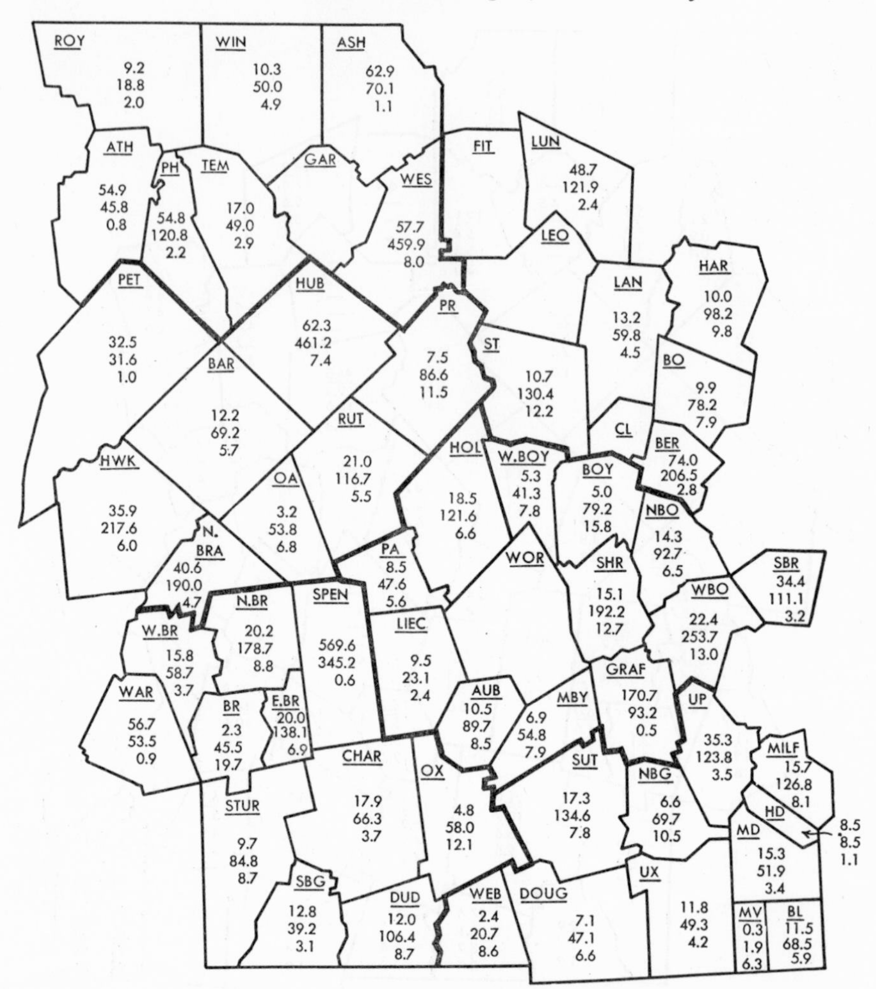

Figure 16. *Distribution of chicken and egg sales by towns in 1950. Upper figure = number of chickens sold (thousands). Middle figure = dozens of eggs sold (thousands). Lower figure = ratio of dozens of eggs sold to number of chickens sold.*

dozens of eggs sold to chickens sold is 3.2. A ratio lower than this indicates that a town is more nearly specializing in the production of broilers and fryers or day-old chicks; and contrariwise.

Turkey production in 1950 was pretty well concentrated in the urban areas and six other towns, in order of number of birds: Uxbridge, Berlin, Paxton, Oakham, Templeton, and Northboro. Only a tenth of them are

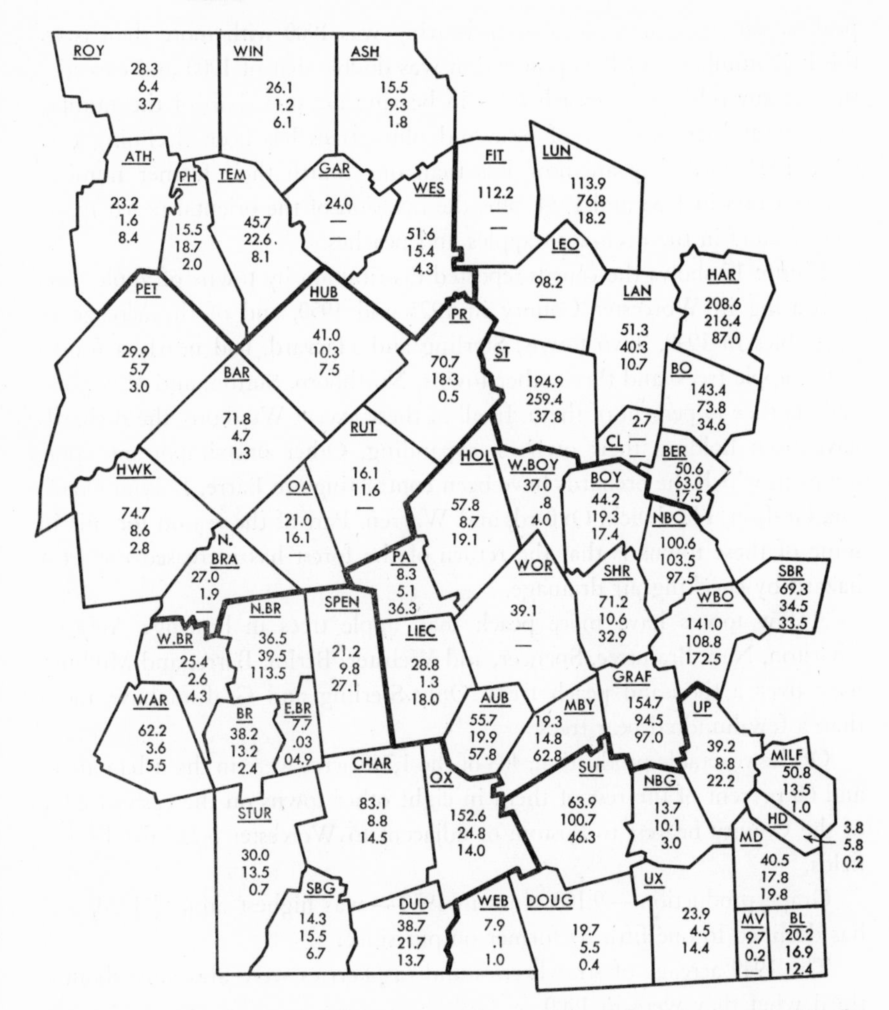

Figure 17. *Distribution of bearing apple trees (numbers in hundreds), by towns in Worcester County, 1925 (upper figure) and 1950 (middle figure); also acreages in vegetables (lower figure) in 1950. (Dash signifies that no apple trees or vegetables are reported for that year.)*

produced in other towns. Worcester County produces a fourth of all the ducks raised in Massachusetts.

Most of the fruit acreage of Worcester County in 1950 — all but around 400 out of 7,266 acres — was in tree fruits, and all but 37,000 of the 236,000 bearing trees were apple trees. A total of 1,744 farmers had one half-acre or more of apple trees. Peaches and pears were a poor second and third. The peak census year in apple trees in bearing was 1900 with more than twice the 1950 number. But 1950 production was double that of 1900 and exceeded that of any other year. Peach trees in bearing are one sixth of the number in 1920, and the number of pear and plum trees has been declining ever since 1900 until they are now less than one fourth their former number. Severe frosts in 1933 and 1934, plus the invasion of the oriental peach moth, were factors in the decline in apples and peaches.

Figure 17 shows the census-reported distribution by towns of apple trees in bearing in Worcester County in 1925 and 1950, and of the acreage in vegetables in 1949. Two towns, Sterling and Harvard, had nearly a fourth of the apple trees, and three other towns, Northboro, Sutton, and Westboro, had another 15 percent of them. In all of these except Westboro, the orchards have been holding their own or expanding. Other once-important apple towns in which the orchards have been contracting are Barre, Bolton, Charlton, Grafton, Hardwick, Oxford, and Warren. Part of the reason for this in some of these towns is that the return of the forest has increased the frost hazard by checking air drainage.

A few towns have more peach than apple trees in bearing: Auburn, Charlton, New Braintree, Spencer, and Webster. Berlin, Barre, and Millbury have over a thousand peach trees. Only Sterling and Grafton have more than a few hundred pear trees.

Of the vegetable production, 408 of the 1,740 acres were in the urban areas, and 60 percent of the rest of them in eight other towns on the eastern edge of the County nearest to Boston, or adjacent to Worcester or in the Brookfields.

Grape production — 9,100 vines in 1950 — was highest around 1920, and has declined to one fifth its former output since.

The 1949 acreage of strawberries and raspberries were also only about a third what they were in 1900.

The vegetables principally grown for market — 1,740 acres on 340 farms in 1950 — were, in order of their acreage, sweet corn, squash, tomatoes, cabbage, green beans, and green peas. The census figures indicate a strong shift out of all the others toward sweet corn production after 1945. Some of this was due no doubt to the exclusion of small farms in the 1950 Census.

WOODLAND

The average sale of forest products per farm in Worcester County in 1949 was only $7.90; per acre of woodland in farms, $0.32. It was as low as this partly because cutting had been at an unusual rate in the war years.

Sales of farm woodland products were four times this rate in 1944. But as managed at present, the 175,900 acres of woodland in farms are yielding a very small return in forest product sales. Neither is the use of timber as fuel, fence posts, and so forth on the farms a very large item. The other farm income from woodland, from the 117,360 acres used as pasture, is also very small.

Furthermore, the woodlands of Worcester County outside of farms, around 500,000 acres of them, are not much more productive than those within farms. The reappraisal Report No. 3 of the United States Forest Service classifies 53 percent of the farm woodlands of New England as under "poor" or "destructive" management, and only 35 percent of that of private holdings generally. Those which are more productive are so because they have not been pastured and natural reproduction has not been disturbed much, rather than because of any positive management measures. Those which have been cut from time to time have in general deteriorated with each cutting.

The ownership of forest lands strongly conditions its management. No detailed inventory of the ownership of the forest lands of Worcester County has been made, but Dr. Solon Barraclough's study of 23 towns in New England indicates clearly enough for present purposes the situation in New England in general and in this part of New England in particular.[3] None of these 23 towns were in Worcester County, but 4 were in Massachusetts, 3 in Connecticut, and 4 more close by in New Hampshire. The towns were selected to give a representation of different forest types, different kinds of farming, and different kinds of rural economy. They included areas primarily agricultural, areas dependent upon income from summer residents and recreational visitors, areas from which people commute to jobs near by, and areas highly dependent upon local wood-processing plants. The information on the tax rolls was expanded by means of interviews with town assessors, selectmen, and long-time residents, to include occupation of the owner, his approximate age, acres of forest land in the property, and apparent purposes of the owner in holding the forest land. This was supplemented by information from 30 percent of the owners who replied to a questionnaire. Only holdings of ten acres or more were included.

The 2,106 holdings of woodland in these 23 towns contained 278,000 acres, or 134 acres per holding. These acres made up from 20 to 85 percent of

[3] Solon Barraclough and James Rettie, "The Ownership of Small Private Forest-Land Holdings in 23 New England Towns," Station Paper No. 34, Northeastern Forestry Experiment Station, Upper Darby, Pa., 1950.

the land in the 4 Massachusetts towns, and 62 percent of that in the 23 towns.

The questionnaire returns indicated that 74 percent of the owners had purchased their land outright, and 25 percent had inherited it. About a fifth of the land had been acquired within ten years by 40 percent of the owners, and over half within twenty years by 70 percent of the owners. It is obvious that turnover at this rate does not furnish a good basis for sustained-yield forestry.

Equally significant is the occupational status of the owner. A fourth of this land was owned by operators of sawmills or other wood-producing plants. Their holdings averaged 830 acres. Business and professional people held 19 percent of it, full-time farmers 12 percent, laborers and clerical workers 8 percent, retired persons 10 percent, and housewives 6 percent. Other owners included clubs and institutions, owners of recreational enterprises, and public utilities.

Of much interest in this connection is it that less than half of the farm woodland reported by the federal census for these 23 towns in 1945 was owned by those who regarded farming as their principal occupation. Apparently much of the decrease in number of farms in the 1950 Census came from not classifying the owners of these woodlands as farmers. Only a very little of this woodland could have been in holdings of less than ten acres. Virtually all of it was in holdings averaging one hundred acres or more upon which enough agriculture is practiced to cause the unit to be called a farm in 1945 but not in 1950.

Absentee ownership of land has always proved to be a large factor in its management. Nearly all of the farmers among the 2,106 owners of woodland in this 23-town survey were living on their land, and a minor fraction of the remainder were residential farmers, and a still smaller fraction had summer homes on their holdings. The tax records showed 65 percent of the owners living in the same or an adjoining town, 17 percent elsewhere in the same state, 10 percent elsewhere in New England, and 8 percent outside of New England.

As already indicated, the acreage of land reported by the census as woodland not pastured has remained fairly constant for Worcester County as a whole, at around 120,000 acres, since 1925. The decline in woodland acreage reported that has taken place has been in woodland pastured, from 164,300 in 1925 to 58,600 in 1950. On the one hand, much woodland once pastured has so little grass that it is no longer pastured, and some of it may even have been fenced off from the pasture land. On the other hand, much

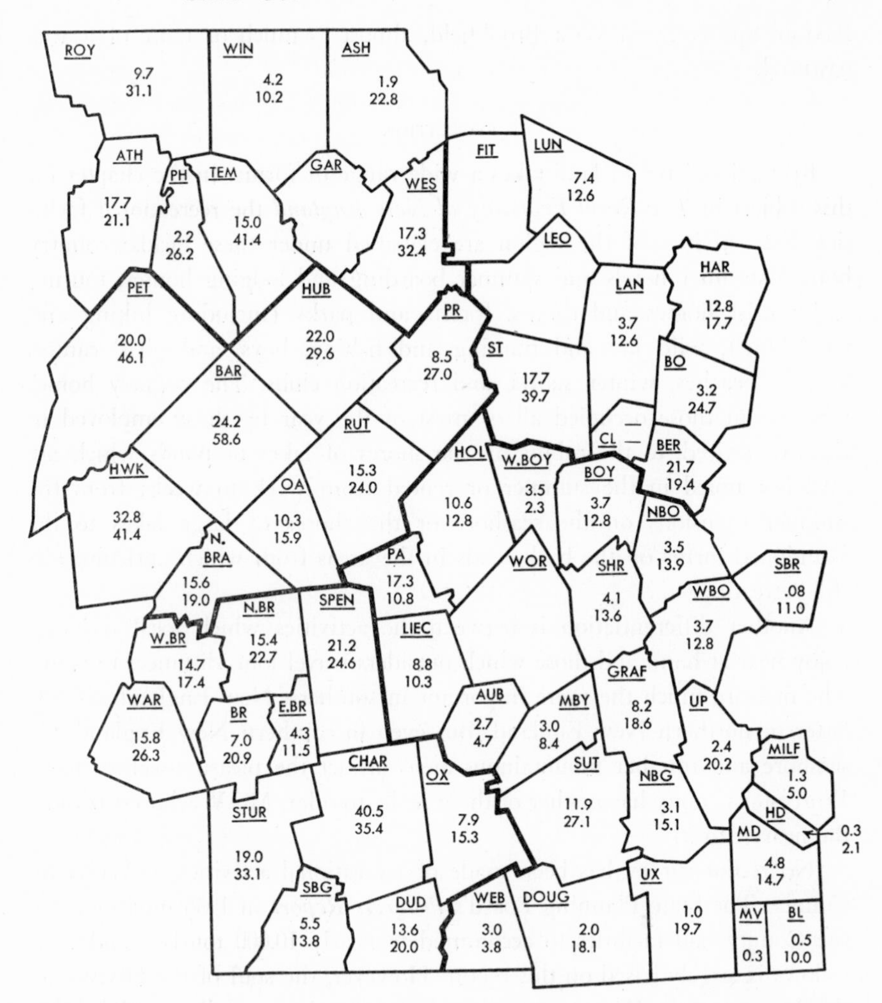

Figure 18. *Acreage of farm land in woodland pastured (upper figure) and not pastured (lower figure), by towns in 1950 (acreage in hundreds).*

woodland has gone out of farms as the places have ceased to be classified as farms. If we assume that the census data are reasonably dependable, these two trends have about offset each other.

However, that there must have been wide differences in this offsetting trend or in the census reporting by towns is evident in Figure 18, in which the acreages of each are shown separately. In Royalston, Winchendon, Phillipston, and Ashburnham side by side, the woodland was mostly not pastured. In Athol, Berlin, Charlton, Hardwick, Holden, New Braintree,

Paxton, Spencer, and West Brookfield, almost as much or more of it was pastured.

RECREATION

Recreational use of land takes a wide range of forms. In the chapter on this subject in *The Rural Economy of New England* the recreational facilities and activities of the region are classified under these heads: country homes, summer hotels and summer boarding and lodging houses, touring and tourist homes and cabins, forests and parks (including hiking and picnicking), wild life and hunting and fishing, boys' and girls' camps, bathing beaches, winter sports, and recreation clubs. The country homes range from those occupied all or most of the year by those employed in cities or retired, to the cabins on the shores of lakes or ponds which are owner-occupied in the summer or rented from week to week; from the summer mansions on the seashore or the shores of large lakes to the abandoned farms on the back roads in the areas from which agriculture is still retreating.

Another differentiation is between the activities which local residents enjoy near at hand and those which outsiders travel long distances to enjoy. The first are much the more important in southern New England and the latter in northern New England. But even in southern New England, the seashore and rougher mountainous areas attract the pleasure-seekers most. Worcester County has neither of these really to offer, Mt. Wachusett coming the nearest to it.

No recent survey has been made of recreational activities in Worcester County. The State Planning Board's *Progress Report* in 1936 indicated that the County had facilities to accommodate nearly 10,000 tourists, and what follows is largely based on this report. However, the staff of the Division of the Massachusetts Department of Commerce writes as follows: "The situation prevailing prior to the war in Worcester County has changed but little, nor will it. The area, while adapted for 'local' recreation, is not of the character to draw or attract vacationers from other parts of the state or other states." Since that time, the staff also reports, "A limited number of new motels — perhaps 20 or so — have been constructed on Routes 9, 20, and 2, mainly for the use of transients." Also since that time, Old Sturbridge Village has come to attract many more from outside the County.

Let us now examine in more detail what the situation was in 1938 as summarized then by Dr. John E. Guthrie on the basis of the Planning Board's *Progress Report* plus some field work. The hotels in the cities in the County were being used to some extent by vacationists. Much more used by tourists were the private-residence tourist homes and overnight cabins designed for the accommodation of motorists and usually located on main highways. These were most numerous in those towns through which main highways pass, and adjacent to or near cities. They were largely concentrated in the towns of Sturbridge, Charlton, Auburn, Shrewsbury, and Northboro, through which federal highway Number 20 passes, and next in order, on Route Number 9 running east and west through Worcester, and then on Number 2 running through Fitchburg, Gardner, and Athol.

As for recreation facilities serving local residents mainly, Worcester County has numerous lakes or ponds and public forests. Of the 35 privately owned camps in the County, two thirds of them were located in the northwest corner. The publicly owned picnic grounds and camp sites were distributed among the state forests and reservations, of which the County then had 21, covering a total area of 22,667 acres. These forests were sprinkled diagonally across the County, from the northwest to the southeast corners. Of these, 17 had picnic facilities only, 2 had picnic and bathing facilities, and 2 were suitable for camping and bathing. The most important local recreational towns were Royalston, Winchendon, Petersham, Templeton, Ashburnham, Princeton, and Hubbardston in the northwest corner of the County and Sutton and Douglas in the southeast corner. There were beaches also in Blackstone, Lancaster, Lunenburg, Mendon, Northboro, Uxbridge, and Westboro.

As for fishing and boating, boats were obtainable for fishing on 31 ponds, 20 lakes, 3 reservoirs, and 2 rivers in the County, and canoe trips were possible on the Otter, Millers, Ware, Quaboag, Quinebaug, Mill, Assabet, and Nashua rivers. Also 16 of the 21 state forests and reservations were open to public hunting, and there were 49 fish and game clubs distributed over 35 towns of the area. The Watatic trail for hiking runs from Mt. Wachusett State Reservation in Princeton northward through Westminster and Ashburnham. Also there are local trails in the state forests.

Little information was available in 1938 as to the number or location of privately owned summer residences. These are usually located near bodies of water, of which there are 56 in the County large enough to permit boating, scattered among 35 towns. Most of these lakes, ponds, and rivers are too small, however, to attract many summer residents from any distance.

Developments since then have been considerably different from what was expected. Most important, as we shall observe in detail town by town, many more workers in urban industry and trade now have their residences in the urban-fringe areas and out in the open country, and this has resulted in many residences being established on or near the shores of lakes and ponds adjacent or close to cities. Also because of the housing shortage, many of the summer cabins have become year-round residences, many of them at the start without the usual facilities of urban houses. The net result on the shores of some of the lakes or ponds has been a reduction in the number of summer homes, though probably not in the recreational use of the water bodies.

Historically a few of the towns have had an experience something like that reported for Petersham in *Planning One Town — Petersham, a Hill Town in Massachusetts*. In the decades after the railroads were built and before the automobile, some attractive interior sites on good roads near railroad cities were chosen for summer homes by well-to-do city families. The houses they built were commonly too large for the families of recent generations, without retinues of servants, who might otherwise enjoy such places in which to live in the summer.

ACREAGES AND RECEIPTS PER FARM

The census acreages of land in an average farm in Worcester County have, of course, been much affected by the changes in the way of counting farms and lands that have been described earlier. Table 6 gives such acreage

TABLE 6

Changes in Size and Composition of Farms, Worcester County, 1925–1954

		Land in farms		*Cropland in farms*		*Open pastures in farms*		*Woodland pasture in farms*		*Woodland not pastured in farms*		*Milk cows, number*		*Eggs produced*	
Year	*Number of farms*	*Acres (000's)*	*Acres per farm*	*Acres (000's)*	*Acres per farm*	*Acres (000's)*	*Acres per farm*	*Acres (000's)*	*Acres per farm*	*Acres (000's)*	*Acres per farm*	*(000's)*	*Per farm*	*Dozens (10,000's)*	*Per farm (00's)*
1925	7094	530.0	75	146.9	20.7	174.4	24.6	164.3	23.2	113.3	15.9	31.7	4.5	242.2	2.9
1935	6464	469.1	73	128.0	20.0	—*	—*	121.3	18.7	109.3	16.9	30.1	4.7	355.8	5.5
1945	6505	452.9	67	133.1	20.5	80.4	12.4	71.1	10.9	124.1	19.1	—*	—*	—*	—*
1950	4230	363.1	89	135.4	32.8	73.4	17.3	47.8	11.3	116.3	27.6	27.6	6.5	693.5	16.4
1954	3267	323.0	100	124.9	38.2	32.3	9.9	43.0	13.2	108.3	33.0	25.8	8.1	—*	—*

*Data not available.

data as are available for the census years since 1925 plus parallel data for number of cows and egg production. The acres per farm in 1945 are low partly because the census enumerators counted in most of the very small farms. The acres per farm have increased since then partly because very many of these were classified as not farms. But also many of the commercial farms have added more acres either by buying or renting them. Cropland per farm, which is more significant, has nearly doubled since 1925. Included in this cropland, however, is plowable pasture, much of which is cropped in rotation with pasture. The acres of open pasture other than this have declined. Acres of woodland per farm have increased as acres of wooded pasture have decreased. The woodland is increasingly being enclosed within fences.

Clearly the number of farms with one or two or a few milk cows is decreasing, and likewise the number with a small flock of laying hens. But still many of these are left, with an average of only 6.5 cows per farm in 1950 and 4 dozen of eggs per day per farm.

As explained earlier, the Census of 1950 classifies farms into commercial part-time, and residential, and by type of farming, and then maps them into "economic areas." Economic Area B in Massachusetts coincides with Worcester County. The 2,452 commercial farms in 1950 averaged 110 acres, of which 43 were cropland used for pasture plus other open pasture and 31 were woodland not pastured. The remaining 23 acres were divided into 16 acres of pastured woodland and 7 acres of land used as farmsteads or roads, and wasteland. The comparable figure for the 535 part-time farms were 52 acres, of which 18 were cropland, 5 open pasture, and 25 woodland not pastured. The 1,210 residential farms averaged 47 acres, of which 16 acres were cropland, 4 acres were cropland plus other open land used for pasture, and 17 were woodland not pastured. The actual harvested acreages of the three classes of farms averaged 28, 10, and 8 acres respectively. The noncommercial farms, especially the part-time ones, thus had relatively more woodland than the commercial farms.

The total sales of the commercial farms averaged $8,250 in 1949, and the cash expenditures listed totaled $5,070 per farm, of which 60 percent was for feed. The comparable figures for the part-time farm were $610 and $835; for the residential farms, $72 and $250. Even the part-time farms — it is apparent if the census reports on sales are complete — are largely places of residence. They do provide, however, besides housing, considerable amounts of the food and fuel used by the family.

The Census of 1950 classified the 2,430 commercial farms in Worcester County as follows:

Dairy	1,134	Vegetables	42
Poultry	791	Other crops	10
Fruit	161	General	66
Other livestock	100	Miscellaneous	126

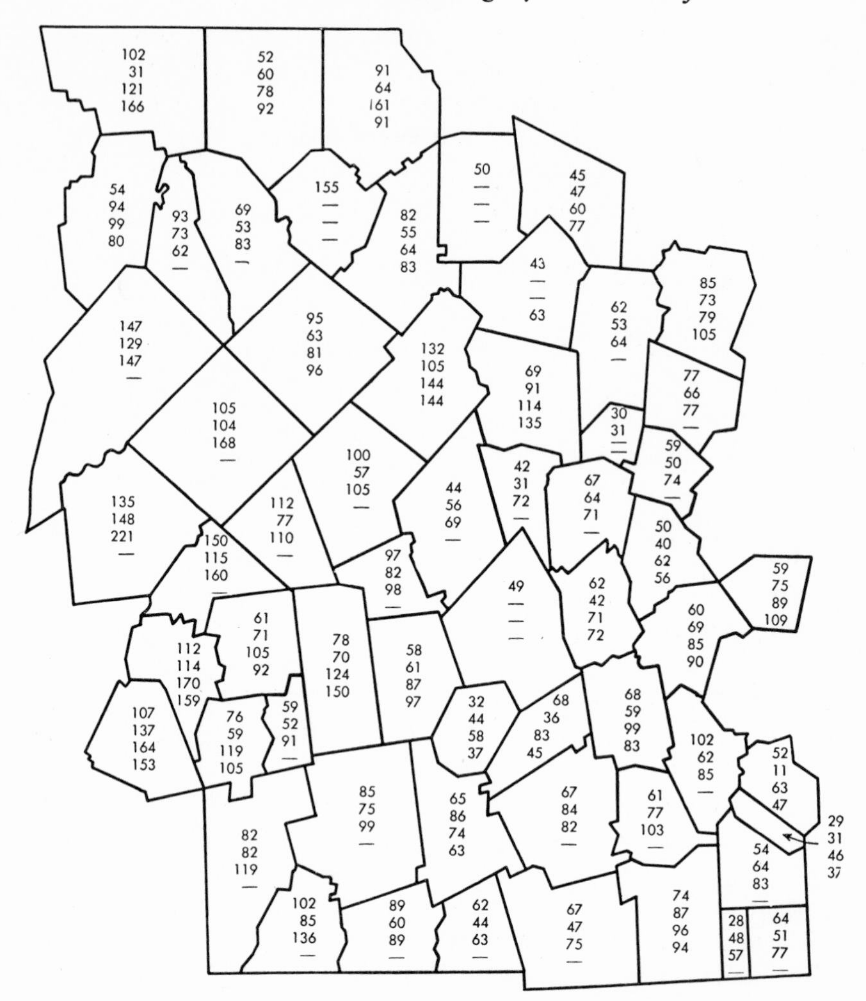

Figure 19. *Average acreage of land per farm, by towns in Worcester County, as reported by the Census in 1925 (upper figure), 1945, 1950, and 1954 (lower figures). (Dash signifies that the data are not available or are highly erratic.)*

The dairy farms reported an average of 20 milk cows, 30 cattle and calves, 2 to 3 swine, and 40 chickens. They averaged 15 acres of corn and 38 acres of hay. These farms averaged dairy product sales of $7,700, livestock sales of $900, and $220 of other receipts. Their feed bills averaged $3,400, and other cash expenses $3,050.

The poultry farms reported an average of 760 chickens on hand four

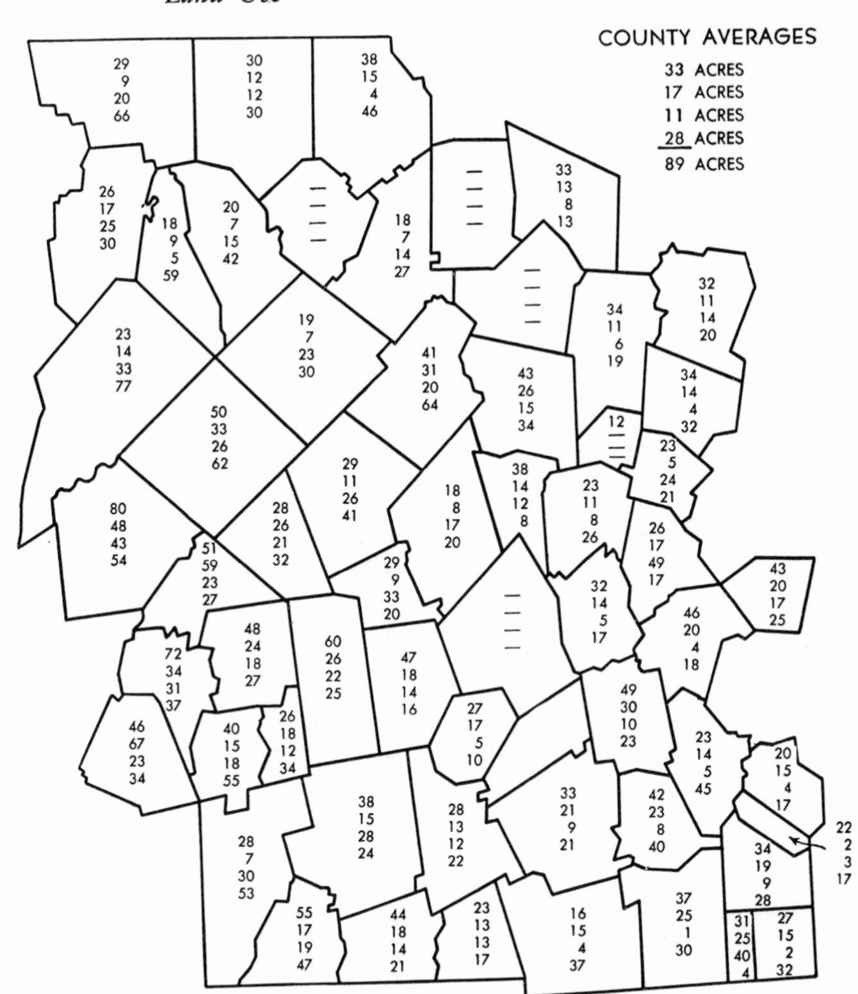

Figure 20. *Average acreage per farm of cropland (upper figure), open pasture land (second figure), woodland pastured (third figure), and not pastured (lower figure) of Worcester County, 1950 Census.*

months old and over at the time of the census enumeration in April. Only 2 in 5 of them had even 1 milk cow and 1 in 6 a pig or hog. Only 41 of them grew any corn and these grew an average of four acres. Their sale of eggs averaged $8,750 and of live poultry $2,850. Their feed bills in 1949 averaged $5,800 and their other cash expenses $1,590.

The fruit farms averaged fruit sales of $7,900, and $300 from other sources. The vegetable farmers reported vegetables sales of $5,500 and $3,660 from other sources, mostly nursery and greenhouse specialities and fruits.

The 112 other livestock farms had sales averaging $5,050; the general farms around $4,700, and the miscellaneous only $1,400.

Figure 19 is included partly to show the wide range in acres per farm among the towns in 1950 — from around 60 acres in eight of them in the eastern half of the County, to 150 acres or more in five of them on the western side — and partly to indicate the general nature of the trends in different parts of the County. The particular series for any one of the towns is not, however, to be taken seriously, because of the obvious erratic character of the census reporting.

With a study of Figure 19 as a background, one can pass on to review the differences among the towns in the acreages of the principal land-use classes in Figure 20. The reader must keep in mind that plowable pastures are counted twice in these figures, in both cropland and open pasture. In this way, he gets at once a picture of the land that could be cropped and of the amount used as pasture.

The acreages of cropland vary among the towns as much as they do largely because of the proportion of commercial as opposed to part-time and residential farms. In Hardwick, Barre, New Braintree, and Spencer, the proportion of commercial farms is high. In towns like Westminster, Holden, Upton, Milford, and Douglas, it is low. Very much of the land in these towns is not in farms at all. Also notable is how large a part of the cropland is in open plowable pasture in towns like Hardwick and Barre and how little of it is in the northwestern section. The towns surrounding Worcester City mostly have very little woodland in their farms — their farms are low in total acres in large part for this reason. This suggests that what land they have is more fully utilized.

THE SIX SECTIONS

Most of the charts thus far presented show Worcester County divided into six sections, A to F. The main reason for this sectioning is that it is not possible to show land use and land-use adjustments in the detail needed for the study for Worcester County as a whole in one map on one page, nor to analyze the adjustments needed all in one chapter. The grouping chosen is a compromise between the wisdom of putting together in one section the towns most alike in land use and most closely associated economically, and the necessity of fitting the sections and maps each to one page or two. Section D contains the towns surrounding the City of Worcester and eastward, Section F mostly the mill towns southeast of Worcester.

Section E is the most agricultural section of the County, but even it had half its land not in farms in 1954. Much of Section B is heavily wooded. Section A unfortunately includes a mixture of heavily wooded and agricultural towns. Section C is as urban-dominated as Section D, but still it includes Sterling, one of the most agricultural towns of the County.

TABLE 7

*Total Number of Farms and Average Percentage of Land in Farms, in Sections A to F, in 1925, in 1948, in 1950, and in 1954 **

	Section A		Section B		Section C		Section D		Section E		Section F	
Year	No. of farms	Percentage of land in farms	No. of farms	Percentage of land in farms	No. of farms	Percentage of land in farms	No. of farms	Percentage of land in farms	No. of farms	Percentage of land in farms	No. of farms	Percentage of land in farms
1925	955	64	1,015	46	1,136	50	1,722	52	1,400	66	819	46
1945	850	49	724	25	958	45	1,469	45	1,226	56	829	36
1950	545	44	463	23	534	33	629	33	777	51	477	30
1954	435	36	470	23	542	24	665	26	751	50	382	26

* The 1954 figures are partly estimates — the 1954 data by towns furnished by the Census Bureau combined the counts for adjoining towns for nearly a third of them.

Table 7 presents summary Census data for the six Sections for the two items, number of farms and percentage of land in farms, for 1925, 1945, 1950, and 1954. The percentage of land in farms has declined just about one half in all but Section E. About half of this came before 1945 in Sections A and F and nearly a third of it in Section D. Changes in census methods had little to do with this decline before 1945. The large declines in the next ten years in A, C, D, and F were probably half or more due to the more rigorous definition of a farm followed in 1950 and 1954. The large declines between 1950 and 1954 in C and D were no doubt due in good part to the spread of cities and contraction of farming operations by many part-time and residential households. Section B apparently did most of its contracting of farming operations before 1945 as did Section E.

The number of farms has reduced by almost a half in Section E and by more than this in all the other Sections. The absorption into nearby farms, by purchase or renting, of land no longer being farmed by those formerly farming it, and in many cases still living on it, has played a large part in this reduction of number of farms and increase in acres per farm, particularly in Sections E and A. In the other towns, contraction of part-time and residential farming figured more largely in this change.

CHAPTER 7

Markets

The pattern of agricultural production in any given area — in this instance, Worcester County — is determined not only by natural and human resource environment but by economic environment, that is, by market outlets and the prices farmers receive for their products and pay for labor, equipment, supplies, and other input factors.[1] These, combined with technical know-how, determine income opportunities in farming. These opportunities, in turn, competing with opportunities in other fields of endeavor, determine the over-all pattern of economic activity in Worcester County as described in preceding chapters.

The framework of prices forming the economic environment of Worcester County is developed by the broad interplay of regional, national, and even international forces. Historically, as explained earlier, these have reacted upon Worcester County's agriculture in such a manner as to encourage the production of commodities that are consumed nearby. From the standpoint of food production and consumption, Southern New England is a deficit area. Worcester County farmers therefore usually enjoy a location price advantage. Hence, as stated in the previous chapter, Worcester County's agriculture is largely oriented not only to New England's markets but particularly to Worcester County markets.

Obviously, in any systematic approach to the development of coordinated policies, plans, and programs for an area such as Worcester County, market opportunities must be analyzed and appraised. The following discussion of Worcester markets will serve to illustrate this need. Unfortunately, factual market information needed for intelligent decision-making is often lacking.

[1] This chapter in its present form was assembled and written by Westcott. But John E. Guthrie assembled information on the organization of the Worcester markets back in 1938, and Alfred Pleasanton helped assemble the recent data on milk receipts and distribution.

Shortcomings will be evident in this brief descriptive analysis of Worcester County markets, especially in the field of poultry marketing.

DAIRY MARKETING

At the beginning of the present century, about 75 percent of the Boston milk supply was obtained from Massachusetts producers, a large proportion coming from Worcester County. Meanwhile the population of Massachusetts has nearly doubled. Worcester County's population has increased by two thirds and that of the city of Worcester by over one half. Concurrent with the growing nearby population was the passage of the Saunders Law in 1910, causing freight rates on milk shipments within the state to be less favorable than those on interstate shipments. Boston dealers began buying a larger percentage of their milk in Vermont and New Hampshire[2] as Worcester County producers shifted to nearby secondary markets in Worcester County and eastern Massachusetts to meet the needs of the growing population. A significant part of the milk in the western part of the County moved to Springfield.

The first successful attempt at organizing a cooperative for milk producers, including those selling in the Worcester area, took place after passage of the Clayton Anti-trust Act in 1914. The New England Milk Producers' Association (NEMPA) began as a bargaining cooperative. Its services to members included (1) negotiating with handlers on prices, terms, and conditions of milk sales, (2) checking weights and tests on delivered milk, (3) guaranteeing payment for milk sold, (4) providing marketing information, and (5) representing the producers in governmental affairs. At present, the NEMPA also provides a plant in Worcester for manufacturing cream or powdered skim milk from surplus milk.

Although the NEMPA introduced the classification or use pricing system used in the market today, it failed to solve other important problems. First, not all producers belonged to the NEMPA. This made it possible for the handlers to make deals to their advantage with some nonmembers. Second, the handlers did not always make a strict accounting according to use of milk sold. Third, the NEMPA faced a difficult problem when attempting to balance supply and demand. If it lowered price when there was an excess of supply, it would lose members. And fourth, the classification plan did not provide a uniform price to all producers because of the varying amounts of

[2] J. M. Cassels, *A Study of Fluid Milk Prices,* Cambridge, Mass., Harvard University Press, 1931, p. 152. See also U.S.D.A. preliminary report, "The New England Dairy Market," by R. J. McFall, 1925 (mimeo.), p. 22.

Class I sales among the handlers. Some handlers paid higher-than-average prices and then sought rebates from producers.

Even though it was unable to solve these problems, the NEMPA was reluctant to give up to public authority what it considered to be functions of its own organization. Nevertheless, with falling prices and the very chaotic milk market conditions of the early 1930's, governmental assistance was sought. Federal regulation was introduced in the Boston market in 1933 and emergency legislation passed by the State in 1934 created the State Milk Control Board (now called the State Milk Control Commission).

In 1935, there were 56 dealers and 23 producer-distributors selling milk in Worcester. In accordance with the regulations of the State Milk Control Board, dealers were required to purchase milk from producers under one of three plans — a flat price for all milk, a price according to use, or a base-rating plan. Prices paid to producers varied in accordance (1) with the plan under which the milk was purchased, (2) with the proportion of Class I sales realized by dealers, and (3) with the deductions for transportation. Producers paid at a flat (Class I) price naturally received the highest return; those paid under a rating plan usually received the next highest composite price; and those paid on a use plan received the lowest.

During the late thirties, almost 90 percent of the milk produced for the Worcester market was from NEMPA members. Dealers were required to pay these members on either the base-rating or the use plan. Only approximately 5 percent of the milk in the Worcester market came from out of the State.

In the thirties over half of the milk produced in the western towns of Worcester County was shipped to the Springfield market. During this period, milk marketing and prices were particularly sensitive in that area because of its location midway between Worcester and Springfield. A brief comparative history of these two markets helps to understand the institutional developments leading up to the relatively stable markets now available to Worcester County farmers.

Springfield was a notably unstable market. After the establishment of the Massachusetts Milk Control Board in 1934, it was hoped that conditions would improve in all markets. Producers supplying milk to Springfield, however, soon found that such was not the case. In an effort to avoid paying prices prescribed by the Board, some of the smaller dealers began obtaining milk in Vermont and dropping their Massachusetts producers. They were thus able to reduce retail prices. Dealers buying from Massachusetts producers, in order to meet the competition of out-of-state milk, and with the reluctant consent of the Control Board, were forced to reduce their prices to producers. Dealers handling milk then had to take on the producers dropped in favor of Vermont producers. This increased the amount of surplus milk in the market. Thus a vicious circle of lowering prices was set up by these competitive forces.

In contrast to the Springfield situation, the Worcester market was remarkably stable during the 1930's. There were several reasons for this. First, although some of Worcester's milk supply came from outside the state, the sources remained the same. Second, the producers were strongly organized through the NEMPA. Third, there was "close cooperation" between the local NEMPA sales committee in Worcester and the New England Dairies representing the northern (Vermont) creamery group. Finally, there was a strong organization of dealers and they cooperated closely with the NEMPA and the State Milk Control Board.

Still the State lacked the constitutional power to regulate the price of milk purchased outside the State. It could use either a handler or market-wide pool for distributing the receipts from the sale of milk among producers, and could, like the Federal government, use the classification plan of payments by handlers. But it could not make the price of milk received by all producers the same or the cost to all the handlers according to use the same when handlers purchased from out-of-state producers. Federal control could regulate the entire supply whether or not it came from within the State.

Following World War II, the farmers in Worcester County and Western Massachusetts began seriously to consider the merits of Federal as opposed to State regulation. The State, it was true, had some advantage over the Federal government in its ability to regulate trade practices of handlers in their relations with their customers. However, in the case of Worcester, the handlers had long maintained stable selling practices. Strange as it might seem, the Federal regulation was the more democratic. Under it, regulations could be voted in or out by a majority of the persons within the milk industry. State regulation, on the other hand, was compulsory upon passage of State legislation. Both provided for a hearing procedure as a democratic way of setting price and settling other regulatory matters.

In 1949, both the producers and the handlers of Worcester County petitioned for Federal regulation. In 1950, following hearings, Federal Milk Marketing Orders were established in the Worcester and Springfield market areas. The Worcester market area consists of Worcester, Auburn, Leicester, Spencer, Paxton, Rutland, Holden, West Boylston, Clinton, Boylston, Shrewsbury, Grafton, and Millbury (See Figure 21). The handlers in this market area get most of their milk outside this market area, as shown in Figure 22, but they pay according to the same schedule for all of it. Handlers in the remainder of the County are under State regulation. The State marketing areas are also shown in Figure 21. It will be noted that these areas are set up without regard to the County boundaries.

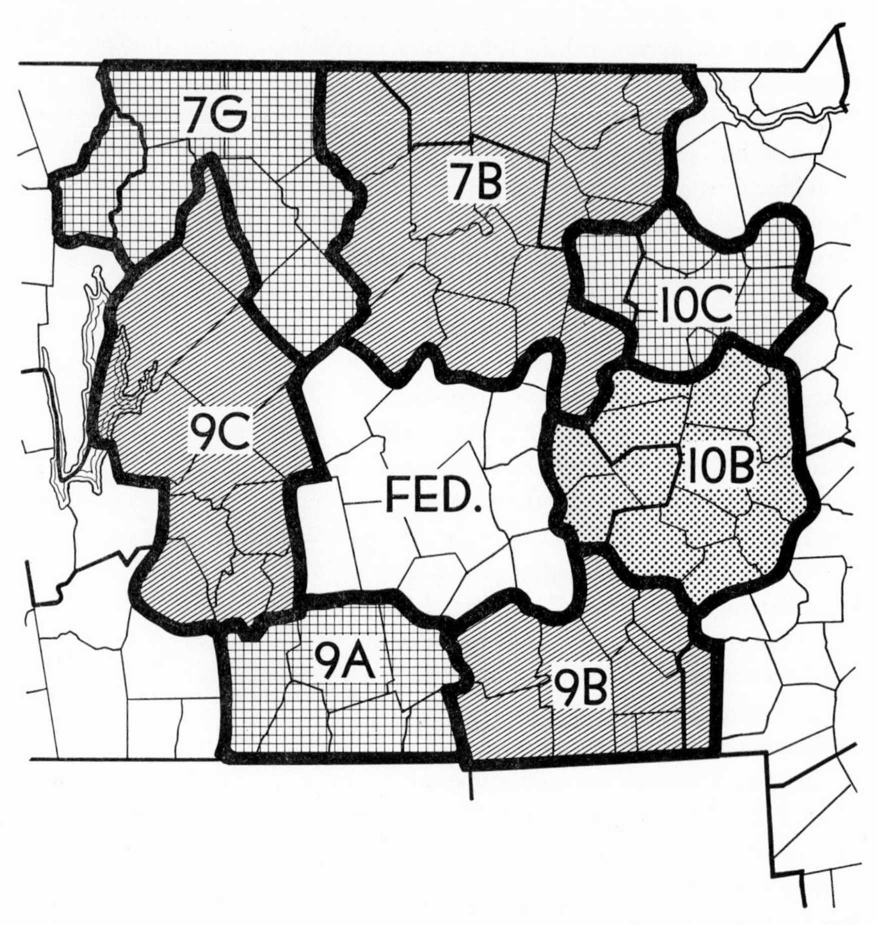

Figure 21. *The Worcester Federal Milk Market Areas and the seven state milk market areas in, or including, Worcester County territory.*

Since 1950, the markets for Worcester County milk have been remarkably stable. Among the factors contributing to this are (1) the Federal agency's power to regulate the entire supply of milk, (2) the setting of the price closely in line with the Boston price, (3) the prompt adjustment of the price to supply and demand conditions, (4) the competent auditing of handler's records, this assuring a strict accounting of the uses of milk (the State of course maintains auditing facilities in its areas too), and (6) the use of the market-wide pool which makes the prices paid by handlers uniform, and those received by producers the same over the whole supply area, except for differences in such items as transport costs. The marketing and production are made orderly because the minimum prices to producers reflect the price and supplies of feed and other economic factors that affect supply and demand conditions in the market. These minimum prices are not support prices, but rather they are supply-demand prices calculated to attract an adequate but not excessive supply. They are determined according to an economic formula that keeps the Class I price in line with changes in the national index of wholesale commodity prices, the New England per capita consumer income after taxes, the grain and labor items in milk production cost, and the over-all milk supply-demand balance. In addition, the formula provides for seasonal price changes which encourage fall and winter production and make milk available to consumers at lower prices in spring when pasture is plentiful. The Class II price is set by a formula based on prices of manufactured dairy products. The producer receives a "blend" of the two prices based on the handler's reports, which show how much milk they received from producers, how much was sold as fluid milk, and how much was used as Class II milk.

As for the dealers, their abilities to compete depend upon efficiencies of transportation, plant operation and distribution, and customer relations. Their selling prices are determined by competition in the market and not by the Federal government.

Federal regulation thus enables all producers, regardless of location, to share equitably in the market for fluid milk and also to bear their proportionate loss as a result of the excess, which has a lower value because of its "lower" use as cream, cheese, or other manufactured products. Assured that he will be paid the full market value for his milk, the farmer concentrates his attention on increasing efficiencies in production and, possibly, on earning a premium on quality milk.

According to the records of the Massachusetts Division of Dairying and Animal Husbandry, during the year 1954 there were 21 handlers of milk in the city handling the milk of 378 Worcester County producers. The location of these producers is shown in Chart Figure 22. Figure 23 shows the location of the 125 Worcester County producers who supplied milk to 32 handlers outside the County. It is interesting to note that all but three producers have shifted away from the Connecticut Valley markets. These

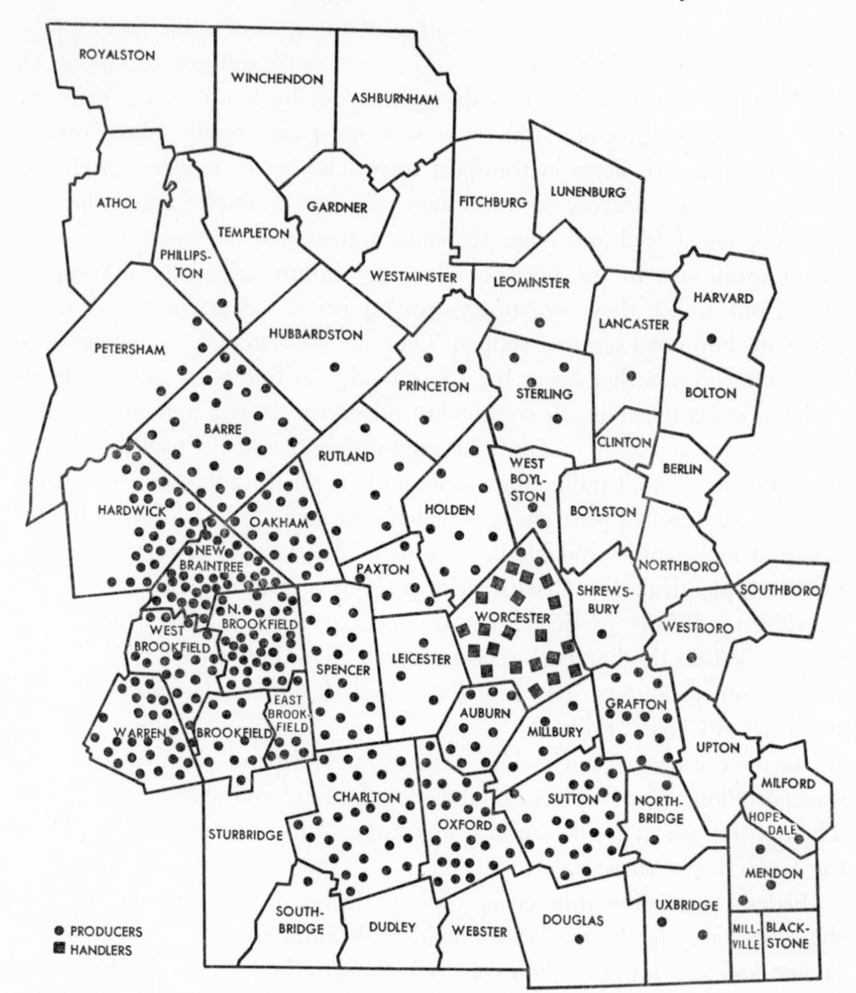

Figure 22. *Location of milk producers and handlers for the City of Worcester, 1954.*

three figures provide an excellent graphic description of the location of milk production, direction of movement, and location of handlers in Worcester County. This is vital information background for analyzing market opportunities.

In what is shown in Figure 21 as the Federal Worcester Marketing Area, there were 68 handlers in 1956, compared with 130 in 1950, the first year under the Federal Order. These handlers received milk from 721 producers in 1956 as compared with 878 in 1950. These figures reflect the trend toward fewer but larger producers and handlers.

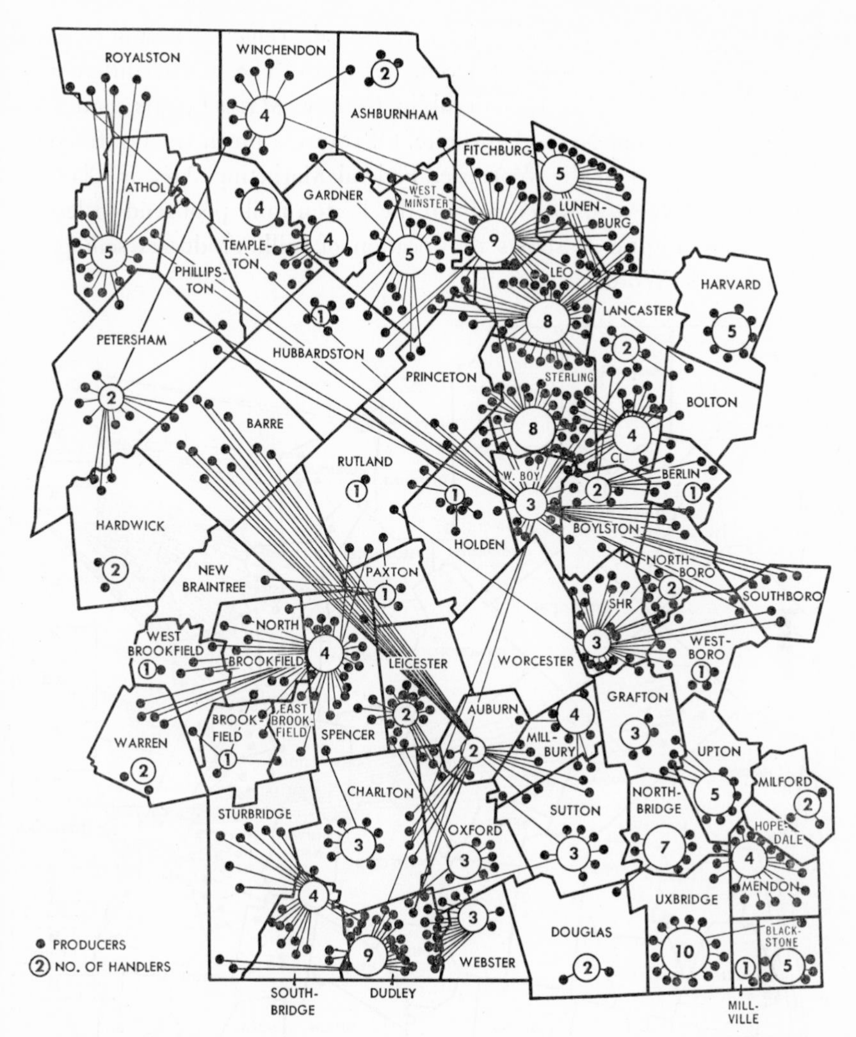

Figure 23. *Location of milk producers and handlers in Worcester County for cities other than Worcester.*

These figures do not of course include the receipts in the Worcester Federal Marketing Area from outside the County, from about 100 producers in Vermont and 75 in Franklin County, Massachusetts, in recent years; also a very little from other Massachusetts counties adjacent to Worcester; nor the Class I milk received directly from the Boston and Springfield milk pools, mostly from Boston's, amounting to about 12 percent of the Worcester Federal Marketing Area's total supply in recent years. The total supply from outside Worcester County has been running around 30 percent in recent months. All milk produced within forty miles of the center of Boston receives a nearby differential premium of a cent per quart. The nearby differential area for Worcester reaches into Franklin County, Massachusetts, and two towns in Vermont and New Hampshire. Of course a much smaller fraction of the milk received in the Worcester Federal Marketing Area is Class II than in the Boston Area. Receipts from the Boston milk pool tend to lessen this difference. Figure 24 shows the location of milk producers selling to handlers outside Worcester County.

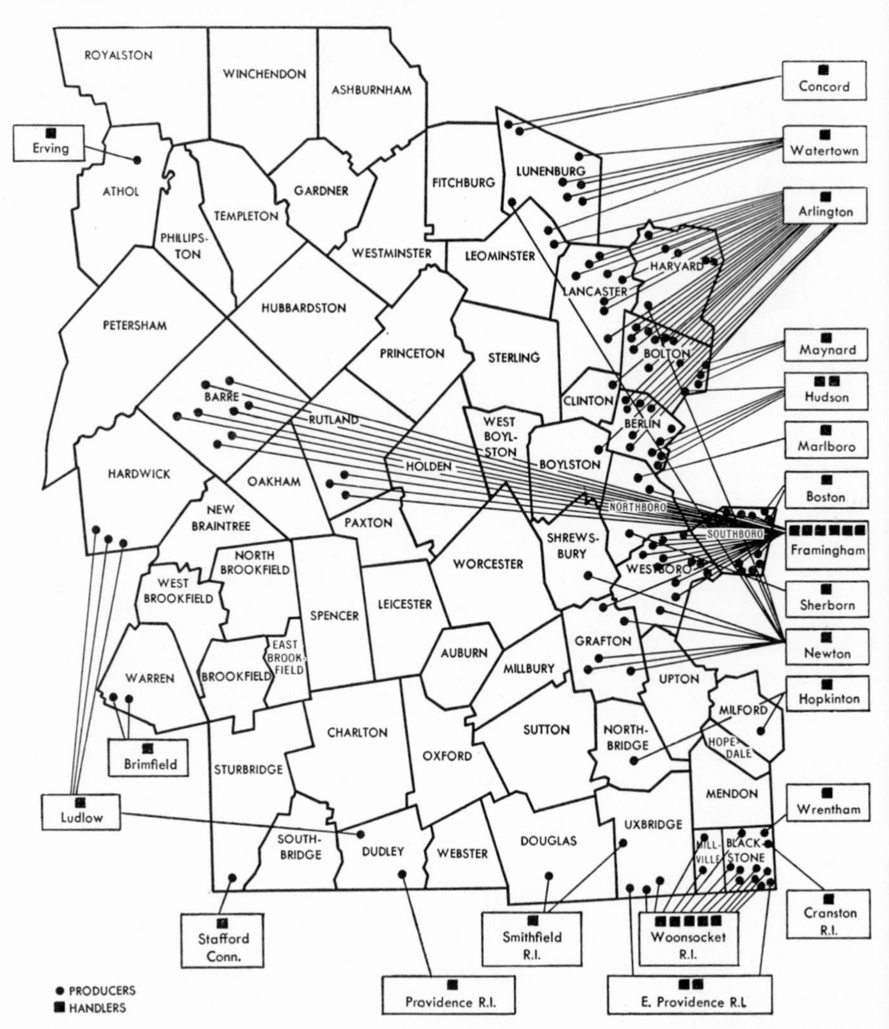

Figure 24. *Location of milk producers selling to handlers outside Worcester County.*

The level of milk consumption in the Worcester Area is relatively high and steadily rising. Total consumption in 1956 was up 3 percent from 1955, 8 percent from 1953, and 11 percent from 1950. Estimates of per capita consumption in the area run close to a pint per person per day. With rising consumption and no increase in nearby production, the Worcester market is "importing" increasing amounts of milk from the Boston market pool.

Tables 8a and 8b give the sources and disposition of milk, with quantities indicating the relative importance of each source and each avenue of disposition for each of the important Milk Control Commission areas in Worcester County. It will be noted that only Areas 9A and 9C lie entirely within Worcester County. Areas 9B, 7G, and 7B extend into adjoining counties. Also to be observed are four towns in eastern Worcester County which are parts of Areas 10B and 10C located largely in adjoining counties. These discrepancies do not materially lessen the descriptive value of the information in Tables 8a and 8b for planning purposes.

This brief review of milk marketing in Worcester County must leave the reader with a vivid impression of an extremely dynamic phenomenon. Techniques, methods, and outlets are ever changing. Though it does appear that techniques for public regulation have brought stability into markets, they have not prevented change. In fact regulation, to be successful, must encourage rather than restrict adjustments. With the increasing tempo of change it behooves individual farmers and their leaders through their planning committees to be quick in understanding developments as they take place and anticipate their direction and meaning in terms of changes yet to come.

Many of the adjustments coming in the field of marketing call for capital to replace labor. This helps to explain the trend to fewer but larger producer and handler units.

Since World War II, merchandising methods for milk have been in a state of flux. Larger retail stores, larger containers for milk, fat and nonfat solid content "tailored" to fit varying consumer needs, and the trend away from door-to-door delivery are examples of change that the industry must watch. These developments will affect Worcester County dairymen, favorably or unfavorably, depending on their alertness in making adjustments.

Since 1952, the outstanding technical development bringing drastic change into the marketing system has been the adoption of bulk tanks on the farms and tank trucks for transporting milk from farms to assembly plants. By the middle of 1957 the Hood Company in Worcester was receiving

TABLE 8a

Sources of Milk by Massachusetts Milk Control Commission Areas

Based on Dealer Reports, November 1955 (thousands of pounds)*

Sources	*7B*	*7G*	*9A*	*9B*	*9C*
Own farm	873	83	142	670	93
Massachusetts producers	1319	605	1034	454	153
Out-of-state producers	397	74	526	8	
Dealers in area	528	111	224	33	
Dealers in other areas	7G—33 9A—73 15B—217	4—1 5A—9 7B—24 9A—1	3A—29	10B—10 14A—31	4—19 5B—3 9E—30
Dealers in other states		Vt—262	Ct—2 Vt—1343	RI—14 Vt—6	
Dealers in federal orders	B—46 W—45 LL—12	W—10	W—46	B—3 W—66	W—40
Standardization Inventory variance	(22)			(2)	
Totals	3521	1180	3346	1293	338

* Detailed figures may not always equal totals owing to rounding. These data do not include route sales in Massachusetts Control areas by Federal Order dealers, nor their receipts from Massachusetts producers. Out-of-state dealer receipts from Massachusetts producers are not included. Abbreviations include B for Boston, W for Worcester, and LL for Lowell, Lawrence (now Merrimac Valley). Compiled by H. Spindler. Massachusetts Agricultural Experiment Station.

all of its milk in bulk. By the same time, 244, or 35 percent, of the suppliers in the Worcester Market Area had converted to bulk-tank handling. For the County as a whole, 290 milk producers had converted by the end of 1956.

Bulk handling of milk is changing the competitive advantages of farmers. The competitive position of handlers in buying and selling milk is also undergoing change. The benefits accruing to individual producers and handlers from the shift to bulk assembly vary widely depending largely upon their location and volume. Milk picked up in bulk can easily be diverted to markets bidding the highest prices. It is evident that the use of tanks on the farm and over the road will bring about much more flexibility in the movement of milk to alternative outlets. Market outlets in Massachusetts already give preference to producers with bulk tanks. Dairymen can lose their nearby market advantages unless they convert soon. Although the pains of adjustment are severe, the rapid changeover by Worcester County dairymen is

TABLE 8b

Disposition of Milk by Massachusetts Milk Control Commission Areas

Based on Dealer Reports, November 1955 (thousands of pounds)*

Disposition	*7B*	*7G*	*9A*	*9B*	*9C*
Route sales					
Within area..........	2607		1257	1065	295
In other areas.........	7G—143 10C—35	4—6 5B—6 7G—1018 9C—3		10B—50 14A—1	5B—12
In other states..........			Ct—18 RI—1429	RI—71	
In federal areas..........	W—3			W—32	
To dealers					
Within area..........	528	111	224	33	
In other areas.........	7G—24	7B—33	5B—53 7B—73 7G—1 9E—11 10B—63	10B—6	
In other states..........	NH—17		Ct—56 RI—128	RI—1	
In federal areas..........	B—10 W—43			W—13	W—25
Total Class I........	3410	1177	3313	1272	332

* Detailed figures may not always equal totals owing to rounding. These data do not include route sales in Massachusetts Control areas by Federal Order dealers, nor their receipts from Massachusetts producers. Out-of-state dealer receipts from Massachusetts producers are not included. Abbreviations include B for Boston and W for Worcester. Compiled by H. Spindler, Massachusetts Agricultural Experiment Station.

favorable evidence of a healthy industry. This is another example of continuous change which must be anticipated if competitive advantage is to be retained. It is already apparent that the bulk-tank development will increase the efficiency of marketing milk in Worcester County.

POULTRY MARKETING

During the last thirty years the poultry industry of Worcester County has grown from a minor farm enterprise to the one in second place. It now accounts for approximately one third of the gross farm income. The progressive development of marketing organization and methods has played an important part in providing a favorable environment for the industry's growth.

Thirty years ago the wholesale houses of Boston, Worcester, Springfield, and the smaller cities sent trucks through the rural areas purchasing farmers' eggs and poultry largely on the buyers' own terms, for there was little dissemination of market information among the farmers. Also there were many independent buyers traveling the countryside. Today the marketing setup is completely changed, with the farmers' own cooperative associations playing the dominant role in the marketing of poultry products. These cooperative associations first standardized the quality of local eggs and then provided outlets. The nature of these outlets has changed rapidly with the demise of the small grocery store in favor of modern supermarkets. The cooperatives have kept pace with these changes. In recent years they have built dressing plants in order to process broilers and fowl to suit consumer demands. At present, in step with modern trends toward vertical "integration," they are providing their members with guaranteed institutionalized returns for the production of broilers and eggs on the basis of contractual arrangements preceding production.

The Brockton Cooperative Egg Auction started operations in August 1932. One year later the Springfield Cooperative Auction Association was organized. Concurrently the United Cooperative Farmers Association of Fitchburg began marketing eggs for its members by selling them through brokers and chain stores in the Boston area.

The Brockton Auction, encouraged by Worcester County poultrymen, soon began collecting eggs by truck in the southeastern, central, and western parts of the County. The Springfield Association did the same in the southwestern part of the County. Thus the thirties marked the beginning of a transition from the irresponsible itinerant buyers to orderly marketing through the cooperatives. They not only introduced efficiencies into the handling and distribution of eggs, but more importantly, they standardized the eggs and improved their quality by strict adherence to grading and inspection.

During the war the shift continued with the volume of cooperative business increasing by leaps and bounds. Since then the transition has been completed. No longer are egg and poultry buyers with their trucks seen in the rural areas. They have been replaced by two new developments. First, there are the poultrymen who deliver and service grocery stores large and small. (A smaller volume is delivered directly from door to door to consumers.) This method of marketing accounts for most of the eggs produced in the central part of the County adjacent to the Worcester area. The smaller cities such as Fitchburg, Athol, Leominster, and Clinton also absorb nearby production in quantity.

Secondly, the cooperatives collect and market the eggs not sold directly to stores and consumers. They process and market practically all of the fowl and broilers. The Fitchburg cooperative services the northern part of the County; the Springfield cooperative a small area in the southwestern area, and the Brockton cooperative the rest of the County.

Since the war the Fitchburg and Brockton cooperatives have built modern dressing plants which constitute most of the processing capacity in the State. A cooperative in Hartford provides a market for some of the broilers and fowl in the southern part of the County. Brockton and Fitchburg provide the markets for the rest.

Brockton and Fitchburg eggs are distributed largely in the eastern Massachusetts area. This is also true for their dressed broilers and fowl, except as they go to satisfy the local Worcester County demands. Some of the fowl and broilers dressed in Hartford are distributed in the New York area.

The poultry industry of Worcester County like that of the rest of the country is rapidly undergoing vertical integration. The chain of integration may extend from the supply of feed and chicks to the point at which the commodity reaches the consumer. By means of this integration, the farmers are securing some of the advantages enjoyed by producers under imperfect competition in the nonagricultural sectors of the economy. Instead of producing a batch of broilers and then taking whatever price the market offers under perfect competition conditions, they know in advance what their returns will be and govern their production plans accordingly. This is the way a manufacturer operates who produces only on the basis of advance orders.

Feed and farm supply dealers are interested because it provides a means for expanding volume for the products they handle. Processors are seeking closer ties with producers as a means of being assured a regular and adequate volume and in order to exercise more control over quality.[2]

Farmers are interested because (1) integration usually provides some assistance in financing; (2) price and production risks are shifted from individual producers and risks are averaged out since marketings are dis-

[2] Seaver's studies indicate that broiler plant costs can be reduced 11 percent and collection costs 27 percent by eliminating seasonality. See S. K. Seaver, *The Effect of Variability in Supply of Eggs Upon Wholesale Marketing Costs,* Storrs Agricultural Experiment Station Bulletin 331, April 1957.

persed over time and space; (3) dealer-producer and processor-producer arrangements and relationships encourage adoption of improved technology, including improved breeds and varieties, the latest knowledge in formulating rations, and disease control, as a consequence of which the quality of product is improved; and finally (4) integration tends to increase scale of production and thereby improves labor and capital efficiency.

The disadvantage of integration from the farmer's viewpoint is that some of his decision-making tends to be shifted to the supplier or processor. Furthermore, he is placed in the disadvantageous position of having to deal with firms that are in strong bargaining positions. But caught up in the sweep of this trend, the individual farmer or group of farmers within an area such as Worcester County has no alternative but to adjust; otherwise he will be eliminated by competition.

Fortunately the Worcester County poultry industry can look ahead optimistically at this point, for through their Brockton and Fitchburg cooperatives, farmers are developing contractual arrangements that will enable them to realize the advantages of integration without completely losing their bargaining and decision-making functions. For as members of the cooperatives they will continue to make these decisions, even though, because it is through group action, one step removed from individual decision-making.

APPLE MARKETING

Apple production in Worcester County has remained steady at approximately 1,000,000 bushels during the past twenty-five years,[3] but the industry has undergone drastic adjustments. Whereas in 1940 there were 276 farms with 100 or more apple trees, in 1955 there were only 93 farms.[4] In 1940 there were 321,000 trees on these farms; in 1955, only 103,000 trees. Changing marketing techniques, along with improved production technology, have had their effect in eliminating the smaller marginal farms.

Twenty-five years ago there was practically no refrigerated farm storage in Worcester County. In 1955, one third (34) of the farms had refrigerated storage with a total capacity of over 400,000 bushels — enough to accommodate almost half of this crop.[5] This has extended the marketing season from the fall months through the winter.

At present, controlled-atmosphere storages are being installed and Worces-

[3] New England Crop Reporting Service.
[4] Fruit surveys made by the University of Massachusetts, 1940 and 1955.
[5] Fruit Survey made by the University of Massachusetts, 1955.

ter County growers already have enough capacity to take care of 10 percent of their crop.[6] This innovation lengthens the marketing season into the following April and May.

These developments have had their influence in eliminating smaller farm units as well as effecting the changing pattern of market channels. The latter has, of course, resulted from the shift to larger retail outlets where apples are now sold largely in one- and three-pound transparent packages.

Table 9 and Figure 25 show the methods used in marketing the 1955 crop of Worcester County apples.[7] It will be noted that approximately 15 percent of the crop is now sold through roadside stands. This compares with only 4 percent 30 years ago.[8] Modern roads and automobiles have brought the orchards of the County nearer to many consumers and thus fruit growers have this added opportunity of obtaining higher prices by direct selling. The Massachusetts Fruit Growers Association promotes roadside merchandising by recognizing "Approved Farm Stands" which meet rigorous standards.

Thirty years ago 10 percent of the Worcester County apple crop was sold and delivered door to door. This practice has been discontinued due to the high cost of labor.

TABLE 9

Methods of Selling Apples, Worcester County, 1955

Bushels and Percentages by Method of Sale for each size of Orchard

	0–199		*200–499*		*500–999*		*1,000–1,999*		*2,000 and over*		*Total*	
Method of sale	*Bushels*	*Percent*	*Bushels*	*Percent*	*Bushels*	*Percent*	*Bushels*	*Percent*	*Bushels*	*Percent*	*Bushels*	*Percent*
Own stand or salesroom	2,203	62.7	15,327	24.0	21,573	16.2	12,627	7.6	67,127	11.9	118,857	12.8
Other stands or salesrooms	0	0	3,592	5.6	4,850	3.6	2,870	1.8	6,208	1.1	17,520	1.9
Direct to retail stores	931	26.5	7,577	11.8	9,048	6.8	27,955	16.9	37,913	6.7	83,424	9.0
Other sales agents	0	0	31,412	49.1	92,733	69.4	114,343	69.1	351,882	62.5	590,370	63.5
Used at home — cider	381	10.8	6,054	9.5	5,391	4.0	7,567	4.6	100,287	17.8	119,680	12.9
Totals	3,515	100.0	63,962	100.0	133,595	100.0	165,362	100.0	563,417	100.0	929,851	100.0

Nine percent of the present-day crop is delivered direct to retail stores. About the same proportion of the crop was sold in this manner thirty years ago; however, more merchandising service to the stores goes with today's sales.

[6] Fruit Survey, University of Mass., 1955.

[7] Fruit Survey, University of Mass., 1955.

[8] Hubert W. Yount and L. P. Jefferson, *An Economic Study of the Massachusetts Apple Industry,* Massachusetts Agricultural Experiment Station Bulletin 228, March 1926.

Thirty years ago approximately 24 percent of the apples were sold on the farm to country buyers and "peddlers." This practice has entirely disappeared. Farmers now deliver their apples to chain store and wholesale warehouses. This accounts for the 63.5 percent sold through "other sales agents." New England wholesalers distribute the New England apple crop to market centers throughout the Northeast including New York, Philadelphia, Washington, Pittsburgh, and Baltimore. New England apple shipments to these markets vary from 15 percent of total receipts in New York to 3 percent for

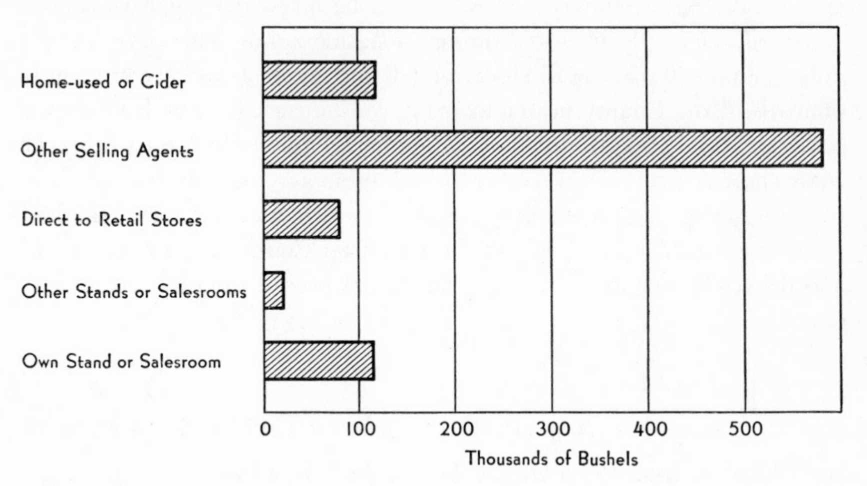

Figure 25. *Methods of selling apples, Worcester County, 1955.*

Baltimore.[9] Thus it may be concluded that Worcester County apples have a broad choice of market opportunities.

VEGETABLE MARKETING

The facilities and organization for marketing nearby vegetables in Worcester County, as elsewhere in the Northeast, have lagged behind modern needs. This has been a decided competitive handicap in the production of local vegetables. To no small degree this explains why vegetable production in Worcester County has never been a vigorous industry.

The charter for the city of Worcester specifies that a free public market must be provided for farmers. For decades, farmers have used Salem Square during the night and until 6:00 A.M. Strict adherence to the 6:00 A.M. closing time was in itself a handicap to farmers, for with the approach of 6:00 A.M.,

[9] Joseph Gartner and J. R. Bowring, *Competition for New England Apples on United States Markets,* New Hampshire Agricultural Experiment Station Bulletin 436, April 1957.

farmers were forced to sell under distress conditions. Usually sales were made between farmers and retail store managers. The produce was transferred from the farmer's truck to the storekeeper's truck in the market place at the time of sale. Following the war, store managers would come into the market and the farmers would then deliver direct to the stores after the market closed.

The Salem Square market was never as important an outlet for farm produce as the Worcester wholesale houses. During the thirties, 60 percent of the local vegetables were handled by approximately 25 wholesalers. In recent years the wholesalers' volume of business has declined. Through-street improvements in Worcester have closed a third of the wholesale establishments. Thirty years ago Fitchburg had 15 wholesale houses and a farmers' public market. Only 3 wholesalers were left in 1957. Lone wholesale houses serve Gardner and Southbridge instead of several as formerly.

Thirty years ago the market garden farmers were located near the cities. With urbanization of these areas, and since distance is no longer a major consideration, the larger operators have moved into outlying areas, where taxes are lower. Only the larger operators moved; the smaller gardeners ceased to exist.

The farmer's markets in the smaller cities have disappeared with the demise of the small farmer and the small grocery store. The Salem Square market in Worcester continues to operate only on a perfunctory basis.

But this is only half of the picture of change. The larger producers are now becoming known in the trade as grower-shippers. They either pair up with large stores or supermarkets or ship directly to service wholesalers who in turn are equipped to provide large stores with all their produce needs — say fifty items — on a one-stop basis, along with such services as packages, advertising, and display materials — hence the term "service" wholesaler.

Actually, 85 percent of the vegetables in Worcester County are presently being supplied directly to large retail stores or to service wholesalers. This calls for responsible growers who can provide a steady supply of dependable quality produce. Only 15 percent is being marketed through the "old line" wholesalers.

At present, attempts are being made to establish a regional market southeast of Worcester at the junction of Routes 20 and 140 on a forty-acre tract of land. Plans are being developed with counsel from the United States Department of Agriculture. The plan has definite possibilities because of its strategic location and space provisions. Such a market could become an assembling point for all of coastal New England. Obviously such a development, should it materialize, would broaden the outlets for Worcester County vegetables.

These drastic adjustments, however, have seemingly left the problem of price determination unsolved. Pricing between shippers and retail store operators is often based on wholesale prices established by a very small segment of the trade under a decadent environment. Such prices are sometimes referred to as "sick prices." On the other hand, supermarket operators are selling their vegetables more and more on the basis of quality and packaging rather than price. Hence, they are willing to pay the producer an attractive pre-agreed-upon price throughout the season if he can deliver a steady quantity of high-quality produce. This practice leads toward a type of integration such as discussed under poultry marketing. Integration between growers and retailers may be the next major development in marketing fresh vegetables.

CHAPTER 8

The County Land-Use Planning Movement

The opening chapter states that this undertaking in land-use planning for Worcester County was conceived at the outset as fitting into and contributing to a nationwide program of land-use planning, with the county as the key unit, that was evolving in this country from 1933 on, and that eventuated in the county planning undertaken under the Memoranda of Agreement between the federal government and 46 states following the Mount Weather Agreement of July 1938.[1] We should know about this nationwide program, its objectives, undertakings, and accomplishments, before setting forth upon an actual planning analysis for Worcester County.

The agricultural leaders of this country had become conscious of land use as a factor in the agricultural problem before 1933. The Agricultural Marketing Act of 1929 had in one brief paragraph designated production and land use as subjects to be included in the program of the Federal Farm Board which it authorized. In the fall of 1931, this Board joined with the U.S.D.A. and other federal agencies in the Chicago Conference on land use, out of which came a national land-use coordinating committee with eleven subcommittees. President Roosevelt scrapped this setup along with the Farm Board itself. What came forth in its stead was, first, a National Resources Board with a National Land-Use Planning Committee under L. C. Gray, and second, a Program Planning Division of the AAA under Howard Tolley.

The Land-Use Planning Committee published a general report in December 1934, and followed this with eleven supplementary volumes. It made

[1] This chapter is largely the work of Westcott, who had the major responsibility for the county land-use planning program in Massachusetts while this program was under way.

further recommendations in its *Progress Report,* June 15, 1936. Among the recommendations were the following:

> (1) That a permanent Land Planning Section of the National Resources Committee or its successor be established, with representation from the Federal bureaus primarily concerned, thus laying a basis not only for continued land planning but for better coordination of policies, research, and public land acquisition.
>
> (2) Federal acquisition of land for retirement of submarginal farms, relocation of stranded people on the land, additions to national and State forests, parks, and wild-life refuges, and enlargements of Indian reservations should be provided for by regular congressional appropriations, with establishment of permanent revolving funds where these are essential to the proper administration and disposition of the lands acquired.
>
> (3) That an adequate zoning by States and counties be encouraged to promote the best use of lands.

The National Resources Board, with the word "planning" subsequently inserted, came under criticism increasingly from 1938 on, and was abolished by Act of Congress in 1943.

THE PROGRAM PLANNING DIVISION OF THE AAA

The Agricultural Adjustment Act of May 1933 provided for reducing the acreage of crops with export surpluses and thus raising prices. The acreage quotas assigned each farmer for each crop were percentages of his acreages in the preceding three years. It was understood from the start that this mechanical procedure would serve only to get the program started and that a much more carefully analyzed program of adjustments would need to be developed shortly. The Program Planning Division was set up in the fall of 1933 to start work on this analysis. Its first large undertaking was a study of regional adjustments needed by agriculture. It divided the country into twelve regions and began cooperating with the state experiment stations in assembling the basic land-use and other information needed. In March 1934 a series of regional conferences were held. The deans and directors of research, the state extension directors, and the heads of the economics departments in the various agricultural colleges and experiment stations took part in these conferences. Plans were made to develop recommendations first on a state and regional basis, and then, in a coordinated national form, for agricultural adjustments to promote good land use; and finally to harmonize good land use with satisfactory economic results.

The experiment stations adopted this program and with funds supplied partly by the Agricultural Adjustment Administration began the necessary descriptive analyses. The experiment stations sought essentially to answer two questions: (1) Into what type-of-farming areas may this state be divided? and (2) What adjustments in the prevailing enterprises in these areas will be necessary to maintain fertility, check soil erosion, and promote efficient management? Representatives of the U.S.D.A. cooperated with the experiment stations in harmonizing their procedures so that the findings in all the states might be approximately comparable.

At a series of regional conferences in August and early September, 1935, the states presented tentative conclusions as to the adjustments desirable within their own boundaries. They based their conclusions on detailed information regarding the total areas in the different types of farming, the land in farms, the land in crops, the grazing and pasture land, the percentages of the cropland in various crops, the number of livestock on farms, and so forth on the supply side, and on the trends in domestic consumption and export on the demand side.

These conferences coordinated the state recommendations into regional reports. Sufficient progress was made to justify a start, in cooperation with the AAA, on plans for interregional coordination of cropping systems, with a view to developing the comparative advantages of different areas in a manner consistent with a sound national adjustment of agriculture to its physical and economic environment.

The analyses made under this regional adjustment project were very largely collaborative between the AAA and the state experiment stations. The state extension services had only a small part in them. More important, the people themselves were having no part in them. In the summer of 1935, however, the Program Planning Division and the Agricultural Extension Service met together in Washington and developed a project to establish county planning committees of ten to twenty members representing the various agricultural interests of the counties. Each committee, with the assistance of community committees and sub-committees, was to develop a long-time agricultural adjustment program for its county, giving first attention to the question of soil conservation. At the first County Planning Project Conference, held in Washington on October 25, 1935, Dr. A. G. Black, then Chief of the Bureau of Agricultural Economics, outlined the function of this project as follows:

It is essential that farmers in the various counties contribute in a very real way toward the building of a more permanent adjustment program. For that reason the County Planning Project has been proposed. We know that groups of farmers, when asked to make recommendations regarding adjustments that should be made within their county, have information that will be of great value in determining what adjustments should be made. We also realize that farm groups must have an appreciation of the general problem of adjustments from the national point of view and must be ready to take full responsibility for their share in the adjustments to be made in the various counties.

It would appear that the present program is the natural growth from the years of economic and general outlook work that have preceded it. The only new elements in the situation are, (1) the participation by farmers in supplying facts to be used in perfecting adjustment programs and securing from them their best judgment as to the direction which adjustments should take in their respective localities, and (2) there is now in existence means by which plans and programs for adjustment can be put into effect.

This project presently became the major land-use planning activity in the states, and project agreements were worked out with the separate states. By 1938, this project was at least begun in something over 2,400 counties. In general, the counties gave major consideration to:

(a) The natural characteristics of the farm land involved, variations in soil types within the county, the extent and seriousness of soil erosion and fertility depletion, and the major causes of such deterioration in the productive plant, such as improper cropping systems, etc.;

(b) the economic status of the farmers involved, changes in economic conditions having some influence on the practices adopted by farmers that resulted in soil deterioration, the long-time outlook as to the general economic situation and specific segments of peculiar interest to farmers;

(c) various ways of attacking the problems revealed or emphasized by such deliberations with emphasis on the need for and suitability of the present programs directed toward agricultural improvement; and,

(d) the economic, civic, and social implications of the various problems and solutions considered.

In order that these committees might consider the situations and problems as carefully as possible, it was necessary to provide them with much basic material pertaining to those forces with which they were not as intimately acquainted as they were with their own local farming conditions. Therefore, one of the first tasks of the extension service was the preparation in usable form of such background information as soil types and their adaptability, trends in crop and livestock production and in market demands and outlets for agricultural produce, price trends, successful farm organization in the different type-of-farming areas, and extent and location of serious soil erosion and fertility depletion areas. In this endeavor, the extension service had the cooperation of the research agencies in the various subject-matter fields, both state and national, as well as the cooperation of the various "action program" agencies such as the Agricultural Adjustment Administration, the Farm Security Administration, the Soil Conservation Service, and others.

To emphasize the undertaking and tie it in closely with the AAA action program, the states were asked to have their county committees provide answers to the following specific questions:

> (1) What production of the various farm products will be expected in 1936, assuming normal weather conditions, present farming practices, prospective prices, and continuation of production and marketing control programs through 1936?
>
> (2) What production of the various farm products would be expected in 1936—
>
> a. Assuming normal weather conditions and prospective prices, but with production and marketing control programs discontinued?
>
> b. Assuming normal weather, prospective prices, *and farming systems so adjusted as to maintain soil fertility and control erosion?*
>
> (3) What production of the various farm products should be expected after all land not adapted to agriculture has been shifted to other uses, and after sufficient time has elapsed to permit such changes in farm management practices as are necessary to maintain soil fertility and control erosion, and to permit those shifts between agricultural enterprises which seem clearly desirable and susceptible of practical accomplishments?

Question (1) was dropped when in January 1936 the Supreme Court declared the benefit payment and processing tax sections of the Agricultural Adjustment Act unconstitutional. Work was continued on the other questions, however, and answers to questions (2a) and (2b) were obtained in almost all of the counties in which the project was started, as well as some answers to question (3). The estimates for (2a) were expected to indicate the effect upon production of the abandonment of marketing or control programs and the return to capacity production, especially in crops, while the estimates for (2b) were expected to indicate the acreages and production that should result were a soil conservation program put into effect.

The estimates of the county planning committees and of the research workers in this Regional Adjustment Project were published in a report[2] which proved to be helpful in determining the general direction in which a soil conservation program should be pointed. The estimates from the two groups agreed to a surprising degree. In general, both groups recommended a significant downward adjustment in the acreage of soil-depleting crops as compared with 1928–1932 levels. A downward adjustment of 10 to 15 percent in the acreage of corn, 5 to 10 percent in oats and barley, 5 to 15 percent in wheat, and 5 to 20 percent in cotton was recommended, and the county planning committees further suggested a reduction of almost 20 percent in the acreage of tobacco. On the other hand, increases of 20 to 30 percent in the acreage of hay, or in the acreage of hay and pasture which might be substituted for hay, were indicated.

In 1936 and 1937, this county land-use planning program was at the same time made more specific with more emphasis on conservation and broadened to include more aspects of agriculture and rural life. The committee setup became more elaborate and included a State Directing Committee, which in Massachusetts included representation from the extension administration, the economics and farm management specialists, the home project work, the junior club work, and the agricultural subject-matter specialists. Membership on the county committees was enlarged to include home and junior interests and activities. The county committees were encouraged to set up numerous sub-committees. In Massachusetts these sub-committees followed along the lines of commodity interests, rural home interests, soil conservation, taxation, and government administration.

The increased emphasis on conservation came as a result of the enactment of the Soil Conservation and Domestic Allotment Act of 1936, provided to take the place of the 1933 Act declared unconstitutional in part. The administration in Washington and the Congress substituted conservation for adjustment as the avowed objective, and the consequent legislation has thus far stood the test of the courts. It was, however, not so much the objectives as the methods of implementation that were found objectionable by the

[2] *The County Planning Project: A Statistical Summary of Results Obtained in 1935–36.* Production Planning Section, Program Planning Division, Agricultural Adjustment Administration, U.S. Department of Agriculture, 1936.

supreme court. The new program compensated the farmer not just for growing less of the crops in surplus, but also according to the land use to which the land was shifted, especially from "soil-depleting" to "soil-maintaining" and "soil-conserving" uses.

The growth and shift in the objectives is indicated by the following statement taken from the project agreement for County Rural Planning in Massachusetts during 1937–38:

A. Long-time and general objectives
   1. To appraise the effectiveness of present agricultural programs (from both local and national standpoints).
   2. To develop future programs of agricultural policy and extension teaching.
      a. Agricultural Programs — This project will lay the basis for and result in the development of sound local, state, and national agricultural action programs which are and will continue to affect local agricultural production.
      b. Correlated Extension Programs — This project will result in increasing the effectiveness, adequacy, and soundness of educational activities carried on by the extension service and other agencies in the field.
         (1) This setup and procedure will result in the bringing together of all lines of extension teaching in the state office, the county, and the community. Through it, the problems of the farmer will first be determined and then extension programs arranged to deal with these problems.
   3. To appraise the means and agencies for implementing the above programs and then to initiate action.
   4. To enhance education and develop agricultural leadership.
      a. Education — The work of farm people involved in this project will, in itself, constitute an educational process. Through this project, the participants should obtain a more thorough appreciation of their own problems and the relationship between the problems of individuals and those which are community, state, or nationwide in scope and character. (The attainment of this objective requires a better understanding of both the basic facts and the problems involved in attaining agricultural equality.)
      b. Leadership — This project will result in the continuous development of new agricultural leadership.

B. Immediate Objectives

1. To determine shifts in the various kinds of agricultural production which should be encouraged for greater utilization of resources.
2. To classify all land as to the future uses for which it is best suited (recognizing that uses vary from time to time under changing conditions).
3. To appraise all agricultural action programs and specifically the Agricultural Conservation Program to determine:
   a. Changes already brought about through the program.
   b. Probable changes to be brought about through the program.
   c. Appraise the soundness of these changes.
   d. Advise with the officers of the County Conservation Association regarding suggestions for future agricultural conservation programs.
4. Coordinate the extension programs of the various extension industry committees (dairy, poultry, fruit, market garden crops, cash crops, and farm woodlots) into a well-rounded, sound county extension program.
5. Continue work on the preparation of a statement of agricultural policy for each county.[3]

It was at this stage of development in land-use planning that the Worcester County land-use planning project came into being, in the manner indicated in Chapter 1, under the joint sponsorship of Harvard University and Massachusetts State College, with aid and support from several of the agencies within the United States Department of Agriculture. The work in this experimental county during 1937–38 was of three types.

(A) First there was an intensive survey of the town of Hardwick. This included (1) obtaining, by means of a short survey schedule, the elementary facts as to occupation, land use, production if any, for each resident outside of the thickly settled areas, (2) making a reconnaissance survey of land use and related factors for the entire town, (3) obtaining the facts as to the town governmental problems and social factors, and (4) mapping forty-two farms located by means of (1).

(B) A less intensive survey was made in nine other selected towns (Northboro, Grafton, Mendon, Sutton, Charlton, North Brookfield, Sterling, Petersham, and Winchendon). In these towns numbers (1) and (2) of the foregoing were carried out and then six or more sample farms were mapped.

(C) A budgetary analysis was made of the farms that were mapped.

[3] Project Agreement, "County Rural Program Planning for Massachusetts," 1937–1938, mimeographed.

This work was basic to preparation of a comprehensive land-use plan for the county. The work on this study continued as a phase of the County Land-Use Planning Project during the period from July 1938 through June 1942.

THE OFFICE OF LAND-USE COORDINATION

By this time another problem had become increasingly acute, namely, that of coordinating the activities of the different action agencies in the federal government. Besides the AAA and later ACP programs, there were the submarginal land purchase program, soil conservation, flood control, water facilities, farm forestry and wildlife activities, rural electrification, farm credit, the tenancy and rehabilitation programs under the Farm Security Administration, crop insurance, commodity loans, surplus disposal, and many others, all developed and launched within the short span of three or four years. Generally, each of these programs had been authorized by a separate Act of Congress.[4] Each made the Secretary of Agriculture responsible for its efficient administration. Each of them usually dealt with only one segment of the complex problem of raising and stabilizing agricultural income and bringing about efficiency and stability in the use of land and water resources. None of them really spelled out the relationships with already existing programs. Hence there was bound to be considerable conflict, duplication, and inefficiency in their application to an individual farm unit, rural community, or even a larger area or region. The most conspicuous feature of this was the number of representatives of different agencies that had contacts with many of the farms.

Moreover, involved in this coordination of the federal agency programs was the whole matter of federal-state-local governmental relations. Bushrod Allin of the Bureau of Agricultural Economics, who had a major role in developing the county program-planning project, writing on this phase of the subject in 1940, identified three problems that had arisen for the United States Department of Agriculture and the Land-Grant Colleges:

> (1) The problem of how to administer a national program in such a manner as to accomplish its national objectives and at the same time to fit the program to the many local variations in physical and economic conditions so that it will serve the needs of each locality most effectively;

[4] For instance, basic legislation included the Soil Conservation and Domestic Allotment Act of 1936, the Sugar Act of 1937, the Agricultural Adjustment Act of 1938, the Federal Crop Insurance Act of 1938, the Marketing Agreements Act of 1937, the Surplus Commodity Acts of 1937 and 1938, the Bankhead-Jones Farm Tenant Act of 1937, the Soil Conservation Act of 1935, the Flood Control Acts of 1936, 1937, and 1938, the Farm Forestry Act of 1937, and the Pope-Jones Act of 1937 dealing with a water facilities program.

(2) The problem of how to unify or coordinate the various federal, state and local agricultural programs so that they are essentially a single program when they reach the individual farms; and

(3) The problem of clarifying the responsibilities and working relationships of the U.S. Department of Agriculture and the Land-Grant Colleges.[5]

The thinking that developed in the U.S.D.A. focused more and more on the use of the land. It was realized that much more than the land was involved, but it began to appear that the best strategy would be to begin with something concrete and tangible like the land and build onto this. The first move was made by Under-Secretary M. L. Wilson by setting up an *ad hoc* committee consisting of one representative each from the Agricultural Adjustment Administration, the Forest Service, the Soil Conservation Service, the Resettlement Administration, and the Bureau of Agricultural Economics, and the senior author of this book, John D. Black, as special consultant. They were to develop a plan to coordinate the activities of these agencies with respect to land. Not only these agencies, but the Extension Service, the Bureau of Public Roads, the Civilian Conservation Corps, the Soil Survey, and the flood control group, made reports to this *ad hoc* committee. The committee's report to Secretary Wilson constituted a noteworthy landmark of relevant thought on the problem. Black's contribution to it was much influenced by the thinking and planning already done in Massachusetts in connection with the laying out of the Worcester County project. Following are excerpts from this report. First of all, it offered five reasons for the coordination of governmental land-use activities as follows:[6]

Review of the activities relating to land use of the various agencies within the Department of Agriculture points to the following as the major reasons for coordination of its land-use activities:

1. State and local agencies, and more especially the farmers, find themselves confused by the number of different government agencies that approach them with respect to undertakings seeming to have much in common.
2. The efforts of the various agencies are not always pointed in the same direction. They may even go so far in places as to nullify each other in part.
3. Much of the effort has not been sufficiently considered from the standpoint of its economic and social advantage. If public funds are going to be available for important undertakings in the future, it is important that these undertakings fully repay the expenditures upon them, and moreover, that

[5] Bushrod W. Allin, "County Planning Project — A Cooperative Approach to Agricultural Planning," *Journal of Farm Economics,* vol. 22, no. 1, February 1940.

[6] Special Committee Report, "Coordination of Land-use Activities within the U.S. Department of Agriculture," unpublished, 1937.

they be the things *most needing* to be done next. Choices have to be made between areas, and between things to do in the same area.

4. The areas selected for projects by the different agencies are not always chosen in such a way as to integrate with each other. Projects having much in common may be under way in different parts of a State under the auspices of different agencies working independently of each other.
5. Considerable waste of public funds arises from deficiencies with respect to the foregoing, certain, before long, to result in public reaction that will set back the whole agricultural program.

The report (never published) then went on to say:

The logical procedure for dealing with such a situation is to have a general plan of desirable land use and a program of orderly steps toward the attainment of this plan, into which the activities of the several agencies can be fitted, and by which the value *at the time* of any proposed public land-use undertaking may be judged.

This calls for what may be called over-all land-use planning. An example of such planning is that which has been done for and by the State of Montana, with the aid of the Land-Use Planning Section of the Resettlement Administration and of the Bureau of Agricultural Economics. The entire state has been laid out in areas according to the most promising future uses of the land. On the basis of eight years of records of production of 90 percent of the farms in the state, the land was laid out into sizes and types of farms, ranches, and cooperative grazing units that promise to produce reasonable livelihoods for families, and then these farms and other units were aggregated into land-use areas.

We need to make clear, before going further, that land-use planning is not an end in itself. Land, as such, occupies no place in the scheme of things that makes it the center or the foundation or the final object of national planning. The ultimate goal of all planning is the wisest utilization of human resources. Land, however, has two characteristics which make highly necessary that all plans and all administration be related closely to it. One of these characteristics is area or extent and the other is the corollary of fixity of location. Associated with any action program relating to land is the necessity, therefore, of travel and communication over distance. There can be no two action programs for the same land area without duplication of these and possible conflict. It follows, therefore, that any national or local program for agriculture must be expressed in terms of a land-use basis if it is to be a clearly defined and workable plan. But the population, families and other institutions reared upon the land are the real objects of concern; the land use is fitted to them. But it should not assume that these are fixed in space or time or form.

It also follows that land-use plans need to be built into and correlated with general over-all plans for all of agriculture, and in the last analysis, for the nation and society. There would seem to be need of still more general plans to form a background for land-use planning, plans which take into account the facts of population, food supply, supply of textiles and timber, recreational resources, trends in production and consumption, international relationships and the like. In such planning, collaboration is needed with other departments of government concerned with land use or with the utilization of human resources.

Then the report proceeded to outline the administrative arrangements that seemed best calculated to achieve in the next few years the planning needed as a basis for the coordination.

1. Set up a new Land Policy Committee that includes the various phases of land-use planning above outlined. (Important to include extension.) The function of this committee is to serve as a board of review and to determine major matters of policy.
2. Set up under this committee a liaison group consisting of one important person from each of the agencies involved who will keep his office in that agency, and keep in touch with its programs, but who will be available upon call to participate in discussions with other members of the liaison group, and be available actually to undertake some of the more important tasks of coordination needing to be done in Washington, ordinarily as a member of a subcommittee. (Such as a subcommittee on air mapping, or on flood control.) This liaison group should have working with it a small staff of full-time specialists in over-all land-use planning. These are needed to make the actual studies of land planning activities and proposals of the various agencies, to guide and direct the actual job of over-all plan-making wherever such plans are needed, and to review any land-use plans offered from the standpoint of their relation to over-all plans. This group should be small at the outset and grow only if and as it demonstrates the value of its services. The liaison group will serve as a first court of general review for the work of its members and its staff, and submit its recommendations to the Land Policy Committee. This liaison group should have a full-time chairman, who is not on the staff of any of the land-use agencies, who will act as a sort of director of land-use planning.
3. Set up this group in the Office of the Secretary of Agriculture so that it can serve all the agencies in the Department.
4. Ask the various agencies to bring before this group for discussion and analysis any "opportunities for coordination" falling within the general types outlined above. The Land Policy Committee and its staff, however, should be free to explore any possibilities upon its own initiative.
5. Have the Committee assign particular jobs of over-all land-use planning, or of research relevant thereto, to existing agencies most competent to do them, or to two or more appropriate collaborating agencies. In many cases, the special staff of the Committee will take an active part in such collaborative arrangements. These assignments may require some work in the field, and in some cases it may be desirable to appoint some member of the staff as director of a land-use planning project. Developing cooperation in such planning with state and local agencies will be an important

phase of the work of the committee, and its staff will need to furnish leadership and guidance in such cooperative effort.

6. The efforts of government toward securing better land use will not be generally effective until the rank and file of farmers individually adopt the necessary measures and practices. If soil is to be conserved, the individual farmers must do practically all of it. It is highly important, therefore, that the extension agencies of the state and federal government be drawn into the work upon an effective basis. This will call for employment of some extension specialists in land use; but it more particularly calls for education and redirection of the efforts of present extension staffs. There will need to be federal guidance and direction of the work of these efforts. The county planning program of the AAA provides the state and local extension workers with one opportunity of this sort; but these workers need training for this type of service, and technical assistance at the start. Working out a good land-use plan in one county in each state in collaboration with the state extension staff would go far toward providing this education.
7. The over-all land-use planning activities of the Department of Agriculture need to be coordinated with those of other agencies of government concerned with other aspects of land-use — credit, grazing, parks and recreation, water supply, residential and other urban uses, etc. Any plans involving these uses should be worked out in collaboration with these agencies in the federal government, so far as federal functions are involved, and in states and localities for more local functions. No attempt at land-use planning should be made anywhere except in collaboration with any state and local planning agencies that have been established. It will be better to concentrate efforts for the present in states where such collaboration is welcome.
8. Careful weighing should be given to the suggestion of a regional land-use planning man for each of 10 or 12 regions, to be stationed in Washington, but keeping in close contact with his region through travel and through participation in the field work. This might involve more of an expansion of the staff of the planning group than is desirable at the outset.
9. Careful weighing likewise of the suggestion that a few "teams" be organized in the Department, made up, for example, of a land economist, farm management man, forester, agronomist, soils scientist, and rural sociologist, and sent out to make a land-use plan in one county in a number of states, having a squad from that state working with them and learning with them how to do it. Regional men from the Forest Service and SCS could also join them. The state man would need to be carefully selected as competent to carry on subsequently in other counties with less and less guidance. Only by training state men to do it is this job going to be done. If this procedure were followed, the regional organization would evolve without effort.

It was on July 12, 1937, that the Secretary created the Office of Land Use Coordination with a small staff under the leadership of Milton Eisenhower, who was in turn a line officer attached to the Secretary's office.[7] He was to serve as a Coordinator of Land Use Planning with responsibility for integrating the Department's land-use activities and for facilitating cooperation between the Department's action agencies and state and local agencies more or less in line with the recommendations of Secretary Wilson's *ad hoc* Committee.

The following year the Office of Land Use Coordination was established as a permanent staff agency in the Secretary's Office, but it had already become almost completely absorbed in preparations for the Mount Weather Agreement. The organization set up to administer the federal end of this Agreement took over most of the tasks that were outlined in the Committee report. The activities of the Office were presently restricted to specific land and water programs such as flood control, the water facilities program and the Wheeler-Case small irrigation program.[8] The Office lost its identity entirely in the latter years of World War II.

The reader will note that the last two administrative proposals were offered only for "careful consideration." This was a compromise statement. Some members of the Committee were not willing to go along with the consultant in these two suggestions, particularly the one about the planning teams. It had been John D. Black's idea for some time that the largest obstacle to progress in land-use planning was the dearth of personnel properly trained and conditioned to do the job, and that the best way to teach such planning was by the learning-by-doing method. He visualized starting out with a few teams working in counties around the state and having them learn practically, under the best leadership available. He expected that the first undertakings of this sort would be a mixture of experimental and pilot operations, but that out of them would come a number of U.S.D.A. planning teams that could then move into counties in other states and repeat the process, having pretty well learned how to do the job from their first experience. At the same time, in each of the states selected, a state team would have been developed that would then work from county to county in that state, and that presently other state teams would be developed. He tried to interest Milton Eisenhower in setting up a planning team and sending it

[7] M. L. Wilson, Announcement, entitled "Coordination of Land Use Planning Activities," U.S. Department of Agriculture, mimeographed, July 12, 1937.

[8] The "Land Use Coordinator" also represented the Secretary in effecting interdepartmental coordination of land-use programs and in all intradepartmental activities concerning land-use coordination. In this latter role he served as Chairman of the Agricultural Program Board and the Secretary's Coordinating Committee. The regional coordinators in the Southern Great Plains and the Northern Great Plains were members of the staff of the Office of Land Use Coordination. (Memorandum No. 814, issued April 6, 1939, by Secretary Wallace.)

to work with the Massachusetts and Harvard group in Worcester County. But he was working hard on the preliminaries of the Mount Weather Agreement and probably did not favor the planning-team approach in the first place.

THE MOUNT WEATHER AGREEMENT

The reason that the Mount Weather Agreement so promptly took most of the coordinating functions away from the Office of land Use Coordination was that at this moment the problem of relations between the U.S.D.A. and the land-grant colleges became particularly acute. What brought it to a head was that Howard Tolley, Administrator of the AAA, in the summer of 1938 suddenly took the state administration of the AAA away from the state extension services and set up separate state and county offices. It was generally agreed in the federal government that, without the work of the state extension service staffs, who took a major part in the operation, the AAA program would never have got off the ground in 1933 and 1934; but it had become increasingly questionable from 1935 on whether the action part of the AAA program should not be under other direction, and whether the extension services should not return to their educational role. Part of the state directors of extension were definitely of this opinion and approved heartily of the change. Others were more or less neutral on the subject. But there was a strong minority group who very much wanted to continue in their role as state directors of the program.

Tolley's reason for making the change was that he did not think he was getting the cooperation he needed from some of the extension services in planning for an expansion of the AAA's program of better conservation of the soil and at the same time in reducing surpluses of export crops and pork products by shifting more and more to grassland and associated livestock farming. It was a common judgment in the federal end of the AAA that some of the state extension services were dragging their heels and that others were essentially opposed to anything like quick progress in such directions. After all, most of the staffs of the land-grant colleges, experiment stations, and extension services in the South were dominantly composed of men who were specializing in cotton or tobacco, and in the eastern Great Plains with those who were specializing in small grains.

It is pertinent in this connection that Elmer Starch, Northern Great Plains Coordinator in the earlier years of the AAA, used to speak of the "land-grant college meridian"—that is, a meridian due southward from the North Dakota state college at Fargo that comes close to all the state land-grant colleges all the way to Texas — and point out that the teaching, research, and extension staffs of these institutions were thinking mostly in terms of the narrow band of semi-humid agriculture in the eastern parts of their states where the colleges were located, and of that of Minnesota, Iowa, and states to the east where most of them had been educated.

Tolley as head of the Program Planning Division of the AAA had promoted strongly the need for the shift toward grassland and livestock farming, and of planning for it, and it was out of such thinking that the new Soil Conservation and Domestic Allotment Act of 1936 was largely shaped. Chester Davis, the first AAA administrator, felt that Tolley for this reason was the logical man to head the new program, and of his own volition resigned in his favor.

As pointed out earlier, the matter of relations between the U.S.D.A. and the land-grant colleges had become more and more of a problem from 1933 on as more federal action programs were organized. Before 1933, the relations concerned research and education only, and these could be handled by the states separately with no directives from Washington except to make sure that the federally provided funds were not misused. The actions of the new federal action programs had to be performed either by federal employees or by state employees delegated to do so under either federal direction or some other form of joint direction. Conceivably, of course, some of them could have been made essentially state action programs. This was in fact proposed in the new AAA program of 1936, but it never materialized.

All that Tolley's action in the summer of 1938 did was to bring this issue to a head. The first move made was a shift in the AAA program direction at the annual meeting of the Association of Land-Grant Colleges and Universities at Houston, Texas, in the fall of 1937. The Association and the Department agreed that each would charge their federal-states relations committees to study the problem.

The U.S.D.A. committee went to work at once. Its members presently came to realize fully that the problem of federal-state relations could not be divorced from the other problems, namely, the fitting of national programs to local needs, and that of coordinating the national programs. It therefore suggested in its final conclusions that all three problems be dealt with simultaneously through a common setup and procedure. It proposed that the Department retain full responsibility for administering its action programs, and that the land-grant institutions and the Department proceed at once in each state, county, and community to cooperate in the development of land-use plans which might serve as bases for localizing and correlating all programs. Its final report was submitted to the land-grant college committee for its study, and then to the administrative officials of the land-grant colleges and universities. Following several weeks of consideration and discussion, a conference was arranged under the joint auspices of the two committees to consider the Department's proposals. It was held at Mount Weather, Virginia, on July 7 and 8, 1938. From their deliberations came the document which was to become known as the Mount Weather Agreement. This Agreement included the major suggestions of the Department Committee. However, it was not as carefully written and was much more general than the Department Report, which spelled out the proposal in logical detail. The agreement plainly showed the effects of the compromise that necessarily had to take place when the federal and state groups came together to seek common ground. However, it did portray a common spirit and because it became the symbol of the spirit during the next four years, it is reported in full.[9]

JOINT STATEMENT BY THE
ASSOCIATION OF LAND-GRANT COLLEGES AND UNIVERSITIES
AND THE
UNITED STATES DEPARTMENT OF AGRICULTURE
ON
BUILDING AGRICULTURAL LAND-USE PROGRAMS
July 8, 1938

Objectives: Both the Department of Agriculture and the Land Grant Colleges and Universities wish to perpetuate and strengthen the harmonious and mutually helpful relations that have long existed between them.

1. The relationships in the field of research and extension have been defined in memoranda and established by precedents. They are clearly understood and mutually satisfactory.

2. New national programs which include elements in addition to research and extension provide payments to farmers on the fulfillment of specific conditions. They present an increased need for planning and action by farm people. They also place a responsibility upon the Secretary of Agriculture for the administration of the programs.

3. The Department feels the need for reasonably uniform procedures whereby farmers may take responsibility for the development of sound land-use plans, programs, and policies for the dual purpose of (a) correlating current action programs to achieve stability of farm income and farm resources, and (b) helping determine and guide the longer-time public efforts toward these ends.

[9] Joint Statement by the Association of Land-Grant Colleges and Universities and the United States Department of Agriculture on "Building Agricultural Land-Use Programs," mimeographed, July 8, 1938.

In order to function effectively and democratically in the national field, these procedures must provide for analysis, planning, and program building beginning in the communities and extending then to county, state, and national levels.

4. The Land Grant Colleges have had many years of experience in aiding and stimulating farm people to build agricultural or rural programs in communities, counties, areas, States, and regions, and in the formulation of agricultural policies at these various levels. This experience has also included program building by commodity groups, type-of-farming groups, and others. These broad efforts to help farm people build comprehensive programs for rural improvement should be intensified.

5. The problem now faced by the Department can best be met by developing special and reasonably uniform methods for land-use planning and program building within the framework of the program-building procedures already established. This can be done as follows:

A Cooperative Plan for Building Land-Use Programs and Policies and Having Such Programs Apply to Varying Local Conditions

1. Each State Extension Service shall set up in each agricultural county an Agricultural Land-Use Planning Committee as a sub-committee of its present County Agricultural Program Building Committee.

2. While the principal county committee consists wholly of farm people, with the county extension agent usually serving as nonvoting secretary, the dual requirement of planning and correlation by the land-use sub-committee calls for some participation by official personnel. Therefore, the sub-committee might well consist of at least 10 farm people, a few forest land owners in counties where forestry is a problem, the county agent, at least one member of the AAA administrative committee, the rural rehabilitation supervisor, and any other State or Federal official in the county who has responsibility for the administration of agricultural land-use programs — such as the Soil Conservation Service project supervisor. The farmer membership shall constitute a substantial majority, and a farmer shall be chairman of the sub-committee. The county agent may be executive officer or secretary.

3. Either through the main county committee or directly, as best meets the situation in each State, the Agricultural Land-Use Planning Sub-Committee shall correlate on a county basis the land-use plans, programs, and policies developed by community and neighborhood planning committees. Where such community committees do not now exist, they should be established as the cornerstone of the whole planning organization.

4. As a sub-committee of any existing State Agricultural Program Committee, or independently if such a Committee does not now exist, there shall be established in each State an Agricultural Land-Use Program or Policy Committee. The Director of Extension shall be Chairman and the membership shall include the Director of the State Experiment Station, the Chairman of the AAA State Committee, SCS State Coordinator, FSA State Director, the Land-Use Planning spe-

cialist of the BAE, a representative of the Forest Service, any other State or Federal official having responsibility for the management of land-use programs in the State, and a number of farm people, usually one from each type-of-farming area within the State. Preferably, the farm men and women should also be members of one of the county agricultural land-use sub-committees.

This statement, dealing only with a few main points, purposely omits details that obviously must be settled promptly. But this can best be done by individual consultation between each Land Grant College and the Department. Each State will wish to have procedures which suit its own situation and experience. This is not to say, however, that essential principles should be sacrificed. Thus, in all States farmer thinking should dominate the work of the county sub-committees; there should be sufficient uniformity in methods of community planning groups to permit correlation of community plans on a county basis; similarly there must be sufficient uniformity to permit correlation of county material on a State basis, and State material on a national basis. In the interest of program coordination, the official representation as outlined for the county and State land-use subcommittees should be uniformly observed.

It should be emphasized that if this system of coordinated land-use planning is to endure, farmers must see tangible results from their work. Officials in charge of each land-use program must assume the responsibility of consulting the State Sub-Committee, receiving its suggestions and criticism before launching a program in the State, and then explaining definitely what portions of its recommendations can be followed and why others cannot. In each county, there must be a direct responsibility upon each official to have the program in his charge carry out, to the greatest extent feasible, the objectives determined by the community and county planning groups.

COUNTY LAND-USE PLANNING UNDER THE AGREEMENT

Organizational Setup. With the signing of the Mount Weather Agreement, nearly all the states began to make arrangements for county and state land-use planning committees. The Agreement outlined procedures for integrating the results of community planning on a county basis by the county committee and the results of county planning on a state basis by the state committee. But nothing was said in it about land-use planning at the national level.

However, the U.S.D.A. was well aware that it must create the means and procedures for integrating the results of state and community planning on a type-of-farming and national basis if state and local planning were to be translated into action and serve as a guide in the formulation and administration of farm programs. Therefore on October 6, 1938, Secretary Wallace issued a memorandum to his bureau and office chiefs announcing an important reorganization of the Department designed to facilitate the carrying out of the Department's responsibility in the land-use planning program. The Bureau of Agricultural Economics (B.A.E.) was designated as "a general agricultural program planning and economic research service for the Secretary and the Department as a whole," and to it were transferred the planning staffs, for the most part, that had been attached to the action agencies in the Department.

To meet this new responsibility the Bureau itself was reorganized to include, among other things, a new Division of State and Local Planning which was given the tasks of formulating general procedures for carrying out the planning program and of reviewing and analyzing reports from state and local planning committees. This Division had a small administrative staff in Washington, and operated in the field through seven regional representatives of the Bureau, and state representatives in each state actively engaged in the program. The state representatives had a highly important role. They were appointed subject to the approval of each land-grant college. The state B.A.E. representative was to have his headquarters at the state agricultural college. He was instructed to work directly with the directors of the extension service and the experiment station and their staffs, with state representatives of the Department's action programs, and with the "appropriate staff of the Bureau of Agricultural Economics in helping to plan, organize, and conduct agricultural land-use planning and research related thereto in the state; and to work with representatives of the extension and experiment station staffs of the agricultural college in coordinating and stimulating planning activities among the several counties of the state, including specifically such activities as bringing to the states information from federal sources needed in planning and coordinating the various Department and state action programs, helping interpret results of county planning activities and recommendations of county committees to the state committee, and helping transmit or make available these results to the various agencies of the U.S. Department of Agriculture."

The next step was the development of a Memorandum of Understanding between the B.A.E. and "the operating agencies" of the Department, which was consummated March 11, 1939. This memorandum defined the functions of the B.A.E. and attempted to distinguish between "general" planning and "operational" planning, admitting that they were "not susceptible of precise, unambiguous definition." The B.A.E. was to be responsible for general planning within the framework of objectives and procedures formulated in the general plans, and in accordance with standards and criteria to be developed cooperatively by the B.A.E. and the operating agencies."

To facilitate cooperation between the B.A.E. and the action agencies of the Department, the Memorandum established an Interbureau Coordinating Committee. This Committee was composed of representatives designated by the several action agencies to serve as liaison representatives between the respective agencies and the Bureau, representatives of the extension service, the Solicitor's office, the Office of Land-Coordination, and the B.A.E.'s division heads, with the Chief of the Bureau as chairman. This Committee and its elaborate system of sub-committees reviewed all procedures developed by the Bureau and all reports and recommendations funneling in from the field. Their findings and recommendations were sent to the Secretary, by way of a general Agricultural Program Board that had been set up, and accepted, perhaps with modifications by the Board, and approved. They were then translated into instructions and transmitted to the various agencies and bureaus as directives from the Secretary of Agriculture. This was the final phase of "putting planning into action."

The next step was the development of a functioning organization to conduct, within the framework of the Mount Weather Agreement, the planning activities within the states in cooperation with the B.A.E. This was provided in Memoranda of Understanding between the B.A.E. and the states that was consummated with all the states but Pennsylvania and California in April to September 1939. (California joined in the program without a Memorandum of Understanding.) These Memoranda provided for a state committee to consist of "at least one representative farmer or farm woman from each major type-of-farming area in the state, the director of the state experiment station, the state representative of the B.A.E., the Agricultural Adjustment Administration, the Soil Conservation Service, the Farm Security Administration, and such other state and department officials as may have responsibility for the management of land-use programs in the State." The state extension director was designated as chairman of the state committee, and the B.A.E.'s state representative as secretary.

The Memoranda also provided that some member of the state extension staff was to act as project leader in charge of administering the county land-use planning project in the counties and with farmers. He was administratively responsible to the director of the extension service.

These Memoranda further provided for a Joint Land-Grant–B.A.E. Committee. This Committee was made up of the state representative of the B.A.E., a representative of the state experiment station, and the state project leader. It was directed to recommend and agree upon the scope of work and the program to be followed by the project leader. This three-man committee functioned not only in an advisory relationship to the agencies it represented, but it was also a working committee for assisting the State Land-Use Planning Committee. It was responsible for developing details of procedure to be followed in the planning work and for encouraging the development of related research work.

As for planning at the county level, the Memoranda all directed the state extension service to "set up or continue in each agricultural county (so far as practicable) a committee composed of at least ten farm men and women, together with a few forest owners in counties where forestry is a problem, the county agent, at least one member of the AAA administrative committee, the Farm Security supervisor, and any other state or Department official in the county who has responsibility for the administration of agricultural land-use programs — such as the S.C.S. supervisor. The farmer membership shall constitute a substantial majority, and a farmer shall be chairman. The County Agent may be executive officer or secretary."

At the local level, the Memoranda instructed the State Extension Service to set up or continue in each agricultural county (so far as practicable) appropriate community committees to assist the County Committee. It specified that these community committees were to consist of representative farm men and women.

Thus was the machinery created for comprehensive rural planning from the local community to the Secretary of Agriculture.

Methods and Procedures. If the land-use planning was to produce results that would be useful as a basis for action and educational programs, the procedures followed would have to be enough alike so that the results would be comparable across both state and county lines. As the first step in formulating a cooperative program of work that would produce such results, the Department was asked to prepare a statement setting forth the needed land-use planning procedures that would be acceptable. After much conferring, the several agencies in the Department and the Land-Grant Colleges agreed upon a procedure that was eventually adopted as a general guide. It soon became commonly known as "Work Outline Number 1." [11] This drew upon the experience of the years 1935 to 1938 with the County Agricultural Planning Project of the AAA Program Planning Division. It divided the planning process per se into four major phases. The *first* major phase consisted of breaking down or subdividing the community (or county, or state) into

[11] U.S. Department of Agriculture. "County Land Use Planning Work Outline Number 1 Covering an Area Mapping and Classification Project Recommended for County Agricultural Land Use Planning Committees," mimeographed, 1938.

a number of land-use areas, each of which was *relatively* uniform throughout with respect to the similarity or pattern of its physical features, present land use, and existing land-use problems. Since logically there can only be one basis for classification, the third criteria, namely, *problems,* emerged as the primary determinant. However, there is a high degree of association between physical characteristics, present usage, and needed adjustments.

The *second* major phase involved the classification of each of the local land-use areas designated in Phase One. The areas were classified into categories expressed in terms of their suitability for selected uses or combinations of uses. The following classification was prepared by the Massachusetts Joint State College–B.A.E. Rural Policy Committee and represents the classification techniques of Work Outline Number 1 adapted to local conditions — in this case, Massachusetts.

AREA CLASSIFICATION FOR MASSACHUSETTS

Class I — Areas immediately suitable for commercial agriculture. (They may also be suitable for part-time farming or residential purposes.)

A. Land now in farms and needing minor adjustments.

Areas where minor adjustments in farm practices or size of enterprise may be made, but they do not need drastic adjustments such as changes in types of farming or in size of farm.

These are, in general, areas in which agricultural income *has been sufficient* to provide, and to maintain in adequate condition, ample facilities for living and for the conduct of the business of farming.

B. Land now in farms and needing major adjustments.

Areas where major adjustments are needed such as in type of farming or in size of farm.

These are, in general, areas in which agricultural income *has not been sufficient* to provide, and to maintain in adequate condition, ample facilities for living, and for the conduct of the business of farming.

C. Land *not* now in farms, but which may be immediately suitable for development into farms.

Class II — Areas which are questionable as being suited for commercial agriculture (except poultry). They may or may not be suitable for part-time farming and/or residential purposes.

A. Land now in farms.

Areas where it is questionable whether or not farmers could conserve their soil and make an adequate living over a period of years, even if desirable changes in farming systems were made.

B. Land *not* now in farms.

Areas where it is questionable whether or not it would pay to prepare the land for agricultural use and whether it would yield a return sufficient to provide, and to maintain in adequate condition, ample facilities for living and for the conduct of the business of farming.

Class III — Areas not immediately suitable for commercial agriculture (except poultry). (They may be suitable for part-time farming and/or residential purposes.) Other uses include forestry, recreation, game preserves, industrial, et cetera. (The most suitable use should be designated in the classification.)

A. Areas which now contain farms.

Areas which now contain farms, but which are not fit to farm and should be put to some other use. By this is meant areas in which farms of any size or type cannot be expected to return enough income to keep farmers off relief rolls or from becoming destitute. Place in this group only those areas which are clearly unsuited to farming. Questionable areas should be included as Class II areas.

B. Areas which do not now contain farms.

Areas which are not now in farms, and which should stay out of farms because they are not fit for commercial farming.

Class IV — Present urban and industrial areas and suitable for such use in the future.

The *third major phase* was the preparation of suggestions and recommendations as to the types of shifts in land use and the adjustments in farming desirable for each of the land-use areas, with due consideration for the class in which any area was placed in Phase Two, and suggestions of measures which might be taken to secure or accomplish the shifts in land use and adjustments in farming deemed advisable.

The *fourth phase* consisted of consolidating, first at county levels and then at state levels, the results of the first three phases as developed at more local levels, making these available for county and state use, and sending a copy of such a consolidated report to the B.A.E. for use by federal agencies.

However, before this planning could be undertaken at the county level, a *preparatory* period was necessary to get the people of the county ready for it and get the necessary organization set up. Counties thus engaged were said to be in the *preparatory* stage. The activities at this stage comprised the following.

1. Acquainting county agents, agency representatives, and others interested in the land-use planning work with the scope and purpose of

the planning program and with various agency programs affecting land use locally.
2. Delineating land-use neighborhood and community boundaries.
3. Building local planning organizations to carry on the work.

The second or *intensive* stage consisted of the actual working out of the plans for adjustments in land use. It called for, first of all, assembling the basic information and developing it into forms suitable for use by planning committees; then for initiating studies and discussions of local agricultural problems, and orienting the analyses to the land-use planning program. When completed, decisions had been reached as to what changes were needed in each of the area units into which the county had been divided.

Then presently a third stage was added, namely, the *unified* stage. Counties of this stage were engaged in translating land-use plans into action. This involved the coordination and revision of existing departmental, state, and local programs, and the formulation of new programs to best achieve recommended adjustments in land use and rural institutions. The work in the unified counties was characterized by its emphasis on the following lines of activities:

1. Formulating specific plans for adoption by particular agencies.
2. Discussing such plans with appropriate officials of the agencies concerned.
3. Obtaining agreements and decisions on the part of these agencies regarding specific lines of action that would contribute to the achievement of the objectives that were agreed upon.

Of course these stages were never as clearly marked as the foregoing would suggest. Nevertheless, it became the practice at state and federal levels to classify the counties as at the preparatory, intensive, or unified stage.

Extent of Operations. In spite of all the effort that went into getting this program into operation, its life was only three years. Congress cut the appropriations for the U.S.D.A. part in it by a half for the fiscal year 1941–42, and cut it out altogether in June of 1942.

The main reason for this action by Congress was, of course, World War II. The state and county committees shifted their emphasis strongly to wartime needs in 1941, but the Congress felt that other things were more important to the war effort than anything that the B.A.E. might contribute by working with the state and county land-use planning committees. The B.A.E. withdrew its state representatives on July 1. Some of the state extension services kept the committees in operation for a year or two, and a few even longer, but the land-use planning ended abruptly. After all, the principal motivations of the planning activity from 1935 on was adjustment of production in order to reduce surplus. After 1942, the pressure was for more production rather than less.

But the onset of the war was by no means the sole cause of the discontinuance of land-use planning under the Mount Weather Agreement. Very soon after it started, one of the farm organizations began opposing it, the real reason for this, not the spoken one, being that it did not want another committee organization in the counties. The farm organizations were unusually well represented on the county committees, but not officially as members of their organizations. Also many of the state and county units in two of the major federal action agencies were more or less antagonistic to the land-planning activities in their jurisdiction. In 1941, the senior author, assisted by Charles M. Hardin and Edgar A. Haff, under a grant from the Rockefeller Foundation, made a field study of the activities of the federal and state agencies involved in action and other programs relating to land use. In the course of the study, he interviewed several hundred regional, state, and county officials of these agencies, no small fraction of whom found major faults with the work of the county committees, and some of them definitely hostile. Their attitudes could be pretty well summed up in the statement that they felt the county committees were proving to be obstacles to the carrying out of their particular programs the way they wanted to do it.

Perhaps an illustration will make this clearer. One of the regional heads in the S.C.S. program said that the B.A.E.–State Committees were fighting the S.C.S. program. As evidence, he cited a county committee in his region which recently had voted against having a conservation district in the county after several meetings in which an S.C.S. representative had participated and told them just how a district functioned. When the committeemen in this county were interviewed later, they said the reason they voted against having a soil conservation district was that after full discussion in their committee, they had concluded that what their largely flat-land county needed for conservation was a county-wide program of obtaining seeds for winter cover crops that would reach most of the farmers quickly, instead of the S.C.S. program of contour cultivation on a few scattered farms under contract.

This farm organization and agency opposition was not confined to the counties and states. It took vigorous form at appropriation hearings in Congress, and within the U.S.D.A. in Washington. The county land-use committees were described at these hearings as wastefully duplicating the work of pre-existing committees. Within the U.S.D.A. the interbureau coordinating activity presently subsided considerably, one reason being that often little if anything in the form of action followed the instructions sent out by the Secretary of Agriculture. Secretary Wallace was not the kind of a disciplinarian needed to obtain such a follow-up. Before the end of the second year, the Secretary appeared to lose much of his interest in the whole program.

What headway did the County Land-use Planning Program make before its demise? By January 1942, more than 2,200 county land-use committees[12] had been organized, and more than 10,000 community committees were participating in the planning process in 47 states. In all, more than 125,000 rural men and women served on state, county, and community committees. Approximately 18,000 federal, state, and local government employees participated. By this time, about two thirds of the participating counties were in the *intensive* stage, and 60 to 70 of these were recognized as having advanced to the *unified* stage. The largest federal expenditure for salaries and expenses of personnel specifically assigned to Land-Use Planning activities was $1,148,000 in the fiscal year 1940–41. Of this sum, $573,000 was spent for B.A.E.'s share of 308 cooperative employees of the B.A.E. and the state extension services.

Of what use were the results obtained in these 2,200 counties, and more particularly in those in the intensive and unified stage? Part of the answer is found in the mapping that was done, even though this mapping was not an end in itself. Over 1,300 counties were developing or had completed county maps and reports when the program came to a close. Except for minor variations to fit local needs, most of the states followed the mapping procedure suggested in the Department's Work Outline No. 1. The area maps and reports developed were particularly valuable as educational devices and as an aid to public agencies in developing their programs and policies. The construction of the maps itself was a valuable educational experience for the farmer committeemen and the agency representatives who participated in the process. The maps helped to narrow down complicated issues to specific areas about which there was local understanding and opinion and a desire for corrective action. They were useful too in informing the agency personnel and the general public concerning the conditions and needs of agriculture locality by locality.

The land area maps also soon proved themselves as valuable aids in the

[12] Over two thirds of the agricultural counties in the United States.

development of local programs. A number of states reported extensive use of the maps in developing work programs for soil conservation districts. The Farm Security Administration used the maps as a guide in making loans, selling and leasing farms, and buying farms for tenant purchase clients. The maps were used in some areas as a basis for zoning by county planning commissions. The Forest Service and the Soil Conservation Service representatives studied the reports to determine how farmers should organize to approach local forest and erosion problems. County agricultural agents found the maps useful in developing their programs and plans of work. The maps were widely used in cooperation with highway officials, utility companies, banks, and others.

County committees in general rendered valuable assistance in obtaining and guiding the increased production of dairy, poultry, and swine products to meet the defense needs of the nation. In the southern states, the committees were particularly active in promoting increased production of food and feed products for home consumption, as a means of developing a better balanced agriculture and partly offsetting the severe decline of export markets for cotton and tobacco.

In areas where defense industries and training centers were located, county and community land-use planning committees moved rapidly in gathering information and developing plans to guide defense and army officials in the acquisition of suitable sites, in making inventories of available labor, in guiding the relocation of displaced farm families, in planning the location of needed housing facilities, in assuring the maximum contribution of local producers to the food needs of army cantonments, and in many other ways.

One has to go to the counties that had been brought to the unified stage, however, to sense something of the real possibilities of such a program. Let us take Teton County, Montana, as an example of such a county. The Teton County Land-Use Planning Committee decided that there were about 20,000 acres of low-grade plow land being tilled that should be taken out of agriculture and put into grass. Consequently, they drew up a plan of action to bring about this adjustment. The Agricultural Conservation Committee agreed to (1) encourage the retirement from cultivation and the reseeding of the low-grade land, (2) not allow any low-grade sod land to come into the AAA program as cropland, (3) make an annual report to the county assessor of all low-grade sod land broken up during the year, (4) stress deferred grazing under the range program, and (5) use land classification data as a guide in determining productivity indexes.

The Farm Security Administration agreed (1) not to make loans for cropping low-grade plow land and grazing land and to try to get land that was controlled by FSA clients put to the recommended uses, and (2) to help increase the size of farms that were definitely too small, and (3) to organize livestock units in the poor areas.

The Farm Credit Administration, in turn, agreed to (1) make a special effort to help increase the size of farm units through loans for the purchase of more lands, sale or lease of lands, and other methods; and (2) give careful thought to the productivity of land before extending loans.

The Forest Service agreed to tie in the use and management of the national forest lands more closely with the use of other lands and the local needs for the services and the products from the forest. They agreed to cooperate in regard to the replanting of burned areas, the protection, the propagation, and transplanting of beavers, and the control of rodents and weeds.

The State Land Department agreed to (1) discourage breaking up low-grade sod and abandoned farm land under its control, (2) make every effort to get its low-grade farm land back to grass to be used for grazing purposes only, and (3) encourage reseeding by charging a lower rental for such land if the renter reseeded it.

The Teton County officials agreed to (1) complete their reclassification of land and correlate it with their assessment procedures, (2) assess at a higher rate low-grade lands that were being cultivated or were broken up for cropping, (3) give a grazing classification to low-grade plow lands that were then in sod or abandoned, and assess them accordingly, (4) make every effort to correct misuse of low-grade county-owned lands, and (5) to make a study of the relation of land values to productivity, in order to improve the tax system.

The county extension service agreed to (1) prepare a program to help bring about the above changes and (2) inform nonresident land owners about the land classification and planning work of the county so that they would know more about the values and best uses of the land.

Thus, the farmers, technicians, and administrators in Teton County worked together toward the solution of one pressing common problem. The process was much the same with many other recommendations made by the committee. Mutual understanding and agreement among farmers and representatives of public agencies on ways and means of getting results was the heart of this kind of planning.

Would the program of land-use planning under the Mount Weather

Agreement have been continued if World War II had not come? It is the authors' judgment that it would have been, and that by now it would have been almost as well established as the state extension service program. The growing support for it from the state extension services would have outweighed the opposition to it. By no means did all the state extension services at the start, it must be admitted, realize fully what this program meant to them. But they were beginning to do so in the years 1939 to 1942 and would have pressed more strongly for its support in the years following. Also in the states they would have brought more pressure on the state and county units on the federal action programs. All of the states, of course, would not have been equally forward in this advance. But there would have been enough that were to furnish strong leadership.

Where was Worcester County in this program? It was still in the intensive stage when the program ended in 1942. In a few of the towns, however, some unified action has been taken in the years since that was based on the intensive work in the earlier years. Progress was as slow as it was in the 1938–1942 years partly because actual planning was delayed by the research that was being combined with it.

As the situation now stands, the results of the mapping still remain, including particularly the division of counties into land-use areas and the body of information about each of these areas. This has been put to considerable use in the years since 1942, and some of it has been kept more or less up-to-date. In most of the states, the extension service has developed county programs, which are made the basis of year-by-year work programs, and these tend to be laid out according to the land-use and community areas that were defined in the planning years for 1935 to 1942. Also each new soil conservation district as it has been organized has developed a work program more or less on an area basis. The new Agricultural Conservation Program with its concentration on enduring practices is calling for much closer attention to differences within counties and needed adjustments by areas. The return to a surplus agricultural economy with crop quotas and diverted areas is essentially reconstructing the situation that the county land-use planning program of 1938 was designed to meet. The result is that there is as strong a need for planning as prevailed in the 1930's.

Recognition of this need is clearly indicated by the joint county "program projection" undertaking of the federal and state extension services, now in its third year. This program calls for looking forward to the next five years to see what direction the agriculture of each county and the subareas within each county needs to take, and laying out the lines of action to meet these needs. It will of course make use of the results of all the planning analysis of the County Land-Use Planning of the earlier years. The schedule set up for this undertaking was a program for one tenth of the counties by the end of the first year and all of them in four years. The leadership in this undertaking is in the extension services, but all the agencies concerned are being called upon to participate in it.

CHAPTER 9

Planning a Farm

The discussion of the foregoing chapters has made clear that analysis of land-use adjustments needs to be first of all in terms of operating units, and that the operating unit in agriculture is ordinarily a farm, and in forestry a tract of more or less contiguous land operated under one management. In mixed farm and forest areas, many of the farming units combine some woodland operations with the agriculture — most of those in Worcester County do this. It has also been explained that although the task of land-use planning for an area or political division is far from complete if all that is done is to determine what adjustments are needed on representative individual farm and forest operating units, still it is well on its way to completion; and until the needed adjustments on such operating units are determined, no other adjustments can be safely designed.

THE FARM

Let us therefore for our next step take one farm in Worcester County, spread it out, as it were, on the table before us, and analyze it and explore its possibilities, to the end that the farmer may lay out the plan and program of operation for it that is in best accord with the family's objectives. The farm which we have chosen for this is located near the center of the County and sells its milk at wholesale in the Worcester market. It is typical of much of New England agriculture in that its principal source of income is dairying. In the past it has also had a small secondary enterprise — an orchard. Many dairy farms in New England have a small supplementary enterprise. It contains 204 acres of land, of which 48.2 acres were in cropland when the farm was mapped in 1938, 6.4 acres were in unimproved open pasture, 83.1 acres in brushy pasture, 56.0 acres in wooded pasture, and 7.4 acres in woodland not pastured. The dairy herd consisted of 26 cows, 8 heifers and calves, and a bull. This farm is larger than the average dairy farm in Worcester County, but not larger than farms need to be to use modern equipment effectively. Smaller units will be considered later.

This farm is also representative of much of southern New England in the character of its land: much of it so stony that man has despaired of ever

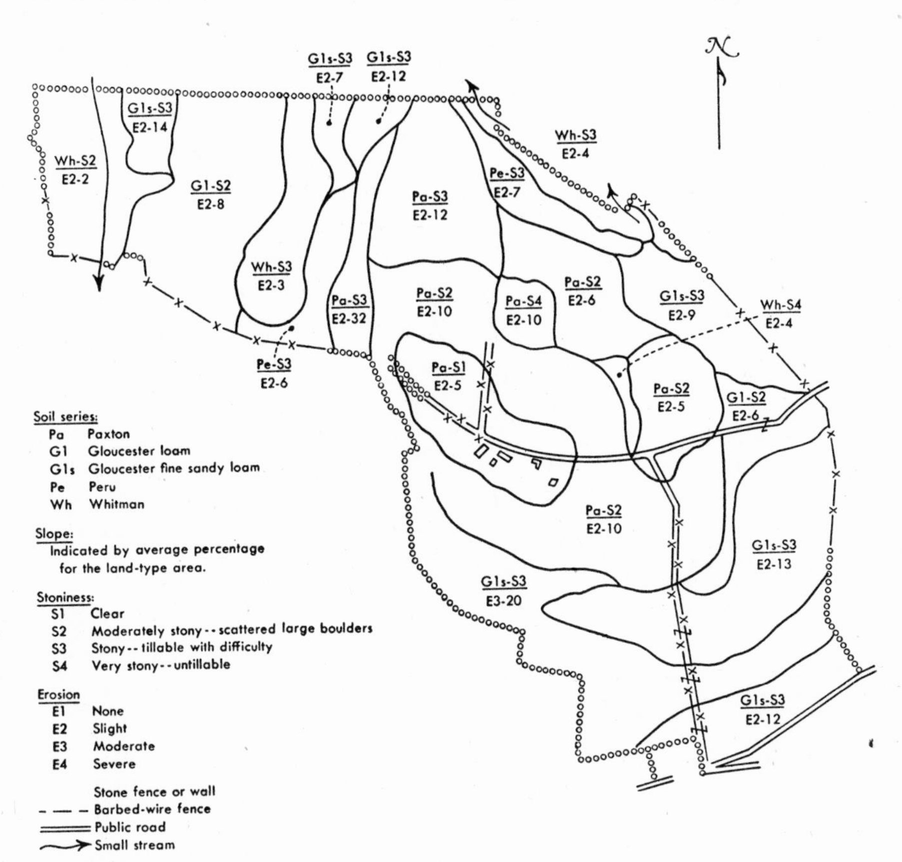

Figure 26. *Map showing soils and physical conditions of a 204-acre farm in central Worcester County.*

reducing it to cultivation. But it includes stretches of land from which the stones have been picked and piled in stone fences or walls separating the farm into many small fields. The central portion of this farm is spread out over the top of a drumlin or low rounded hill of heavy ground-moraine soil deposited under the glacier by the overriding ice. It has been explained that such soil grows good crops when freed of stones, and good pasture if enough of the stones are removed so that the sod can be broken occasionally to allow reseeding. Other than the Paxton soils of the drumlin, the soil on this farm is mainly stony Gloucester, but a few low undrained tracts have Peru or Whitman soils. These are all acid soils needing applications of lime every five to seven years. The land between this farm and the main road a mile away is mostly in woodland now, but the houses are occupied by part-

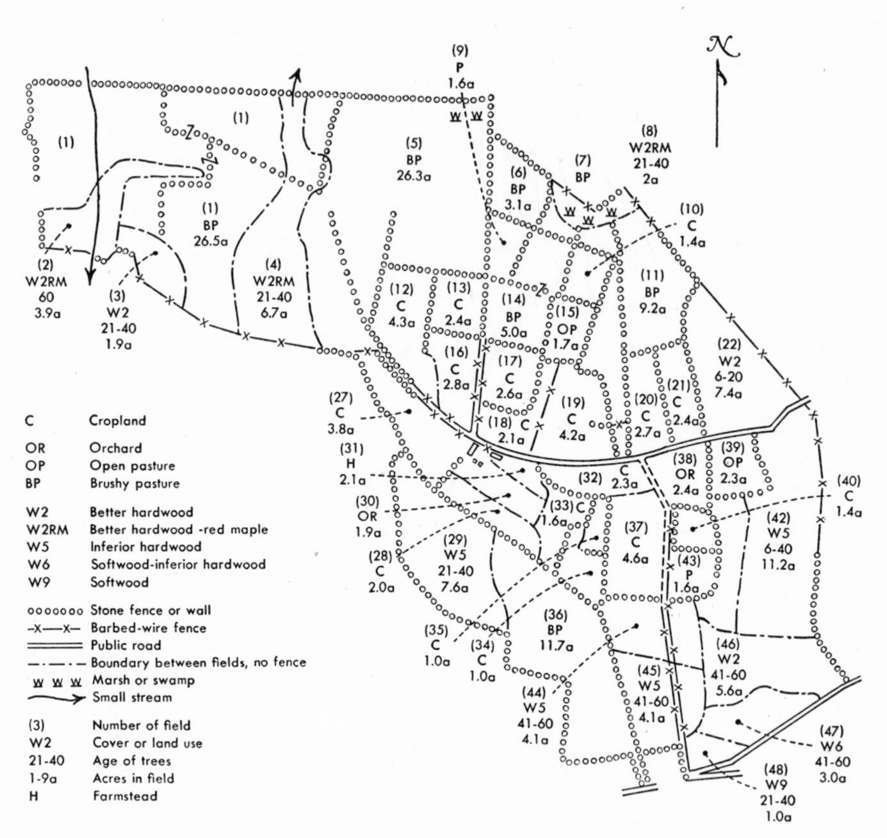

Figure 27. ***Map showing field boundaries, cover, and land use for same farm as Figure 26.***

time and residential farmers. The land along the main highway at the south end of the farm is in farms.

Figure 26 shows the layout of the land comprising the farm as it was mapped in detail in 1938. The farmstead is located on the nearly level land now free of stones on the crest of the drumlin. Much of the rest of the land has a slope of 8 to 13 percent, but on the steep hillside toward the west the slope averages 32 percent. The Gloucester soils on its eastern side have slopes running from 6 to 13 percent. Most of the Paxton soils are only moderately stony whereas the Gloucester soils can be tilled only at large expense. One small patch of Paxton classified S4, however, has many large boulders. The Peru soils are at the foot of the slopes, and the Whitman soils on still lower stretches and on the bottomlands of small streams. These marsh soils tend to be as stony as the Gloucester soils.

Figure 27 also shows the manner in which the soil-type areas were broken up into small fields when the farm was mapped in 1938. The stone fences enclosed 28 separate fields, 15 of these having less than three acres. The cultivable fields were all small. When the land was cleared, the stones picked up were built into fences near at hand; with the methods of cultivation then followed, small fields were no serious handicap. The property-line fences and the fences around the pastures and woodland were assembled from surface rock abundantly at hand. The few poor stone fences now running through the pasture and woodland mark what were once separate fields or pastures. This farm, like most others in this part of New England, had by 1938 already gone a good distance on the road to abandonment to brush and trees.

Figure 27 also shows the use of the land in the fields enclosed within the stone fences and in the soil-type areas of Figure 26. The 48.2 acres in cropland in 1938 were used as follows: silage corn, 12.0 acres; clover, 2.4 acres; mixed hay, 21.9 acres; poor hay, 2.6 acres; oats, 2.8 acres; millet, 1.0 acre; garden, 1.2 acres; orchard, 4.3 acres. In addition, 12 acres of hayland were rented and some pasture. The two orchard tracts were at that time in apple trees with peach trees as fillers. Hay was also cut between the trees. The only really open pasture on this farm was 5.6 acres in Fields 9, 15, and 39. A total of 83.1 acres were classified as brushy pasture. Cattle also ran in most of the acres classified as woodland. The woodland on this farm was classified as shown in the accompanying tabulation.

		Acres
W2	— Better Hardwood	19.4
W2RM	— Better Hardwood-Red Maple	17.1
W5	— Inferior Hardwood	22.9
W6	— Softwood-Inferior Hardwood	3.0
W9	— Softwood	1.0
	Total	63.4

The dominant species in the Better Hardwood stands are red oak, white ash, hickory, and red maple; in the Inferior Hardwood stands, gray birch and red maple; in the Softwood stands, white pine; and in the Softwood-Inferior Hardwood stands, white pine, gray birch, and red maple. The dominant age classes of the trees is indicated for each stand in Figure 27. There were 16.6 acres with the trees mostly 41 to 60 years old; 23.7 acres with the age classes mostly 21 to 40 years; and 11 acres of 6- to 20-year growth. Finally, Field 42 had trees ranging from 6 to 40 years. In recent years before 1938, an average of 20 cords of wood had been cut for fuel to supply the farm needs, and in addition an average of 18 cords had been sold. The cutting had been mostly of middle-age stands. The hurricane of 1938 destroyed most of the white pine. Pasturing had prevented reproduction of sawtimber species on much of the woodland.

The next step in planning this farm was to assemble the information concerning crops, livestock, feed and labor inputs and the like, shown in the first column of Table 10, and the expenditures and receipts data, shown in the first column of Table 11, for the farm as then being operated.

This farm in 1938, as stated above, was carrying 26 milk cows and 8 head of other young stock for replacements. Its actual gross cash receipts at prices then prevailing were $3,815; its cash outlays, $3,120; and its net cash income, $695. But at the prices that have been prevailing since World War II until recently, the gross cash income would have been $5,525, and the net cash income, $1,355, as indicated under Plan I in Table 10. The major receipts calculated on this latter price basis were: milk, $5,055; cows, $270; calves, $140; apples, $60. The major expenses were: feed concentrates, $1,525, and labor, $1,200. The farmer and his son, then 26 years old, were doing all the work, the son working on a wage basis. The farm had both a tractor and a truck and one team of horses. It was therefore amply supplied with power.

ALTERNATIVE PLANS

The next step in the planning was to go into conference with this farmer and members of his family, with someone from the county agent's office present, and get from them their ideas as to how the land use on this farm could be changed to advantage and the farm business reorganized. This discussion was designed to bring out any preferences of the family as to the kind of farming it wanted to do, any plans of the family as to the future of its members that would affect the farming, and any limitations on its freedom of action such as debt and lack of credit.

The next step was to work out, first, a farm plan closely in accord with the operating program favored by the farm family and an operating state-

TABLE 10

Farm Reorganization Worksheet — Physical

Item	Plan I 1938 normal*	Plan II 1945 normal*	Plan III	Plan IV	Plan V	Plan VI	Plan VII
			1. Crops (acres)				
Corn	12.0	10.2	7.9	10.2	10.2	11.7	4.0
Millet	1.0	2.0					
Oats	5.2	5.5	7.8	10.2	10.2	11.7	11.8
Alfalfa		14.5					
Mixed grass	41.3	17.7					
Apples and hay	(2.4)	(2.4)	(2.4)				
Ladino hay mixture			28.1	30.5	33.0	44.3	42.6
Hay-pasture			(10.0)	(10.0)	(10.0)	(15.0)	10.0
Rotation pasture		5.2	7.8	17.4	15.9	11.7	11.7
Grass silage			3.5	3.0	2.0	2.5	11.8
Total cropland	59.5	55.1	55.1	71.3	71.3	81.9	81.9
			2. Pasture and woodland (acres)				
Open improved pasture			10.3	12.3	21.1	30.8	30.8
Open unimproved pasture	6.4	10.1	.8	.3	.3		
Rented pasture	100.0	100.0	100.0				
Brush pasture	83.1	72.8	71.8	14.7	5.9	25.8	25.8
Wooded pasture	56.0	56.5	17.3	0.0	0.0	2.1	2.1
Woodland	7.4	7.4	46.6	102.9	102.9	63.1	63.1
Other	3.7	2.2	2.2	2.6	2.6	2.2	2.2
Total	316.1	304.1	304.1	204.1	204.1	204.1	204.1
Less rented land	112.0	100.0	100.0				
Total land owned	204.1	204.1	204.1	204.1	204.1	204.1	204.1
			3. Supplies purchased (tons)				
Hay		15.0	6.0				
Concentrates	25.0	34.4	36.3	36.6	41.0	55.0	51.0
Fertilizer	2.2	4.5	25.6	10.5	21.0	27.6	28.5
Lime	15.0	5.0	18.0	23.0	24.6	30.0	29.4
			4. Labor (months)				
Total labor	19.0	29.0	29.0	28.0	29.0	36.0	36.0
			5. Crop production (tons of hay equivalent)				
Silage	90	140	152	152	167	197	196
Hay	77	70	80	85	99	133	118
			6. Livestock				
Cows	26	37	37	37	42	56	52
Heifers	8	14	16	16	18	22	20
Bulls	1	1	1	1	1	2	2
Horses	2	2	2	2	2	2	2
Hens	40	25	25	25	25	25	25
			7. Livestock products				
Production per cow (pounds)	5270	5310	5600	5900	5900	5900	5900
Total milk production (cwt.)	1397	1955	2070	2180	2480	3300	3068
Milk sold (cwt.)	1330	1882	1970	2075	2360	3150	2922
Grain fed per cow (pounds)	1640	1675	1675	1690	1685	1700	1700

* "Normal" means that any inputs or outputs that were abnormal because of unusual circumstances — such as unusual weather, unusual losses due to accidents or disease — were adjusted upward or downward to correct for this.

ment to go with this; second, plans and operating statements for any other promising programs in which the family showed an interest; and third, plans and operating statements for still other programs that the county agent or the planners believed were worth considering. For each of these, a budget was prepared showing the expenses and receipts that were most reasonable to expect, assuming normal weather and other operating conditions, at the set of prices, wage, and other cost rates most reasonable to expect.

The third step was to take these different plans and operating statements back to the farm family, show them the results, discuss these in detail, and get from the family then, or shortly thereafter, their decision as to the one they wished to have drawn up in detail for the purpose of carrying it out when they were able. The plan worked out at that time called for putting the cropland in an eleven-year rotation consisting of corn two years, oats one year, and hay eight years, for using a low-alfalfa mixture on part of the seeding, for seeding 7 acres of ladino clover for pasture, for fertilizing considerable of the pasture, and for clearing the brush and surface stones from Fields 6, 9, and 14 so as to make them ready for pasture improvement. The main objective of these proposed changes was to increase the supply of pasture feed on the home farm so that no pasture land would need to be rented, and to increase and to improve the feed supply so that less feed would need to be bought. It was expected that with these changes the farm would grow its own replacements at a sacrifice of only 1.5 milk cows and increase the output per cow from 5,275 to 6,000 pounds of milk per year. The proposal for the woodland consisted mainly of fencing the cattle out of most of it.

The onset of the war interfered with the follow-up extension work on this farm. The staff of the Worcester County extension service was kept busy with war-service problems relating to farm machinery, farm labor, the rationing of fuel oil, and the like.

Plan II in the second column of Tables 10 and 11 shows how far this farmer, working almost wholly by himself, had been able to carry out this plan in the years from 1940 to 1946, when the farm was revisited in the summer of 1946. The eleven-year rotation system had been adopted. Not only had 7.5 acres of land in Fields 6 and 9, and the upper part of 14, been cleared of brush and converted to cropland to the extent of removing part of the stones, but the crops and hayfields were being systematically limed and fertilized, and some alfalfa was being included in the grass-seed mixtures. These had included only timothy and red clover in 1938—which meant that most of the hay was timothy and "red top" after the second year. The fertilization was light, however — 400 pounds of 4-12-4 per acre in corn, and 2 tons of lime plus 400 pounds of phosphate and 100 pounds of potash when seeding down. In 1946, the crops consisted of 10 acres of corn, yielding 90 tons of silage, 32 acres of hay plus the hay cut in the orchard, these altogether yielding 70 tons of hay; and 5 acres of oats and 2 acres of millet yielding 50 tons of grass silage. The peach trees had been killed by the severe winter of 1940 and had been removed; and one part of the orchard (Field 30) had been converted entirely to meadow. The farmer was still buying feed — 34 tons of grain and 15 tons of hay — and still renting 100 acres of poor brushy and wooded pasture. But the dairy herd had been increased to 37 cows and 14 head of young stock for replacements. The production per cow had increased only to 5,300 pounds. The total milk sales were now 1,882 cwt. which sold at $4.14 per cwt. The farm receipts totaled $8,880 and the farm expenses $6,725, leaving a net cash income of $2,155 at the same assumed level of prices. The labor cost consisted of year-round wages for the son at $115 per month plus wages for an extra hand during five summer months. The farmer, then well over 60, was no longer doing a full man's work.

Obviously a wide range of alternatives as to intensity of land use are possible on this farm. At one extreme, all but a few acres of it can be brought into use in cultivated crops. Land no more difficult to bring into such use is now cropped in the densely populated agricultural lands of the Orient. To convert this land to crop use would require, first of all, the removing of vast tonnages of stones still in the upper levels of the soil. Some fields would also need to be drained. Then if they were to be used regularly in crop rotations including cultivated crops, much of the land would need to be terraced and strip-cropped. Finally, lime and fertilizers would need to be applied to all of it regularly.

But there is little prospect that the pressure of the population on the land of the earth in the United States and in Massachusetts will ever be severe enough to force this maximum intensity of use. A reasonable expectation instead was that the father would presently turn the farm over to his son, who would operate it with as little as one year-round hand, or this plus an extra hand during the crop season, or with two year-round hands, or possibly even more hired help, depending mainly upon how much land was cropped, how much pasture was improved, how much feed was bought, how many cows were kept, and how much equipment was used. It is the operator of this farm who must make the decision as to the intensity of his

TABLE 11

Farm Reorganization Worksheet — Financial (in dollars, at 1950 prices)

Item	Plan I 1938 normal*	Plan II 1945 normal*	Plan III	Plan IV	Plan V	Plan VI	Plan VII
		1. Expenditures					
Seed	44	50	82	105	105	144	133
Fertilizer	68	123	520	446	719	986	1037
Lime	90	12	40	51	55	67	66
Hay		525	210				
Concentrates	1575	2175	2300	2318	2592	3456	3217
Outside pasture	75	75	75				
Livestock purchase	200	20	20	20	20	30	30
Hired labor	1200	1800	1800	1700	1800	2400	2400
Electricity and other power	85	100	115	110	115	130	128
Truck and tractor costs		600	640	700	720	930	900
Auto	100	100	100	100	100	125	120
Machinery repairs	70	350	380	400	410	460	420
Building repairs	100	100	100	100	100	160	150
Fencing	10	10	20	25	28	20	20
Insurance	30	130	130	130	140	200	190
Taxes	276	290	293	300	305	380	370
Rent	40						
Telephone	40	40	40	40	40	40	40
Veterinary services	40	75	75	75	78	105	100
Spray materials	12	20	20				
Miscellaneous supplies	30	40	40	40	43	62	59
Miscellaneous services	85	90	90	90	90	90	90
Total expenses	4170	6725	7090	6750	7460	9785	9470
		2. Receipts					
Cows	270	465	465	465	534	665	540
Calves	140	240	240	240	279	335	286
Poultry							
Milk	5055	7861	8323	8766	9965	13300	12333
Apples	60	278	278				
A.C.P. payment**		36	269	254	372	530	521
Total receipts	5525	8880	9575	9725	11150	14830	13680
Total expenses	4170	6725	7090	6750	7460	9785	9470
Net income	1355	2155	2485	2975	3690	5025	4210
		3. Cost of Improvements					
Cost of land improvement	—	—	—	3590	3850	4820	2900

* "Normal" means that any inputs or outputs that were abnormal because of unusual circumstances — such as unusual weather, unusual losses due to accidents or disease — were adjusted upward or downward to correct for this.

** Agricultural Conservation Payment under schedule then prevailing.

land use and the scale of his operations. To make a wise decision on these points, he needs to know what is involved in each alternative — how much labor and other expense, how much expenditure on land improvements, how much total investment, how much additional demand on management, and, paralleling each of these, how much addition to his net income he can anticipate. Tables 10 and 11 have five other columns, each showing the receipts and expenses and net income with five different plans of organization of this farm, all of them more intensive than the one followed in 1945, but in varying degrees. Some of these were suggested in the first conference with the farm family and some were not. Following is a brief description of these. Table 10 shows the cropping and livestock programs accompanying Plans III and VII, and Table 11 the prospective receipts and expenditures of each.

Plan III

Under Plan III, no additional land is improved, except for liming and fertilizing ten acres of open pasture and changing to a grass-seed mixture including 2 pounds of ladino clover, 4 pounds of alfalfa, 4 pounds of red clover, and 5 pounds of timothy. The use of fertilizers, however, is increased from 4.5 tons to 25.6 tons, and of lime from 5 to 18 tons. The rotation system is changed from ten to seven years with one year of corn, one year of oats and five years of hay. This reduces the acreage of corn to 7.9, but the yield is increased so that 110 tons of corn silage are produced. The oats are pastured, and 42 tons of hay, mainly ladino clover, are converted to grass silage. The extra pasturage is obtained by rotation grazing on 7.8 acres and pasturing after hay on 10.0 acres. The increased output of hay and forage is fed to the same cattle as under Plan II, but the yield per cow is increased 300 pounds because of better summer grazing. It is still necessary to buy a little hay and rent the 100 acres of poor pasture. No additional labor is hired, but the present labor force has the extra labor of applying the extra lime and fertilizers and harvesting the extra hay and forage. The gross income is increased to $9,575, and the net income to $2,485. The hay and feed bill is reduced $190 and the milk receipts increased $462.

Plan IV

Under Plan IV, the cropland is increased 16.2 acres by clearing the brush and removing the stones from Fields 6 and 7, and parts of Fields 5 and 12, at a cost of $930, or $58 per acre. Also the remainder of the orchard (Field 38) is converted to cropland by pulling out the trees. Finally, the remaining stones are removed from a total of 55 acres of mainly Paxton soils on both sides of the main road. These fields had been cropped over the years by plowing and cultivating around the many large boulders still remaining. The cost of their removal is estimated at $727, or $13 per acre. To get these fields into units large enough to use tractors effectively also requires removing 1,870 yards of stone fence figured at a cost of $1.30 per yard.

The pasture improvements under Plan IV are limited to removing the brush and surface stone from 10.6 acres of land in parts of Fields 5 and 11, and Field 25, at a cost of $345. The purpose of these improvements is to make it possible to use a bog harrow to break up the soil and then to seed it down to improved grasses with a small admixture of ladino clover. Pasture thus improved and fertilized may have its carrying capacity increased tenfold.

As for the woodland, Plan IV includes erecting a fence between Fields 4 and 5 to shut off that whole end of the farm and permitting the brushy pasture of Field 1 to grow up to woodland eventually. The farm under this plan thus has no woodland pasture.

The 71.3 acres of cropland under Plan IV are used in the same seven-year rotation as with Plan III. Of the additional 16.2 acres, 9.6 are used in rotated grazing and the rest divided among corn, oats, and hay. The farm now has enough hay and pasture for its 37 cows and 16 head of young cattle and the output per cow is increased 600 pounds over Plan II. Most of this is the result of better pasture from the ladino clover in the latter part of the summer when pastures otherwise become short. The same amount of concentrates is fed. The rate of fertilization, especially the top dressings on the pastures, is much lower under this plan than under Plan III — down to 10.5 tons — but more lime is applied to the pastures. The expenses are $340 less than with Plan III and the receipts are $150 larger. The increase of $720 in net income thus obtained is combined with a sizable reduction in operating labor because of time saved in use of the tractor on larger fields free of stone. The farm will be much easier to work. The total cash outlay involved in the improvements is $3,590 divided into $737 for new cropland and improving old cropland, $345 for pasture improvement, $2,430 for fence removal, $70 for filling water holes, and $20 for pulling out fruit trees. These are the cash costs only. It is assumed that the work will be mostly done with specialized power equipment as provided through a Soil Conservation Service district, or by a custom operator under contract. The stone fences will be pushed into prepared trenches with bulldozers, the trenches being dug with special equipment. The boulders will be hauled off the fields in heavy scoops attached to tractors, or on stoneboats, the larger boulders being blasted first. The regular farm labor force will help with some of the work.

If the money for these improvements were borrowed at 4½ percent and the improvements were all made the first year, the annual interest would be $160 only. If all the $820 of increase in net income were used to pay interest and principal, the $3,590 would be reduced to nothing in less than six years. The item of expense showing the largest gain is the pasture improvement.

Plan V

Plan V is like Plan IV except that it includes 8.8 more acres of improved pasture from Fields 11 and 5 and fertilization of crops and pasture at the heavy rates employed in Plan III. The extra hay and pasture resulting will support 42 head of milk cows and 18 head of young cattle. The extra pasture improvement would cost only $360. The expenditures under this plan total $7,460, extra fertilizer and feed being the largest items. The net income, however, would be raised $715 above that of Plan IV. It is apparent that if the land improvements of Plan IV are made, the further additions of Plan V are needed to give them full use. By hiring a month's extra labor at the peak season, the farmer would find himself with little or no increase in the work load for the regular labor force. The difficulty with this plan is that the 60 head of cattle is more than the present barn and shed will hold, and the enlargement of the shed would entail a sizable investment, especially if badly needed repairs are combined with it. But the increase in income would redeem these outlays in a few years.

Plan VI

This plan provides for still another 10.6 acres of cropland, and 9.7 more acres of improved pasture; also removing another 470 yards of stone fence. The additional cash outlays on these are $970. The crops and pastures would be limed and fertilized heavily as under Plans III and V, and the old barns and shed torn down and replaced by a modern barn that would house 56 milk cows and 22 head of young stock. The barn would be built on a new location across the road so that it would be on a lower level than that of the house. The cropland would be increased to 81.9 acres, of which 44.3 acres would be in hay, and the improved pasture would be increased to 30.8 acres. This farm thus organized would produce 197 tons of corn and grass silage and 133 tons of hay. Enough more concentrate would be purchased to provide for the 14 more milk cows. The labor load would be increased by seven months. This farm would now be a full three-man farm according to the methods and standards of labor use prevailing in this area. The cash expenses of the farm would be raised to $9,785 and the cash receipts to $14,830, leaving a net income of $5,025. No estimate is here included as to the cost of the new dairy barn, but even though it were as high as $12,000, this and the $3,500 spent on land improvements could be paid off in seven years from

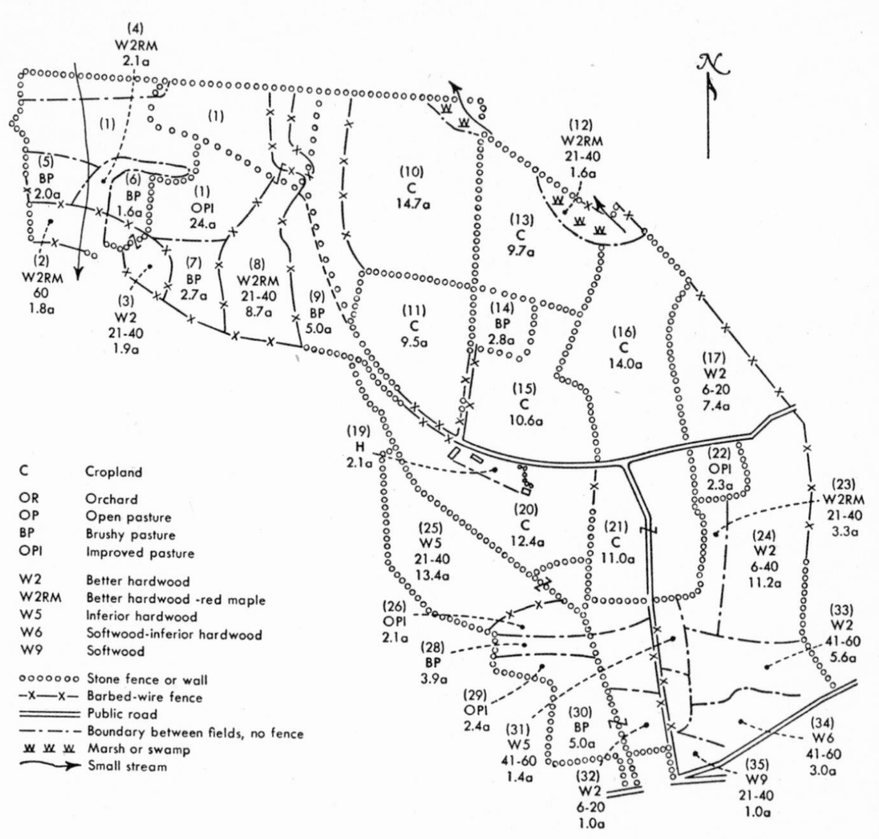

Figure 28. *Same farm as in Figure 27 replanned according to Plan VI.*

the increased net income of $2,870, plus interest at 4½ percent on a covering loan.

This farm organized as under Plan VI would be a modern dairy farm. Its cropland would be laid out in seven fields ranging in size from 5.4 to 14.7 acres, as indicated in Figure 28. These fields would all be farmed in a seven-year rotation. It might be found that some of the slopes eroded too much in the one year when the field would be in corn, even though the corn was rowed on the contour. Should this prove to be true, strip cropping could be introduced where needed, or a few terraces could be built. The 30.8 acres of improved pasture would be limed and fertilized regularly, and worked over and reseeded often enough with a bog harrow to maintain a fair stand of ladino clover for late summer grazing.

Plan VII

Though Plan VI might repay the farmer for his extra management and additional investment, a somewhat smaller business and smaller investment might fit in better with his desires and with market conditions. The most costly type of land improvement is clearing fields of stones sufficiently so that they can be used in rotations including cultivated crops. Plan VII calls for clearing all the stones from only 27.0 acres, leaving Fields 10, 13, 15, 16, and the eastern half of 21, a total of 54.4 acres, in condition for use in a rotation including hay for six years and one year of oats used as silage and at the same time as a nurse crop for the new seeding of the hay crop. With 27.0 acres in the seven-year rotation including corn, this farm would grow only 4 acres of corn silage a year, and would depend upon grass and clover for the rest of its silage. The cost of the land improvements would be reduced to $2,900 and the carrying power of the farm by 4 milk cows and 2 replacements. The net income of the farm would be reduced only from $5,025 to $4,210. The labor load would probably be reduced a little. An argument in favor of using Plan VII might also be that the more sloping fields would need no contour farming if they were never planted with corn. Under this plan, the 25.8 acres of pasture in Fields 5, 6, 7, 9, 14, 28, and 30 would be left in brush pasture. The stone fences in the pasture and woodland would not be disturbed. Removing the relatively few stones in the fields designated OPI would make possible the use of a bog harrow and reseeding. Field 14, designated BP, would be cleared of brush, but it is too stony to permit intensive management. The crossroad splits Field 21 in two, but the road need not be fenced except alongside the pasture.

Woodland. This farm with either Plan VI or Plan VII would still have 60.5 acres of woodland in Fields 2, 3, 4, 8, 17, 23, 24, 25, 31, 33, 34, and 35, all of it but Field 4 being fenced off to allow reproduction. This woodland would yield the 20 cords needed annually on the farm, once the stands were improved, and in addition, after the oldest trees, now 60 years, had reached the age of 80, would yield an annual cut of sawtimber of 14 cubic feet per acre. The average annual growth of 50 cubic feet of wood per acre possible under such management should be worth $6.00. The annual growth under present management is worth only $1.50. The first step in such management would be an improvement cutting that would remove 92 cords of fuelwood. This would require 135 man-days of labor. After that, one day per acre per year would suffice.

It is obvious that the work on the woodland needs to be integrated with that on the dairy enterprise. After the first improvement cutting, it could be fitted in between work on the crops. If the farmer does not want to do this much work on his woodland, he can do nothing more than remove for fuelwood each year the trees that would be marked for an improvement cutting, instead of removing the best trees. This alone would almost double the yield of his woodland. Further details of the woodland management of this farm are left for discussion in the next chapter.

Market Factors. The final decision as to which of Plans II to VII would be best to follow depends upon important factors outside of this farm. If only a few farmers in Worcester County increased their dairy herds from 26 cows to 56, the supply of fluid milk reaching the Worcester and adjacent markets would not be increased enough to affect prices received. Any particular operator may conclude that only a few farmers will recognize the opportunities to increase their incomes in the manner here outlined, or will be sufficiently interested to make the required effort, and hence decide he is safe in going forward with even Plan VI. If only a fourth of these, however, were to improve their farms to the extent of Plan VI, much of the milk would need an outlet in other markets; and if production in these markets expanded at the same time the increase would have to sell at Class II prices. Availability of what will otherwise be Class II milk in the Boston milkshed may also need to be taken into account. It is entirely possible, therefore, that dairy farmers generally would fare best if this farmer and others like him improved their land to the extent of a half increase in their output instead of doubling it. Similarly, the rate at which it would pay best to apply improvement cutting to woodland would depend somewhat on the local market for fuelwood.

It will be apparent that the operating statements for the alternative plans for this farm in Tables 10 and 11 could not have been worked out without considerable basic data. These include the probable yields of hay, corn, and other crops on the different soil types with systems with different grass and legume mixtures and in different years of the rotation; also similar data for different pasture mixtures and the feeding of dairy cattle, and finally data as to the use and depreciation of machinery and other equipment and as to alternative methods of clearing of land of brush and stones.

Data on the relation between amounts of fertilizer, feed, labor, and the like used and the resulting products are now commonly referred to in the simple language of input-output ratios. The operating statements for these plans are no more dependable than are the input-output ratios upon which they are based, and there is seldom enough of such data. In the planning of the farms in Worcester County, the results of all of the experiment station work done by the Massachusetts Experiment Station were used, as well as pertinent data from other experiment stations in the Northeast. These were supplemented by some data from farm management surveys in the region, and in some cases by limited special surveys of recent experience with different practices of farmers in the area. The "data book" recording this material had grown to more than a hundred pages by the end of the Worcester County study. Still, a good deal of judgment was required in applying these data to particular farms and fields, even though several hundred soil tests were made of the soils on the different farms.

At this point, it will be well also to explain more carefully the price system followed in estimating receipts and expenses in Table 11. The intent was to approximate a set of prices and cost rates which was likely to continue on the average for a period of a decade or more beginning as soon as demand-supply relations for farm products got back to normal. The absolute level of these prices and cost rates is not very important — the major concern is that prices of products sold, wages of farm labor, and prices of feed, equipment, and supplies are in the right relation to each other. The prices followed in Table 11 meet these specifications as nearly as possible. They were the prices for feed, fertilizer, hired labor, and other expense items that prevailed in 1950, and prices of dairy and other farm products figured at 90 percent of parity against these cost rates.[1]

Finally, the reader should know that the method of analysis in the foregoing that provides a basis for choice of farm plans and programs to be followed has come to be referred to commonly as a *budget analysis,* and the operating statements for the different alternatives as *budgets.* They will be referred to by these terms in the pages following.

OTHER DAIRY FARMS

In Chapters 11 to 18 following, the planning alternatives on a wide range of other dairy farms in this area will be analyzed. But it will be helpful to consider briefly at this point some of the more prevalent of the variant types

[1] If the projection were being made as of 1958, a level of 85 percent of parity or even lower would be more reasonable.

of dairy farms. For example, a very common type is a farm with so little land in reasonably productive condition that it will not feed enough cows to give the family an acceptable income. Many of the so-called one-man or "family-size" farms in Worcester County answer this description. On the particular farm in the county chosen for illustration here, the farmer had been milking ten cows and raising enough heifers for replacements, and supplementing his farm income by earning $600 a year at off-farm work. His family had lived on the farm for several generations but had let the land run down gradually. It included 152 acres, but only 37 acres of cropland and open pasture remain. Another 13 acres of pasture had reverted to a thin growth of brush and poor grass. Altogether, 83 acres were then in woodland. The remaining 13 acres were idle muck lands needing drainage.

The plan chosen by this farm family does not call, however, for any clearing of woodland or drainage. It calls only for raising the productivity of the present open pasture by fertilizing it more heavily in a rotation of corn silage, oats, and alfalfa with reseeding every four to eight years; for using part of the present open pasture in a hay-and-pasture combination in which a ladino mixture is the base, with liming and fertilization as needed for good yields; and for clearing the brushy pasture and removing enough surface stones from some of it to permit use of a bog harrow, and liming, fertilizing, and seeding to improved pasture grasses. The additional corn silage, hay, and pasture grass resulting will provide feed and pasture for 21 milk cows plus replacements, except for the purchase of concentrates at the same rate per cow as at present. The barn can be made to house this larger herd and additional hay by moving the stable from the first floor to the basement. This, with modern dairy barn equipment, and an adequate silo, will cost $3,000. The farm also needs a modern tractor with equipment. (It is now operating with a very old tractor and a team of horses.)

The total new investment called for by this plan, including initial liming and fertilizer, will be $6,500, and the cash outlay on raising the additional heifers to milking age is estimated at $1,000. The amount of credit necessary will depend upon the rate at which the plan is put into effect and on the amount of current income which the operator is willing to put back into the business. A practical plan for financing the investment should take into account the estimated year-by-year needs for credit and the expected year-by-year earnings available for repayment of indebtedness after meeting minimum family living expenses. Table 12 shows the proposed schedule of borrowings and repayments. This schedule assumed that the land clearing would be undertaken in 1951, that the equipment would be purchased in the same year, and that the new stable would be needed in 1953. Part of the investment would be financed out of current income.

This schedule of repayments of course takes account of the expected increased earnings of the farm. The net income would be almost doubled, with the farmer doing very little off-farm work, and having to employ hired labor for only about a month.

TABLE 12

Proposed Schedule of Borrowings and Repayments (dollars) in Plan Chosen for Family-Size Dairy Farm

Date	Amount borrowed	Payments on — Interest (4½%)	Principal	Total	Balance due
April 1, 1951......	2,500	—	—	—	2,500
April 1, 1952......	500	113	—	113	3,000
April 1, 1953......	1,500	135	—	135	4,500
April 1, 1954......	—	202	—	202	4,500
April 1, 1955......	—	202	500	702	4,000
April 1, 1956......	—	180	1,000	1,180	3,000
April 1, 1957......	—	135	1,000	1,135	2,000
April 1, 1958......	—	90	1,000	1,090	1,000
April 1, 1959......	—	45	1,000	1,045	0

An alternative plan considered in 1951 when grain threatened to be scarce and expensive included substituting 4 acres of corn for grain and buying half as much concentrate per cow. At 1951 prices, this would have increased the net farm income by over $200, assuming that no extra labor would be hired.

Another alternative called for spending $1,000 additional on converting 8 acres of the brushy pasture to cropland and raising 8 acres of corn for grain. This would have added another $200 of net income under the same assumptions. Whether the family would be willing to do the work of caring for and harvesting 8 acres of corn for $400 more net income is a decision which they had to make. At the time, they decided not to include this in their plan, but held it in reserve as a possibility when the thirteen-year-old son would be able to help more in the summer.

The fifth alternative considered called for growing no corn and using the whole 45 acres of open land in hay and pasture and buying only half as much concentrate per cow as under the plan chosen. Production per cow would be

10-to-12 percent less under this feeding schedule, but the net income would be as high as with the plan chosen.

An important issue on this farm concerned haying equipment. The plans considered all provided for the purchase of a hayloader and side-delivery rake. An alternative, especially with Plan V, would be using a field hay-chopper and grass silage. Certainly using a field hay-baler would reduce the labor load. But it is ordinarily considered that one-man farms cannot afford to maintain such equipment even after taking account of the better quality of the hay when it can be harvested promptly and usually between rains. Depending upon custom hiring of such equipment of course introduces the hazard that it may not be available just when it is wanted. Analyses that will appear in later chapters will show that two-man dairy farms can generally afford to own and operate either field hay-baling or field-chopper equipment, and more often the latter, and that three-man dairy and larger farms are commonly able to afford both.

The farm just analyzed is able to produce all it needs as a family-sized farm with its present acreage of open cleared land. Should the son want to remain on the home farm after he finishes high school, however, additional cropland will be needed. The land now in woods is rough stony Gloucester and will not repay clearing. Draining the muck land would be expensive because there is no ready outlet for the water. This problem is being met in part on another dairy farm in the same town by renting 79 acres of land from a farmer nearby which the owner does not farm because it does not provide his family with as good a living as an off-farm job. But although the owner would give a five- or ten-year lease with one year's notice of termination, he will not sell it — he fears that he may lose his present job in the next depression. Also, the family has owned this land for generations. Under these circumstances, the first farmer does not feel safe in spending much on lime and fertilizer to apply to this rented land, and even more important, on enlarging his barn to hold the additional cows needed for a larger income. The plan which he is now following calls for high rates of fertilization of the crop and pasture land on the home farm, for raising only a few replacements and feeding a heavy ration of corn silage and purchased grain to use present barn room as efficiently as possible, and much less intensive use of the rented land.

POULTRY FARMS

The land used in actual poultry production on farms in New England is limited, 2 or 3 acres at the most being all that is used for building sites, range shelters, and range on a family-sized poultry farm with ordinarily around 2,000 laying hens or the equivalent. For largely historical reasons, however, many of these farms include anywhere from 20 to 100 acres or more of usually poor woodland. These were once general farms, and many of them were dairy farms later. They were too small to provide the family with an adequate income, especially after the land had been allowed to run down, and poultry was taken on as a supplementary source of income. Once the family had learned how to manage poultry, it was easy to expand it to a full-time enterprise. At the start, these poultry farmers grew part of the grain for their flocks. Eventually it proved to be more profitable to keep more hens and buy all the grain.

In general, the poultry farms tend to be located near markets in the larger cities, and on the lighter soil types such as Merrimac, Hinckley, and Carver. They need well-drained soils, but they also need land that will grow grass for poultry range. These statements apply, of course, to the common type of poultry farm that sells eggs, the culls from its laying flocks, and perhaps the male chicks from its baby-chick purchases when they reach broiler or fryer age. They do not apply to the specialized broiler, hatchery, or turkey farms.

The most common sizes of full-time poultry farms at the time of this analysis were one-man or family-size farms and two-man farms. At the time of the 1930 Census when all the farms in the United States were classified by type, the family-size poultry farm in New England usually kept from 800 to 1,000 hens. Today enough of the operations have been standardized, or performed off the farm — hatching of chicks and preparation of feed, for example — so that keeping 2,000 hens is common on such farms. The farm which is here being taken as the first example started in 1940 with a poultry house, hereafter referred to as No. 1, 24-by-86 feet with laying pens on the first two floors and space for brooding in about half the width of the third floor. A space of twelve feet at the west end of this building was used for grain storage. In 1949, a two-story, 40-by-46 foot house, here referred to as No. 2, was added, and four small range shelters. The equipment includes an electrically operated egg grader, a conveyor for raising feed to the second floor of the poultry house, and two coal brooders.

This farm as it was operating in 1950 bought only pullet chicks, starting one brood in December and another in February. Both lots were brooded under the two coal stoves on the top floor of the No. 1 house. The first brood was moved to the No. 2 house in time to make room for brooding the second lot of chicks. The second lot of chicks spent the summer on the range and then was housed in the No. 1 house. Chicks were grown on a "standard" mash[2] purchased from a cooperative. The mortality and culling during the rearing period were low, and approximately 2,850 pullets were housed. This pattern of brooding requires selling birds from the No. 2 house about the first of March, but even so a majority of the birds housed are held through most of their first laying year. The first column of Table 13 summarizes results under this plan of operation. The average number of layers per year was about 2,000, egg production averaged 16.4 dozens per layer, and the average price received for these eggs was 45.8 cents a dozen. It will be noted that the family did about all of the work. A neighbor was hired from time to time to help pack eggs or dress chickens, or to take care of the flock during brief absences of the operator. Some eggs and poultry were retailed at the farm by the operator's wife, but most of them were marketed wholesale through a cooperative.

Alternative Plan II

This farmer was much interested in reorganizing his business so as to increase the net income. The obvious way was to enlarge the business. This meant enlarging one of the buildings to get more space for the laying flock, but this would also involve hiring more labor. Accordingly two other plans were considered along with this. These are Nos. II and III in the table, the No. IV plan being the one with the enlarged plant. The farmer chose No. II, which continues with the same housing space and other facilities and merely starts the two lots of chicks each two months earlier. It is generally recognized that fall-hatched pullets tend to produce a larger share of their first year's egg production during their first six or eight months of laying than do birds hatched at other seasons. Moreover, their first few months' egg production includes relatively few small eggs, and the average value of eggs produced per bird kept during the first six or eight months of laying is higher than for other seasons of hatching. Thus these birds fit in particularly well in cases where use of dual-purpose houses requires marketing layers after only six or eight months of production. Moreover, the greatest space requirement for a group of fall-hatched pullets comes at a season when yards adjacent to the laying house can meet part of the need. This therefore becomes a way of making fuller use of available buildings. Also, when a good range is available for the layers, some saving in feed purchases results.

Operating along these lines, this farm would start with 1,810 pullet

[2] The term "standard" is used to indicate a mash not corresponding to the recently developed "high efficiency" formulas.

TABLE 13

Poultry Farm Business Summary

Item	Plan I (Present)	Plan II (Proposed)	Plan III	Plan IV
Farm acreage				
Total	3	3	3	3
Poultry range	1	1	1	1
Crops	—	—	—	—
Floor space (sq. ft.)				
Permanent houses	No. 1 4820	4820	4820	No. 1 4325
	No. 2 3680	3680	3680	New 4325
				No. 2 3680
Shelters (range)	400	400	400	400
Chicks started				
(P = Pullets, C = Cockerels,	Dec. 1800 P	Oct. 1810 P	Oct. 2410 P	May 3600 P
SR = Straight-run)	Feb. 1500 P	Jan. 2000 P	Jan. 2670 P	Aug. 3750 SR
Layers housed	2830	3050	4065	4380
Average No. of layers	2020	2122	2830	3052
Egg production				
Per layer (doz.)	16.4	17.5	17.5	17.5
Total (doz.)	33,079	37,034	49,500	53,314
Egg sales				
Number (doz.)	32,779	36,734	49,200	53,014
Average price (wholesale basis)	45.8¢	46.3¢	46.3¢	46.1¢
Fowl sales				
Number	2588	2795	3727	4014
Total weight (lb.)	15,528	16,770	14,908	24,084
Average price (wholesale basis)	26¢	24¢	17¢	24¢
Other meat birds				
Number sold	235	381	507	2236
Total weight (lb.)	940	1524	1268	8942
Average price (wholesale basis)	26¢	26¢	19¢	26¢
Grain purchases				
Laying flock — cwt.	2220	2334	2660	3357
— price	$4.25	$4.25	$4.25	$4.25
Growing flock — cwt.	889	980	1102	1694
— price	$4.25	$4.25	$4.25	$4.25

Financial Summary*

Receipts				
Eggs — wholesale value	$15,013	$17,150	$22,800	$24,439
— retail margin	100	100	100	100
Fowl	4,037	4,020	2,540	5,780
Broilers and roasters	244	396	241	2,325
Total	19,394	21,666	25,681	32,644

TABLE 13 (Continued)

Item	*Plan I (Present)*	*Plan II (Proposed)*	*Plan III*	*Plan IV*
Expenses				
Labor	400	400	700	1,820
Feed — poultry	13,213	14,090	16,000	21,467
— other	45	45	45	45
Lime	30	30	30	40
Chicks	957	1,105	1,775	1,682
Supplies — litter	10	10	10	20
Fuel	30	40	40	60
Gasoline and oil	20	20	20	30
Repairs and maintenance	300	300	300	375
Auto upkeep (farm share)	20	20	20	20
Water, electricity, telephone	120	120	120	180
Taxes	229	240	240	300
Insurance	50	50	50	100
Interest	225	225	225	607
Replacement of building	150	150	150	350
Replacement of equipment	100	100	100	300
Total	15,899	16,945	19,825	27,396
NET FARM INCOME	$ 3,495	$ 4,721	$ 5,856	$ 5,248

* Prices received have been estimated at levels which seem reasonable in relation to prices paid in late 1950 and the long-term outlook. These prices are not intended as forecasts, and the budgets will certainly not be entirely applicable to any specific year, either past or future.

chicks hatched during October, brooding them on the top floor of the No. 1 house and then moving them to the No. 2 house. With the range available nearby, space would be adequate for 1,450 pullets when they reach laying age on April 1. This flock would be reduced at the end of November and again in December to make space available for the new brood of chicks. The 2,000 pullet chicks started in January would also be brooded on the top floor of the No. 1 house. These would provide about 1,600 pullets for the laying flock on July 1, to be housed on the three floors of the No. 1 laying house. A slight reduction in this flock would be made in October to clear the top floor for brooding purposes. The remaining flock of about 1,230 would be carried through until the end of June, except for normal mortality and culling.

On this basis, the average number of layers for the year would be 2,122, which is 102 more than under the present plan, production per layer would be expected to average 17.5 dozen eggs, and the value of eggs on a wholesale basis to average 46.3 cents per dozen. The financial summary indicates a net farm income under this plan $1,226 higher than under the present plan.

Alternative Plan III

This plan is like II except for the substitution of the Leghorn breed for Rhode Island Red. Leghorn flocks had mostly disappeared from New England by the end of the 1930's, but price relationships and production methods have changed greatly since that time and current discussions are again beginning to consider possible advantages of a lighter-weight laying bird. With Leghorns, floor space on this farm would probably be adequate for at least a one-third increase in the size of the laying flock. With a cross between Leghorn males and Red females, the possible increase in flock size would probably be nearer 10 to 20 percent. Production of such cross-breds is on a very limited basis at present, and any shift to lighter-weight layers would have to be approached experimentally at present. To indicate the financial possibilities, however, the program of Plan II has been recalculated as Plan III on the basis of a Leghorn flock one-third larger than the heavy-breed flock of Plan II. Using Leghorns, the October hatch would be about 2,410 pullet chicks and the January hatch would be 2,670 pullet chicks. On this basis, the average number of layers would be 2,830, production per layer would average 17.5 dozen eggs, and the average value of eggs on a wholesale basis would be 46.3 cents per dozen. The amount of feed to be handled would be increased only by about 10 percent over Plan II, and the birds would be kept in the same pens. The extra work of collecting and packing the additional eggs would amount to about two months' more hired labor. Estimated net farm income would be $1,135 higher than under Plan II, if the white eggs could be sold for the same price per dozen as brown eggs of equal quality. A discount of two cents a dozen for the white eggs would not quite wipe out the income advantage of this plan over Plan II. Before the farmer makes this shift, he should investigate local outlets for white eggs and possible sources of chicks. Also within a few years, he might find that he could purchase Leghorn-Red crosses locally, and that such crosses offered more promise than the straight breeds.

Alternative Plan IV

This plan calls for enlarging the No. 1 house to provide nearly double its present floor space. Under this plan 3,600 May pullet chicks could be brooded in the No. 2 house and moved out onto range. This would provide 2,880 pullets for the laying flock in November. These birds would be housed in the expanded No. 1 house and kept through the year, except for mortality and culling losses. In August, 3,750 straight-run chicks would be brooded in the No. 2 house and would provide 1,500 pullets on February 1. Of these birds, about 260 pullets would be added to the flock in the No. 1 house and the remainder kept in the No. 2 house until such time as space was needed for brooding. Then the No. 1 house could be filled to capacity again and the remaining birds sold.

On this basis, the average number of layers for the year would be 3,050, production per layer would average 17.5 dozen eggs, and the average value of eggs on a wholesale basis would be 46.1 cents per dozen.

This plan would call for the employment of a full-time hired man. It would convert this family-sized poultry farm to a two-man farm. It would have the advantage of providing a reliable person to care for the flock in emergencies when the operator could not do the work himself. But it would increase net returns only $500 over Plan II.

Other Alternatives

If straight-run or unsexed chicks are bought, either more brooding space is needed or fewer laying hens can be housed. The extra cost of the male chicks is small. Which pays the better depends upon special circumstances on each farm and in each market and on relative market prices at the time.

Another area of choice is in the number of broods started each year, whether two, three, or four. This alternative was tested out on another family-size poultry farm in Worcester County. Shifting from broodings in January and April to January, March, and May reduced the net income because it reduced the number of layers unless additional brooding space was provided, and when it was provided, the extra income resulting little more than paid for the extra building and labor costs. Using unsexed chicks in these three broodings brought $135 more net income than using pullet chicks only would have brought, but relatively lower meat prices could have wiped out all this advantage.

Adding an October brooding to these three promised to add another $100 to the net income because it increased the average number of hens by 200 over the present plan and brought slightly higher average prices. It also provided a more even labor load throughout the year.

DAIRY-POULTRY FARMS

Although in the past many of the dairy farms that took on poultry as a supplementary enterprise shifted entirely to poultry, many others did not and on many that did the restoration of the pastures by liming, fertilization and reseeding, and parallel rehabilitation of the cropland would have paid better than adding more poultry. The combination of dairy farming plus a part-time poultry enterprise offers a good solution to the problem on many Worcester County farms with too little good land.

This alternative has been tested out on a farm which contains 88 acres, of which 30 are cropland, 15 are moderately good open pasture, and 40 acres are woodland, and which in 1950 had 14 cows. One method of supplementing the income had already been adopted, namely, growing 4 acres of sweet corn for the local market, but this was not enough. Adding a poultry enterprise with 400 layers housed in the fall and 500 sexed chicks raised for replacement promised to increase the net income by $475, with 15 dozen eggs produced per hen, allowing nothing for extra labor of the regular farm labor force. An investment of $1,000 in building and equipment would be involved.

On an occasional dairy farm in Worcester County, the wife handles a small poultry business. On one analyzed, an average flock of 180 layers, with 300 pullet chicks started each year, and 250 housed in the fall, added $240 to the net cash income of the family, in addition to the eggs and poultry meat used in the home.

FRUIT FARMS

The fruit farms chosen for illustration in this chapter are all farms with apple orchards. The one reported here in most detail was a 62-acre farm with 21 acres in apples and 8 acres in hay, and 1 acre in potatoes and sweet corn. The other 30 acres were in brushy pasture. When the farm was mapped in 1938, the operator was a man 65 years old who was not interested in planting replacements. The plan worked out with him called simply for somewhat heavier fertilization with complete fertilizer to increase yields and about one additional spraying. This farmer was, however, already managing his orchard pretty well, his yield in 1938 being 300 bushels per acre. When the farm was revisited in 1946, it had been purchased by a younger man who was interested in a much longer future. The yields from the present orchard would be expected to begin to decline considerably beginning in ten to twenty years, and none of the trees were old enough to remove.

This raised the question as to available land for the new planting. The slopes on the present orchard land range from 3 to 15 per cent. The erosion had been slight on most of this, and moderate on only 3 acres. Field 4 was mostly too low for apples, but Field 1 contained 25 acres of Gloucester soils of the same type as the present orchard land, and with B slopes mostly. The difficulty was that the stones had never been cleared from it.

The plan worked out with the farmer in 1946 called for clearing this 25 acres and planting at an average rate of 3 acres per year, and in addition removing the stone fence from within Field 2 and the surface boulders to make the use of equipment much simpler and perhaps even to help with pest control. No trees would be planted on the low Whitman soils or on the ledge in the corner of the field.

Another decision this young farmer had to make was whether to plant only permanent trees, 27 per acre, or semi-permanents, to be removed in 25 years, along with the permanents, or these plus fillers in addition to be removed in 18 years. With land scarce on a farm, the planting of semi-permanents and fillers is likely to be advantageous. This farm has the land, but only after an investment in clearing estimated at $50 per acre. The budgeting of alternatives showed that, with $0.90 per bushel assumed as the price of apples per bushel on the tree, and labor and other costs at prevailing rates, the fillers, although coming into bearing at 7 years would not cover the investment in them by 18 years of age, and the semi-permanents would yield only a small net return by 25 years. The farmer concluded therefore to plant only the permanents. If he had been short of land, or had considerable family labor to help with the planting and other overhead work, the answer would have been different.

This farmer was also going to look into market outlets for vegetables that he can grow among the trees the first several years after planting.

The farmer on this place in 1938 kept a horse and 2 or 3 head of young stock to run on the pasture in Field 1 and consume the hay grown on Field 4. The revised plan called for tractor power only and renting the pasture till it was converted to orchard.

While the young orchard was coming on, this farmer would be making a growing investment in land clearing, tree stock, and fertilizer. It would grow steadily to over $2,000 in about 10 years when the fruit harvest would begin to cover part of the current annual out-of-pocket expenses. The hired labor expense on the farm in 1946 was around $1,000. With both the new orchard and the old in production, the labor expenditures would rise, but so would the receipts.

The budget of this farm for 1946 with a yield of 215 bushels of apples per acre was as shown on the next page.

This farmer would have decisions to make each year as to how much fertilizer to apply, and how much of this would be nitrogen and how much a complete fertilizer, as to intensity of spraying and pruning, as to how much mulching of his trees was necessary, and as to several other cultural prac-

Receipts		
Apples 4,500 bu. $1.80 per bu.	$8,100	
Sweet corn	80	
		$8,180
Expenses		
Spray	$ 750	
Fertilizer and lime	165	
Boxes and crates	500	
Labor	900	
Insurance	180	
Depreciation and repair on machinery	450	
Gas and oil	150	
Building depreciation and repair	150	
Selling costs	800	
Storage	800	
Taxes	275	
Miscellaneous	125	$5,245
Net farm income		$2,735

tices. Then he would have decisions as to sorting, grading, storage, and market outlets.

Also nothing has been said in the foregoing about the choice of varieties.

The planning analysis of several larger apple orchards in Worcester County revealed very little in the way of change from established cultural practices. These orchards were all being well managed so far as fertilizer, mulching, spraying, and pruning were concerned. The major issue with all of them was replacement planting. Few of the orchardists were planning to expand their enterprises. In general, they were planning to start young trees to take the place of the old trees as fast as these were cut out. This would mean, in the case of one of the older orchards with a nearly even-aged stand, a decline in total output below present levels for a while. The others already had trees in several age groups. But when these orchard farms were revisited in 1946 part of them had not carried out their pre-war planting intentions. Their operators, however, were expecting to make up their arrears in a few years. They gave as their reason for the delay the wartime shortage of planting stock and labor.

The largest changes planned were on farms with the smaller orchards. Part of them chose plans in 1938 that would have nearly doubled their use of fertilizer and their sprayings. In general, they proposed to use all the grass grown in the orchards as mulch. Those with orchards in combination with dairying, however, while proposing to increase the yields from present orchards, made few plans for replacement plantings. When these farms were revisited after the war, several of the smaller orchardists had been neglecting their orchards and others had already converted them to cropland.

CHAPTER 10

Planning a Forest Operating Unit

It should be evident by now how much the use of land within farms is conditioned by the types and sizes of operating units among which the land is distributed. This is true even though most farms in a region are family-type farms and most of these are either family-size or two-man units. The part-time and residential units so prevalent in New England furnish the major exceptions to the prevailing pattern of agricultural operating units in the region, and it is now obvious that most of these are not very agricultural.

The character of the operating unit is even more determinative in forest use of land than in agricultural use.[1] First of all, the amount of land in one individual ownership varies widely. At one extreme a survey of ownership of forest tracts in one town in southern New Hampshire showed 444 owners of such tracts averaging 17 acres. Also 69 summer homes in this town had an average of 13 woodland acres attached to them. At the other extreme, in New England as a whole in 1945 there were 45 owners of forest tracts of 50,000 acres or more, altogether owning 32 percent of the private commercial forest land. Another 7 percent of it was owned in tracts of 5,000 to 50,000 acres of 194 owners.[2]

Worth showing in detail are the data in Table 14 as to the distribution of size of holdings in the 23 towns surveyed by Dr. Solon Barraclough. Nearly half of the holdings are of less than 50 acres, but these occupy only 9 percent of the timberland. Over half of the land is in holdings of 250 acres or more.

[1] This chapter is very largely the work of Dr. Ernest Gould, Forest Economist at the Harvard Forest, Petersham, Massachusetts.

[2] "The Management Status of Forest Lands in the United States; Report 3 from a Reappraisal of the Forest Situation," USDA, Forest Service, 1946.

The table shows a group of 63 owners in these towns with 500 or more acres, and 97 more with holdings between 250 and 500 acres. Dr. Barraclough says of these groups: "A systematic effort to locate and assist this comparatively small number of forest owners would go a long way toward getting better forestry on a large block of the forest land in small holdings."

TABLE 14

Distribution of Forest-land Acreage and of Forest-land Owners in the 23 New England Towns According to Size of Holding

Size of holding (acres)	Forest land (acres)	Owners (number)	Percentage distribution: For each size of holding		Percentage distribution: Cumulative	
			Acreage	Owners	Acreage	Owners
5,000 and over*....	54,292	8	19.5	0.4	19.5	0.4
2,500 to 4,999......	13,277	4	4.8	0.2	24.3	0.6
1,000 to 2,499......	30,195	21	10.9	1.0	35.2	1.6
500 to 999.........	20,838	30	7.5	1.4	42.7	3.0
250 to 499.........	33,691	97	12.1	4.6	54.8	7.6
100 to 249.........	66,141	448	23.8	21.3	78.6	28.9
50 to 99...........	34,842	509	12.5	24.1	91.1	53.0
10 to 49...........	24,765	989	8.9	47.0	100.0	100.0
Total.........	278,041	2,106	100.0	100.0	——	——

* In these towns there were no private holdings that contained more than 12,000 acres.

Secondly, the character of the timber varies widely, as pointed out in Chapter 3, from stands with no merchantable timber at all, with only seedlings and saplings, to those with sawlogs ready for harvesting.

In the third place, associated with this wide range in size of forest holding is a wide assortment in type of owner, all the way from large-scale commercial operators down to thousands who are doing nothing more than to pay taxes on small pieces of woodland that they have never seen. It is this third difference among forest tracts that has the largest effect upon the kind of management that forest land is now receiving. Dr. Barraclough undertook to find out why the owners of the 2,106 tracts in the 23 towns were holding their forest land. Many of them cited two or three reasons. In the accompanying summary of the reasons given in his questionnaire returns, the percentages therefore add up to more than 100.

By class of owners, 7 percent of the processing-plant owners gave recreational purposes as well as timber values as their reason for ownership. The business-professional group divided their reasons into 28 percent timber

Forest properties being held for —	*Percentage of owners*	*Percentage of land*
Timber values	43	62
Recreational purposes	20	23
Satisfaction of owning land	15	12
Residential use	15	9
Sale later at a higher price	15	10
Use as pasture	8	6
Other uses	9	10

values, 35 percent recreational, and 24 percent residential. The retired persons gave more weight to the satisfaction of owning land — 29 percent — than any other group, but also gave large weight to timber values and residential use. The housewives had apparently inherited holdings in most cases and were hoping to get some returns from timber values, or to sell later at higher prices, in about half the cases.

In keeping with the foregoing, 72 percent of the owners of wood-using plants had harvested timber products in the preceding ten years and also 72 percent of the farmers, in the latter case no doubt in considerable part for use on the farm. For the other groups, the range was from 40 to 62 percent.

The expectations as to harvesting in the next ten years averaged only 44 percent as compared with 53 percent in the past ten years. The market for timber products was strong during the war years.

Dr. Barraclough concludes:

It is clear from these reports that a great many of the small woodland owners hold their properties over long periods of time without cash income from the sale of forest products or even income in the form of forest products harvested for the owner's personal use. In spite of this, only 20 percent of the owners were willing to say that their forest property is a financial liability. Some 19 percent gave no indication of their feelings about the financial status of their forest properties. It is entirely possible that many of these people felt that the question of whether the property is a *financial* asset or liability was not of primary importance to them. At any rate, this question was conspicuously left unanswered by many respondents. Those who took a positive stand by saying that their forest property is a financial asset made up 61 percent of the forest-land owners.

One more strong piece of evidence that financial inducements are not the all-important factor in the holding of small forest properties in New England is the extremely low rate of tax delinquency. In the 23 towns that were covered in this survey, only 1.2 percent of the forest-land owners are now delinquent in the payment of their taxes. The acreage held by these people is even less: 1.1 percent of the total. The 39 percent of the forest-land owners who do not look on their property as a financial asset apparently find other values in it that are sufficient to justify continuous payment of the taxes.

The foregoing description does not altogether fit either northern or southern New England. Half or more of the forest land in 3 of the Vermont towns and in 2 of the Maine towns was in holdings of 1,000 acres or more and none of it in 2 of the Massachusetts and 2 of the Connecticut towns. But in 10 of the 23 towns, 6 of these being in Massachusetts and Connecticut, the largest fraction of the forest land is in the size-group 100 to 250 acres, and it is units of this size that will receive most attention in this chapter.

In the 10 Worcester County towns studied most intensively, 78 percent of the timberland acreage was not in farms of any description, not even residential, and no doubt the major portion of this is held in units of 100 to 250 acres.

Attention will be given in this chapter also to farming units, including residential and part-time, whose land is dominantly in timber. Chapter 6 has presented the necessary facts about these units for the 10 Worcester County towns studied intensively.

It follows from the foregoing that a wide range of forest operating units may need to be planned in a county like Worcester. There is even need for considering some which do not now exist because they represent the most promising way of utilizing existing tracts.

Because the woodland of Worcester County is broken up into so many separate holdings owned for a variety of reasons by people in all walks of life, no blanket prescription for forest production is likely to meet all the requirements of the present situation. The diversity in size of holdings, in ownership objectives, and in the capacity for forest management of the people involved is of first importance to any plans for the development of forest operating units. In spite of these complicating factors, some typical cases may point the way that development can wisely follow.

It should be recognized at the outset that any kind of forest management will require something more than the simple ownership or control of a forest tract. The more intensive forestry programs especially call for using such resources as labor, equipment, and managerial ability along with the forest land. If these resources are lacking, it will generally be possible for an owner to use only the lowest intensities of forest management. Many forest landowners lack the resources that they need to take full advantage of forest production possibilities. Because of this, one of the largest problems that must be solved is that of devising forest operating units that will bring together under a single decision-making head all of the resources needed for forest production.

Any moves in this direction must start with the realities of the present patterns of landholding, resources, and objectives of ownership. Unless a great expansion in federal, state or local government ownership is contemplated, forest production problems will have to be solved within the present context of private enterprise. Certainly a great deal more analysis is needed before the relative advantages of public and private ownership can be clearly stated.

FARM WOODLOTS

In many ways farmers are better equipped to solve their problems of forest production than are most of the other private woodland owners of the County. Farmers frequently have much of the capital equipment, managerial ability, and all or part of the labor needed to undertake a variety of forest management programs. They also live near their woodlots, are familiar with the peculiar problems of raising crops, and can keep track of local outlets for wood products. Farmers also tend to have forest landownership objectives that center around the income-producing possibilities of their woodlands.

About 30 percent of the forest land in the County is in farms. A study of how a forest enterprise can be developed as an integral part of these active operating units is a logical place to start analysis. The following case study of Farm A illustrates some typical problems and possible solutions in the use of farm woodlands.

Farm A

At the end of World War II, this 434-acre farm included 56 acres of cropland, 106 acres of open pasture, and 190 acres of woodland. In addition, about 12 acres of cropland were rented. Forty-five cows with enough young stock for replacements were kept and about 1,600 pounds of grain were fed each cow annually. Milk production averaged 7,100 pounds of 3.6 percent milk per cow.

The buildings were in good repair. The barn had enough tie-ups for the herd and enough space for 15 additional stanchions. The equipment included two tractors and tractor equipment, a hayloader, a side-delivery rake, and a milking machine. The labor force consisted of the operator, his father (part-time), and two hired men, who between them worked a total of about 18 man-months each year. About 20 cords of wood were cut each year to meet farm needs, most of this being harvested by clear-cuttings in pole-sized stands.

A major problem on this farm was how far to go in improving land and expanding the dairy herd. If 52 acres were improved for ladino clover pasture by removing surface stones and some brush, adequate roughage production for a herd of 60 cows and replacements could be maintained. If land improvement were limited to top-dressing permanent pasture, adequate roughage for a herd of 48 cows and replacements could be supplied. This would require little outlay for stone removal, but could not be expected to yield as high a net farm income as the larger business.

Also if more intensive woodland management were used, 90 acres of woodland could be developed into stands producing high-quality sawtimber. The remainder of the woodland was swampy, but could produce sizable quantities of red maple fuelwood or pulpwood. Altogether, the forest enterprise could be developed into an important part of the farm business.

The condition of the forest growing stock on this farm is shown in Table 15. The small area of inferior hardwood supports a gray birch stand that has seeded in an old pasture. Eventually better hardwoods such as longer-lived oak, ash, and maple will take over this site.

TABLE 15

Acreage of Forest Cover Types and Age Classes of the Growing Stock in Farm A

	0–20	21–40	41–60	0–60	Total
Better hardwoods	6	23	10	44	83
Inferior hardwoods	7	—	—	—	7
Red maple swamp	—	100	—	—	100
Total	13	123	10	44	190

An important fact brought out in Table 15 is that most of the stands are at least 21 to 40 years of age, and 54 acres contain older trees. Thus some mature products can be cut without any long waiting period for growth. This contrasts with many forest areas in the County which, as a result of past cutting and hurricane damage, contain very few older stands. With a preponderance of young stands on a property, a long period may have to elapse before salable products can be cut regardless of the management program used. The problems posed by this situation will be discussed later.

Three general intensities of forest management have been analyzed. Although these alternatives do not explore all the possibilities, they do fairly well span the range of management programs feasible under present market conditions.

Low Intensity of Forest Management—A low intensity of forest management would entail clear-cutting stands in much the same way as has been practiced in the past. No steps would be taken to promote regeneration. Stands would be cut as soon as they contained salable trees, frequently at the beginning of their most productive period of growth. Returns would be sporadic under this program — during the next decade the average yearly cut would be about 20 M.b.f. (thousand board feet) of low-grade sawlogs plus about 200 cords of red maple fuelwood or pulpwood. No cutting could be done during the following decade and then a cut of 10 to 15 M.b.f. could be made each year for the next two decades. After that, no more cutting could be done for ten to twenty years by which time some more fuelwood or pulpwood would have matured.

This schedule of clear-cutting interspersed by periods without cutting would lead to an average production rate of about 0.25 cords per acre per year. The total labor required each year during the next decade would be about 340 man-days, but the long-run average would be about 70 man-days per year. Of course this program could be put into effect by periodic stumpage or lump-sum sales of standing timber, with no labor furnished by the farm. The owner would then only have to negotiate the sale and supervise the cutting enough to make sure he was paid for the material cut. Stumpage sales would provide no profitable work for farm labor and equipment that might not otherwise be used.

Medium Intensity of Forest Management—Alternatively, stands could be held until they had made the bulk of their rapid growth and some form of partial cutting could be used to harvest them. This system would allow the more valuable trees to grow about a decade or so longer than under a low intensity of management and would promote more prompt and valuable reproduction. No steps would be taken to improve the volume and quality of the stands before they were mature.

The effect of this program would be to postpone some cutting for the sake of greater volume and quality of growth and better regeneration. Harvest cuttings would also be more regular over time. Average annual harvests during the next decade would be about 15 M.b.f. of sawlogs plus 40 cords of fuelwood or pulpwood. If the stands regenerated promptly and natural losses were not excessive, this level of yearly cutting could be kept up indefinitely. The proportion of high-quality sawlogs should be appreciably increased and the stands should be easier to operate after partial cutting. This should lead to an increase in sale values. Productivity over the years would be equivalent to about 0.35 cords per acre per year.

If this management program was carried out largely by farm labor, about 90 man-days of work would be needed each year during the next decade. The average labor load would be slightly more than this later. The public forester could give any technical help needed to mark the stands for partial cuttings. This program could also be carried out through ordinary commercial sales of marked stumpage. The owner would merely have to mark the timber and negotiate a contract for its sale.

High Intensity of Forest Management — A higher intensity of forest management would include the partial cuttings planned under a medium intensity of management together with a program of weedings or cleanings, improvement cuttings, and thinnings throughout the life of any stand of better hardwoods. These intermediate treatments would remove poorly formed, diseased, and dying trees to speed the growth of selected crop trees and to salvage material that would otherwise die and be wasted. No attempt would be made to improve the volume and quality growth of the stands of swamp red maple; these would continue under medium management. Average annual cuttings during the next decade would average about 15 M.b.f. of sawlogs plus 70 cords of fuelwood or pulpwood. This amount could be cut more or less indefinitely, barring catastrophic losses, and would lead to an average annual production rate of about 0.50 cords per acre. After a few years, sales values should increase substantially because of the better quality and greater accessibility of the stands.

Although harvest cuttings could be made by the sale of marked stumpage, most of the intermediate treatments could not be accomplished by commercial sales. It would be necessary to use farm or special hired labor, at least supervised by the owner, to carry out much of this program. About 130 man-days of work would be needed each year during the next decade for harvest cuttings and intermediate treatments. Slightly more than this would be needed in the longer run.

Proposed Plan — The proposed farm plan was for increasing the number of cows to 60 and the number of heifers raised each year to 12. The necessary stalls for the care of this herd would be added in the barn. Fifty-two acres of pasture were to be improved for ladino pasture. Heavier fertilization of the present cropland, 5 acres of corn raised instead of 10, and grass would supply the remainder of the silage needed.

Because milk production was already moderately high in relation to the grain fed, no change was anticipated in production or feeding rates. The following estimates of milk and livestock sales and grain purchases at the then expected prices should be reasonable once the agricultural adjustments became effective.

4,180 cwt. of 3.6 percent milk at.....	$ 3.80
11 cull cows at..................	90.00
43 bob calves at.................	5.00
8 pigs at........................	8.00
960 cwt. grain for cows at..........	3.00
200 cwt. grain for other stock at....	3.00

The owner also wants to undertake a high intensity of forest management in view of the probable future values of high-quality sawlogs and an improving outlet for hardwood pulpwood. In addition to 20 cords of fuelwood for home use, this program will provide about 15 M.b.f. of sawlogs and 20 cords of pulpwood for roadside sale.

The operator intends to fit woods work into his regular farm program. The labor needed to carry out the revised farm program plus high-intensity management of the forest enterprise can be supplied by the owner with part-time help from his father, plus about 25 man-months of hired labor. The proposed adjustments will make it possible to keep two full-time hired men and depend very little on part-time labor.

Using long-term planning prices based on the 1943–1945 expense level, the estimated cash income of the farm during the next decade, after adjustments have been made effective, are shown in Table 16.

Farm B

Another dairy farm with two men and only 52 acres of woodland illustrates a situation where with careful management it is possible in the immediate future to supply the farm wood needs from the woodlot. Later on, when the stands are more mature, a surplus will be available for sale. The owner has a well-equipped dairy operation with 37 cows of milking age. In order to fill the barn, he can expand the milking herd to 43 head, raise his own replacements, and enlarge the business handled by himself and one hired hand. Some land improvement will be required, but no heavy investment in buildings or equipment.

The owner estimates that he is fully equipped to do about 30 man-days of woods work. He uses on the farm the equivalent of about 15 cords each year, including fuelwood and a few sawlogs. He could use any of the three intensities of management outlined for the previous farm, but because he has only a 52-acre woodlot he wants to use the higher intensity of management

TABLE 16

Condensed Financial Summary for Farm A, Present Plan and Proposed Plan, Based on the 1943–1945 Expense Level (in dollars)

	Present plan (45 cows and low-intensity forest management)		Proposed plan (60 cows and high-intensity forest management)	
Income				
Agricultural enterprises		13,020		17,355
Forest enterprises				
Sawlogs		none sold	(15 M.b.f.)	270
Fuelwood or pulpwood*		none sold	(20 cords)	180
		13,020		17,805
Expenses				
Farm and forest enterprises		5,715		8,065
Labor	(18 mos.)	1,800	(25 mos.)	2,500
		7,515		10,565
NET FARM INCOME		5,505		7,420

* The value of fuel used at home is not included with the cash income. About $250 worth of growing stock inventory has been accumulating, over and above wood cut for home use, each year. At current prices the proposed cut would be worth about $680 at the roadside.

that will be most productive over the years. Also he can fit the required woods work for such intensity of management into his farm business.

The acreage and condition of the present stands is shown in the accompanying tabulation together with a brief description of the operations needed to start a program of high-intensity forest management.

Acres	Present condition	Proposed treatment
30	Even aged, 20–40-year-old stand about one-third hemlock and the balance mixed hardwoods. Some trees are older and there are a few open areas. Stands are of medium density with fair reproduction.	Make improvement cuttings every 5–10 years to release and thin hemlock, ash, and red oak as final crop trees. Gradually harvest mature trees at 16″–18″ diameter breast high. Some smaller logs can be used for farm lumber.
22	Even aged, 0–20-year-old stand of mixed oaks, maple, hemlock, pine, and gray birch. Medium to low density and only fair reproduction.	Make improvement cuttings every 5–10 years as above, starting when material removed will be usable. Fence in to protect from grazing.

The proposed system of frequent partial cuttings will yield an annual harvest of 10 to 15 cords of fuelwood and other products from the older stands during the next five to ten years. This will require fifteen to twenty man-days of labor. As all the stands mature and become fully productive, the yearly cut will increase to about 25 cords of material, including fuelwood or pulpwood and an increasing proportion of high-grade sawlogs. Some sales can then be made. About 30 to 40 man-days of labor would be required. It is estimated that returns from the suggested management will be about double those of infrequent clear cutting, due to better growth of crop trees, better salvage of defective trees, production of high-grade sawlogs, and the elimination of delays in restocking.

PART-TIME AND RESIDENTIAL FARMS

About a fourth of the farm forest land in the County is owned by part-time farmers or people who live on their land and work elsewhere. The part-time farmers work off their farms most of the time, but frequently have as much of the resources needed to develop their forest enterprises as do regular farmers. Owners in this category with forest holdings like those on the farms just discussed could follow any one of the three alternative intensities of management outlined. Even the highest intensity could be used to advantage if the necessary managerial ability and equipment were available and the labor could be fitted into the owner's schedule or be hired and supervised by him. The technical help needed for any kind of management can generally be obtained from the public forester free of charge.

The same general statement can be made about the owners of residential farms, although it is unusual for such people to have the needed equipment and labor. Not infrequently, however, these owners have the necessary local knowledge of markets and can find time to supervise and lay out the forest operations. If the owner is content with a medium intensity of management, it is ordinarily possible to find local operators who will buy and cut marked trees. In this case little more is needed than a knowledge of how to sell and mark stands for partial cutting and enough time and interest in forest production to perform these simple management functions.

Of course many of these owners have very small holdings that can be expected to produce salable materials only at long intervals. Especially is this true of holdings that were severely damaged by the 1938 hurricane. It may be hard for such owners to find the necessary buyers or operators for the small amounts of material that they have to sell. It is also difficult to find reasonably skilled woods workers in the County who will accept the sporadic work that the owners of small lots can offer.

In addition, larger operations can take better advantages of the new mechanical aids to forest operations that have appeared in the last few years. There are also advantages to larger-scale operations that continue over a long time, such as developing and improving market contacts, learning through practice the most efficient logging methods and forest-management techniques, taking full advantage of mechanization, and training and improving the efficiency of permanent woods labor. Few small or sporadic operations can realize all these economies of scale.

It is difficult to say how large a forest enterprise is required to realize fully all the possible economies of scale. However, a business that could profitably employ a three- to five-man crew using chain saws, a tractor, and truck with full-time trained management could realize many economies that are unlikely to accrue on smaller operations or holdings.

Of course the flow of wood products from any tract will depend on the condition of the growing stock as well as the size of the holding. Young growing stock will yield no usable products for some time, and having 5,000 acres rather than 50 acres cannot change this fact.

LARGE HOLDINGS

Large privately owned areas of woodland used exclusively for forest production are rare in Worcester County. However, the presence of a few indicate some of the problems and possibilities of developing larger-scale forest enterprises. It would be possible for an owner to assemble 2 or 3 thousand acres of forest land almost anywhere in the County. The following is an analysis of the 2,196 acres in Tract A described in Table 17 that might be selected to form a large forest operating unit.

Tract A

This tract would consist of several holdings, and although these probably would not be contiguous, they would be close enough together to be worked effectively as a single operating unit. Much of the area has been farmed once, and town and old woods roads make it fairly easily accessible. Typically, little work will be needed to complete an excellent network of roads.

The bulk of the growing stock now in the County developed either on abandoned fields or after clear-cuttings, so that the stands are generally even-aged. In this tract, the 831 acres supporting white pine are largely outwash soils favorable to the growth and regeneration of this species. Hardwoods occupy most of the more moist upland till soils. The stands have suffered very little damage from fire and insects and from the 1938 hurricane.

Table 17 shows that this acreage is fairly evenly distributed among the various forest age classes. Although such an even division among young-, middle-, and old-aged stands is exceptional in the County, tracts can be selected which approximate this distribution. Given such a "normal distribution of age classes," about the same amount of cutting will be possible every year in the future, and with a little care, this relatively even flow of production can be maintained, that is, if the stands regenerate successfully and there is no widespread damage due to fire, insects, disease, or wind. Barring these catastrophic losses, it is estimated that the average inputs, outputs, and stumpage returns likely to result from any specific management program will not vary much from year to year.

TABLE 17

Acreages of Growing Stock by Age Classes and Forest Cover Types in Tract A

Forest cover type	*0–20*	*21–40*	*41–60*	*61–80*	*Total*
White pine	210	190	200	231	831
Mixed hardwoods with some pine	375	340	350	300	1365
Total	585	530	550	531	2196

If the owner wants to create a forest enterprise that will provide him with full-time work, a satisfactory income, and at the same time build up values that will accrue later, several factors outside the operating unit will have to be considered. First, there are relatively good market outlets in the area for all kinds of softwood logs and for most of the better grades of hardwood sawlogs. Both hardwood and softwood pulpwood markets have developed recently, and a limited amount of hardwood can be sold locally for fuel each year. Also there are a number of sawlog stumpage buyers and sawmill operators in the area. Some difficulty might arise from the fact that there are practically no part-time woods workers available. However, if full-time work were offered, a woods crew of three to five men probably could be assembled from the resident population. A certain amount of training would undoubtedly be needed to bring these workers to a high degree of efficiency.

As a first step toward initialing a detailed plan of management for this forest enterprise, the owner would need to decide upon the general intensity of forest management to use. He would need to know what level of production he could expect from using relatively little labor and management over the years and how much greater output he might expect from using more inputs over time. The three alternative intensities of forest management previously suggested can be analyzed for this tract to illustrate the range of possibilities.

Table 18 shows the probable results of each of these alternative programs of management on this tract. The stumpage returns represent minimum values that would be available for the payment of taxes, interest, and returns to the owner. The owner could earn an additional sum for the amount of productive work that he was able to do in the woods. The amount might be considerable, especially if he acted as the working foreman of the whole operation.

TABLE 18

Average Annual Input of Woods Labor and the Volume and Stumpage Value of the Output of Forest Products from Three Intensities of Forest Management on Tract A

Intensity of forest management	*Input of labor (man-months)*	*Output of forest products*	*Stumpage returns**
High	65	500 M.b.f.	$3,000
		400 cords	800
			$3,800
Medium	35	400 M.b.f.	$2,400
Low	25	330 M.b.f.	$1,980

* Long-run stumpage values of $6 per M.b.f. of sawlogs and $2 per cord of fuelwood or pulpwood were assumed. Current sawlog prices would average about $15 per M.b.f. but pulpwood and fuelwood prices would be very little more than those above.

Low Intensity of Forest Management—This program could be carried out by making ordinary stumpage sales to local mill owners or woods operators. Or the owner could hire a helper, get the necessary equipment, and do the woods operating himself, and sell the logs at the roadside or delivered to a mill. Harvesting could also be concentrated in larger periodic cuts rather than spread out evenly over the years. The average annual figures, however, would be about the same under any of these procedures.

It is likely that this kind of management will eventually degrade the growing stock and lead to lower returns, especially if low-grade hardwoods are difficult to market and bring a low price. However, if the owner sells stumpage and doesn't keep a crew, he can carry out this program with very little effort. It will be necessary only to arrange stumpage sales and supervise the cuttings enough to ensure prompt payment for the products cut.

Medium Intensity of Forest Management—Stumpage sales of marked timber could be made to carry out this program, or the owner and two helpers could do all of the work. Alternatively, the owner could use marked stumpage sales and do most of the weeding and marking himself; he would still have some of his time left over for other work. If a woods crew is maintained, however, this program of operation will take up all of the owner's time.

The quality and growth-rate of the growing stock is likely to be maintained or increased by this kind of management. Over time, some increase in stumpage values can be anticipated for the better trees left in partial cuttings. The increased value of the growing stock should be reflected in the value of the property within a few decades. In addition, a better road net will be maintained over the property by the more frequent operations. This will add to land values and will tend to reduce fire risks and make the salvage of wind or insect-damaged trees easier.

High Intensity of Forest Management—It is unlikely that the intermediate cuttings planned under this program will attract a stumpage buyer. Therefore, in addition to working in the woods most of the time himself, the owner will have to maintain a crew for these cultural operations. If he does all the woods work with his own crew, he will need about four men and the necessary equipment.

This plan will produce more high-quality sawlogs than either of the other programs, and in addition there will be a considerable volume of pulpwood and fuelwood from thinnings and improvement cuttings. Over the years there will be a marked improvement in the quality of the growing stock, which will lead to a substantial quality premium for any logs sold, and will also increase the value of the property. The advantages of a better road net will also be realized.

Tract B

This is a large tract like A, but it is more nearly typical of such tracts in Worcester County because it has an uneven distribution of age classes.

Table 19 shows the age and composition of this tract. Only about 3 percent of this 1,863-acre area supports mature sawtimber; the rest is divided among stands of seedling and pole-sized trees.

TABLE 19

Acreages of Present Forest Cover and Size Classes, Tract B

Forest cover	Restocking and seedling	Pole-timber	Sawtimber	Total
Hardwood	539	649	0	1,188
Softwood	366	260	49	675
Total	905	909	49	1,863

Market and labor conditions are much the same in this area as in the Tract A area. However, the drastically different growing stock has a large effect on the timing and size of returns. The analysis in Table 20 shows the way cash income will accumulate by decades over the next ninety years. Taxes and interest on operating deficits have not been included as an expense. Two sets of roadside prices were used to estimate future returns. The upper section of the table shows returns based on the assumption that roadside prices of $18 to $21 per thousand board feet of sawlogs and $9 per cord of rough fuelwood or pulpwood remain unchanged throughout the planning period. Labor at $6 per day throughout is also assumed. The lower section of the table is based on the assumption that sawlog prices will remain at the $18–$21 level for the first thirty years, then rise to $24–$27 for the next thirty years, and then to $30–$34 in the last thirty years. A $6 wage rate is assumed as fixed throughout the period, however, together with $9 fuelwood and cordwood prices.

Table 20 shows that even on stands with this uneven age distribution the lowest net returns will be made by using a low intensity of forest management. Moreover, stumpage returns will fluctuate more from year to year under this plan than under the others. In addition, the increase in the value of the growing stock will be only about a tenth or less of the values built up by the alternative programs. But the differences in total returns are not large if constant prices are assumed over the ninety years.

The returns from medium management show clearly that some income is postponed for the sake of later returns. Some time is required, in this instance about three decades, before the cumulative returns of medium- exceed those of low-intensity management. A good deal of time is needed

TABLE 20

Average Annual Forest Enterprise Income (hundreds of dollars) During Each Decade of a Ninety-Year Planning Period*

	Intensity of forest management used		
Decades in future	*Low*	*Medium*	*High*
	Assuming constant prices		
1	5	**	−16
2	2	3	−7
3	31	18	22
4	8	39	54
5	132	95	119
6	**	36	101
7	62	48	−7
8	67	92	69
9	46	31	71
Total income for 90 years	3,530	3,620	4,060
Increase in stand values	30	296	553
Total return	3,560	3,916	4,613
	Assuming rising prices		
1	5	**	−16
2	2	3	−7
3	31	18	22
4	12	58	87
5	204	144	185
6	**	55	158
7	117	90	50
8	131	175	186
9	89	73	157
Total income for 90 years	5,910	6,160	8,220
Increase in stand values	91	890	1,519
Total return	6,001	7,050	9,739

* Income measured by roadside value of products less operating costs. Taxes and interest on deficits not included as operating expenses.
** Less than $100.

to build up the productivity of a forest enterprise that includes so much young growing stock.

A high intensity of management will require a considerable investment in the form of weedings and early improvement cuttings that yield little or no immediate return. However, this early investment, and more frequent cultural operations later, will increase forest production more rapidly than medium management. After about five decades, cumulative returns will exceed those of the other management programs.

With the rising sawlog prices assumed in the lower section of the table, the higher intensities of management will yield relatively much greater returns in the long run. This results from a greater emphasis on the production of high-grade materials under medium and high forest-management intensity. The necessity for postponing income, or actually making an added cash investment for several years in order to adopt a program of medium or high forest-management intensity, will weigh heavily with any owner who must make this management decision.

Joint Management

The analysis of Tract B has assumed that all of the 1,863 acres are under one ownership. Actually the land is divided about evenly among three separate owners. The three owners have different objectives and command widely different capital, labor, and managerial resources. One is a businessman and another is a professional man. Both are well past middle age and keep their lands for summer home, recreation, and sentimental reasons. Although each could hire the labor and management help and buy any equipment needed to operate his woods with the highest degree of management intensity analyzed, neither one wants to make the long-term investment that seems necessary. Neither one alone has enough land to keep a permanent crew busy — and cooperative management would require a long-term commitment to a specific forest production program. Some agreement would be needed to share not only the early investment costs but also the future returns that would be generated.

Such an agreement is unlikely, especially in view of the fact that the third property needed to round out a forest operation based on an intensive management program is owned by a farmer who works very hard to get even a modest income from his small acreage of arable land. This man has practically no surplus money, labor, or managerial ability to invest for long-deferred returns.

Of course, any one of these men could practice medium or low intensity of management on his own property. Stumpage sales could be larger and attract better bids, and the district forester could help more effectively with any necessary marking, however, if they pooled their operations.

These owners have temporarily decided to adopt a program of medium management intensity, more or less independently of one another. Most of the harvest cutting during the next ten years is on one ownership, and the first partial cutting has just been completed by making a sale of marked stumpage. No sales of any consequence that could benefit from cooperative action will be needed for another decade. At that time the situation can be reviewed again.

This situation illustrates some of the problems that would be encountered in building up a forest enterprise large enough to enjoy some of the economies of scale. If a cooperative effort is made, the people must have ownership objectives and resources that are compatible with the kind of management proposed. If it is possible to assemble properties with a relatively even distribution of age classes, the even flow of income and cutting makes the whole enterprise easier to operate and widens the choice among feasible management programs.

Several methods could be used to bring together separate forest ownerships for management purposes. Some agency such as the soil conservation district could take the lead in organizing cooperatives that might jointly maintain the marketing and management services needed, including not only technicians but also woods crews and equipment.

Long-term leases of timberland to a company for use under some agreed management program would also have advantages for both parties.[3] The owner could realize a steady income from rents and would not be burdened with the management of his land. At the same time, he could preserve most of the intangible values of forest ownership. The lessee could assemble land enough for an efficient forest enterprise without the expense of land purchase. Possible leasing agreements are flexible enough to cover most of the conceivable conditions found in the County. The possibilities of such leasing certainly deserve more study and trial.

Most forest landowners in Worcester County are practicing at least a low intensity of forest management. Some of them, however, believe that present clear-cutting and high-grading methods are incompatible with the residential or recreational values of their land and therefore do no cutting. But most of these properties eventually change hands and frequently the timber is then clear-cut and high-graded and sold. Of course, many use low-management intensity because they know of no other course to follow. They simply hold their timber until a buyer discovers it and makes an offer

[3] John R. McGuire, U.S. Forest Service, Northeastern Forest Experiment Station, Upper Darby, Pa., "Leasing Forest Land" (unpublished).

that seems fair to them. Because the owner frequently knows little about the value of the timber he has to sell, he may realize only a fraction of the real market value of his trees.

Analyses of actual operating units in the County indicate that most farmer, part-time farmer, and residential farmer landowners have the time necessary to practice at least a medium intensity of forest management rather than the low intensity commonly used. With this group of owners, such an adjustment would be compatible with intangible ownership values and at the same time would increase the long-run productivity of their forest land. For many owners with woodland mostly of young growing stock, no action will be required for many years, except to pay taxes on their properties, make more use of the public forester's advice and time, and do a modest amount of improvement work in young stands. Those with large enough resources can purchase the necessary help from consulting foresters.

This leaves the owners who lack the time and resources for forest management, especially those with very small holdings, with very little alternative but that of using a low intensity of forest management. Some change through cooperative action, private or public ownership, leasing or the like, is needed to combine these forest lands with the necessary labor, capital, and management ability for more valuable and effective forest production. New operating units and special arrangements need to be analyzed and tested to explore the problems and possibilities of increasing the number of alternative forest management programs feasible for these private owners to follow.

CHAPTER 11

Planning One Town — Hardwick

As explained in Chapter 1, ten of the sixty towns in Worcester County have been analyzed in more detail than the others, and two of the ten, namely, Petersham and Hardwick, in the most detail of all.[1] Also as already explained, the analysis of Petersham has been published in *Planning One Town — Petersham, a Hill Town in Massachusetts*. Petersham was selected for such analysis partly because of its highly varied pattern of land use with only about a third of it left in farms, thus making it a good subject for a research seminar group drawn from agricultural and forestry economics, political science, and regional planning. Hardwick was chosen largely because it adjoins Petersham on the south and yet has retained much more of its agriculture. The 1950 Census reported 66 percent of Hardwick as still in farms, as compared with 38 percent for the County. As to the number of farms, nearly as many were reported for Petersham as for Hardwick, 60 as compared with 76, but Hardwick's farms averaged 42 acres of cropland as compared with 18 acres for Petersham. Much less of Hardwick's farming is residential and part time.

For the purpose of this study, what is most important to note in this chapter is the degree of detail to which the land-use planning is carried when the effort is concentrated on a small area like a town. This should be

[1] The work on this project in Hardwick has at all times had the full cooperation of Mr. Ernest Ritter who for the past thirty-seven years has worked as an agricultural extension agent in this Town, supported by the Calvin Page Agricultural Fund created in 1914. The income from this fund has been increasingly inadequate over the years, but the Cooperative Farmers' Exchange which he helped organize and which operates from the same offices has expanded to the point where it now employs two regular helpers. Mr. Ritter has maintained over the years a close personal contact with all the farm families in the Town.

contrasted with the detail possible in the eight towns, and that in the remaining fifty. No doubt there are circumstances to which each of these three degrees of detail is best fitted. Or what is more likely, they may represent stages through which land-use planning may need to pass under actual working conditions. Whether, or in what circumstances, land-use planning needs to be, or is best carried to the detail outlined already for Petersham, and here outlined for Hardwick, is, however, a large question upon which a careful reading of this chapter will throw much light.

THE TOWN

First, a few general summary facts about Hardwick Town. Topographically, Hardwick lies toward the western edge of the Worcester County plateau described earlier. Some of it at the northwest is now covered by the Quabbin Reservoir and a larger adjoining area by the Reservoir Reservation. The rest of it is within the watershed of the Ware River which forms its southeastern boundary. The Ware River is in the watershed of the Chicopee River, which joins the Connecticut River at Springfield. Five separate brooks flowing southward in the town form well-defined tributary valleys of the Ware. The upland elevations of 800 to 1,100 feet drop rather sharply one to two hundred feet into these valleys and to around 500 to 600 feet in the Ware Valley and Muddy Brook Valley. The land surface is therefore mostly rather hilly, and much of it stony or sandy. The soil types are primarily Gloucester, except for a narrow band of Merrimac and Hinckley along the Ware River. Most of the cropland is in the eastern part.

The original forest was mostly coniferous in the western sandy areas, with scatterings of pine and hemlock mixed with oaks, chestnut, maple, birch, beech, and hickory elsewhere. White pine had come in on many of the old fields from 1850 on and much of it had been logged. What was left, and the stands that had followed after logging and other cutting in the western sector and elsewhere were largely blown down in the hurricane of 1938.

The principal facts about the agriculture of the town of Hardwick as compared with that of the other towns are presented in the figures in earlier chapters. For convenience, they may be briefly summarized here as follows: First of all, it appears that Hardwick is on the northern edge of the group of towns in the west and southwest part of the County which have the most agriculture of the towns in the County, and whose agriculture is most nearly holding its own, and also where the farming is predominantly dairying. In terms of percentage of all land that is in cropland, Hardwick's 24 percent in Figure 13 of Chapter 6 is exceeded only by New Braintree, two of the Brookfields, Spencer, and Dudley in this part of the County, and Sterling, Berlin, and Westboro in the eastern part. The number of farms reported in 1950, shown in Figure 14, is in about the same relation to total land area as in the other towns to the south of it if allowance is made for the tract in the northern corner transferred to the Quabbin Reservoir and Reservation. There were, however, only 13 farms in this tract in 1938. Most of these towns, like Hardwick, reported around a half as many farms in 1950 as in 1925, New Braintree, Dudley, and Berlin being the exceptions. Figure 15 shows only one town, New Braintree, with more milk cows than the 1,200 reported for Hardwick. The ones nearest to Hardwick in number of cows are all in this same southwest part of the County except Sterling and Sutton, and Barre adjoining Hardwick in the northeast. There were, however, only four towns that reported selling more eggs than Hardwick in 1950, namely, Westminster, Hubbardston, Spencer, and Westboro, but the sale of chickens is partly a sideline of egg production in Hardwick. As for the orchards, Hardwick reported less than a tenth as many bearing fruit trees as five other towns.

How the land reported in farms in Hardwick was divided into land-use classes in 1950 is indicated in acres for the Town, and as an average per farm, in Table 21, the plowable pasture part of the open pasture being counted both in cropland and in open pasture.

The average farm size of 221 acres reported for Hardwick was the

TABLE 21

Distribution of Land in Farms in Hardwick among Different Uses, Total Acres, and Average Acres per Farm

Uses	*Town*	*Per farm*
Total land in farms	16,806	221
Cropland	6,096	80
Harvested	3,185	41
Plowable pasture	1,046	14
Other	1,865	24
Open pasture	3,653	48
Plowable	1,046	14
Other	2,607	34
Woodland pasture	3,282	43
Woodland	4,144	55
Other land	677	9

largest reported for any town in the County in 1950, the nearest to this being 169 for West Brookfield and 165 for Warren. This 221 was a jump from 148 acres in 1945. This resulted from a decrease of a fourth in the number of farms reported, with land in farms at the same time increasing nearly a tenth. The more thorough enumeration in 1950 must have offset the weeding out of a considerable number of small places by bringing in a number of places with a large acreage of woodland per farm. The average woodland reported rose from 49 to 98 acres per farm. But the cropland reported also increased from 3,500 to 6,100 acres, or by 45 acres per farm. It would appear that a good part of this came from classifying more open pasture as plowable in 1950 than in 1945.

Of the cropland harvested in 1949, all but 15 percent was hay. A total of 28 farms grew 236 acres of corn. No oats or other grain was threshed. The hay was two-thirds clover and/or timothy. Seventeen farmers grew 268 acres of alfalfa, or one tenth of the total hay. Poor "june grass" stands made up most of the rest.

Of the 76 farms, 64 reported 1,200 cows, plus 500 heifers born before January 1, 1950, plus 95 born afterwards. They thus averaged total dairy herds of 27, of which 19 were cows or heifers of milking age. All the milk reported sold, 4,950,000 pounds, was sold as fluid milk.

Of the 76 farms, 30 sold an average of 3,280 dozen eggs and 1,200 chickens per farm in 1949.

Finally, 28 of the farms had an average of an acre of land in orchard.

HISTORICAL BACKGROUND

The discussion in the preceding section is mostly confined to Hardwick Town as it now is. More information is needed as to how this bit of the economy of southern New England got to be the way it is. The general outline for this is of course presented in earlier chapters. But special circumstances of geography and history are likely to affect the course of development of particular areas.

The settlement of the Hardwick area began in 1729, which was 43 years after a group of eight Roxbury men had bought it and some surrounding territory from three Nipmuck Indians for twenty pounds. Hardwick Town was incorporated in 1739. The population had increased to 1,400 by the time of the Revolution, declined a little in the hard years from 1790 to 1810, then risen to 1,900 by 1830. Shortly thereafter came the period of agricultural decline for all of southern New England with the number of farm workers falling off nearly a half by 1880, most of this coming in the first thirty years.

The assessors had reported 200 farms in 1781, and 172 in 1832. From then until 1870, the number fell off to 120. The younger farmers and the farmers' sons either migrated westward or northward or took jobs in the growing industrial cities. The general reversion of farm land to brush and trees probably did not begin until after 1840. Up to that time, the clearing of new land had about offset the abandonment of old fields and pastures. By 1870, the acreage reported as "improved" by the federal census had fallen off by a fourth; by 1925, by another 30 percent.

The agriculture of the early years had been almost wholly self-sufficing. All the farms had at least a few cattle for meat, milk, butter, and cheese; also a few swine and even sheep for wool. With the completion in 1800 of the South Massachusetts Turnpike northward through the center of the Town, some of the farms began to specialize in butter and cheese for the Boston and New York markets. The industrialization after 1850 also provided a local market for meat, milk, eggs and poultry, and fruit. The railroad widened the market still further, particularly as it stimulated the growth of industry in railway cities like Worcester and Springfield. The agriculture thus became more and more commercial. In 1900, the assessor reported only 130 swine and 70 sheep, with the number of cows at an all-time peak of around 1,500. Some of these cattle, however, were still of beef types. The decline in cattle numbers after 1900 was mostly on farms with less than 6 cows. By 1937, nearly half the farms had 20 or more cows.

The first industry of towns like Hardwick was also of a local self-sufficing type. It processed locally produced farm or woodland products for local use, or produced tools and equipment for local use. In 1840, Hardwick Town had 5 sawmills, 4 gristmills, 2 tanneries, 1 distillery, 1 plant for making paper, 1 for making carriages and wagons, 5 shops for making leather goods, 1 for hats and caps, and of course some blacksmith shops. In the decade following, several types of small woodworking plants appeared — producing finished lumber, furniture, barrels and pails, boxes, wheels, and the like. All of these were small, part of them carried on along with farming.

The real industrialization of Hardwick, however, came after 1850, and was based largely on shipped-in materials. In 1840, all but 15 percent, or 78, of the workers of the Town were engaged in agriculture; by 1919, only 18 percent of them were. By 1865, there were 831 industrial workers in the Town; by 1915, the count was 1,279. The map in Figure 29 shown later in this chapter indicates the location and dimensions of the four village or urban centers of the Town. Industrially, Gilbertsville, almost an appendage of the Town, and Wheelwright, on the Ware River, have played by far the largest roles. Most of the 1,279 industrial workers of 1915 were employed in the woolen mills of the George H. Gilbert Manufacturing Company, which had been incorporated in 1867 and was in full operation by 1870, the year that the Ware River Railroad from Palmer northward through Hardwick began operating. The paper mill at Wheelwright at one time employed nearly a hundred workers. The mill hands were mostly immigrants. The first wave of these was a large group from Ireland shortly after 1850. The Irish kept coming until about 1885. The next wave was of French Canadians around 1865. Then came the Poles, who by 1915 made up nearly half of the foreign-born population of the town. By then 43 percent of Hardwick's population was foreign-born.

Although the first employment of these immigrants was almost entirely in the mills, they soon began to replace native American stock on the farms. Professor Carle Zimmerman in his study of Hardwick as an industrial town compared the assessors' lists in 1832 and 1937. None of the names of farmers were "foreign-sounding" in 1832, whereas over a third of them were in the latter years.[2]

The history of Hardwick as a political and economic unit has since 1870 largely been in terms of the fortunes of the industries of Gilbertsville and Wheelwright on its southern border. The woolen mill began retrenching in 1928 and shut down entirely in 1932. The big Depression of 1929–1936 was the immediate cause of this, but no doubt competition with other regions was an important factor in it. At any rate, the situation called for vigorous entrepreneurship, and the following generation of Gilberts did not provide this.

One of the serious consequences of the decline of Hardwick's industries has been the loss of tax revenue. In 1867, the woolen and paper mills of the Town were assessed at 10 percent of the total valuation; in 1920, at 60 percent of it. Moreover, the political control of the Town was taken over by the industrial population in the Depression. The tax burden on agriculture therefore increased greatly. The tax rate rose from $25 to $49 per $1,000 from 1930 to 1935.

But although the industries of Hardwick may have imposed a tax burden on its agriculture in the 1930's, without them the agriculture would have declined much more than it did from 1850 on, and in the present would be much more like that of Petersham than it is.

The peak years in census-reported population for Hardwick were 1910

[2] *The Changing Community,* New York, Harper and Brothers, 1938. Hardwick is called Hamlet in this analysis.

and 1915, with close to 3,600. The decline following was to 2,154 in 1940, followed by a rise to 2,271 in 1954. Gilbertsville has shared somewhat in the general industrial recovery of the postwar years. Smaller enterprises are now using space in the principal factory buildings. The leading products are now plastics, clothing, and foundry and machine shop products. The factory at Wheelwright that was producing paper products before the depression is now under new management and prospering. The tax rate has risen only to $56, but part of the reason for this is that no large new expenditures, such as for school buildings, have been undertaken.

POPULATION OUTLOOK

Land-use planning is related to the human factor in two ways. In the first place, people, not land, must be served by such planning. In the second place, the farm operator and his family are major elements in land-use adjustments. Too frequently, recommendations are made that seem to assume that the farm family is a constant factor in the situation, unaffecting and unaffected by other changes. A good land-use plan considers the operator and his family as active participants in the program. It is in this connection that the population outlook of Hardwick is extremely important.

Before planning for this area, several questions must be answered. Is the birth rate sufficiently high to maintain the existing farm population? Are the children of Hardwick families planning to remain on the farm and are they preparing themselves for that end? What has been the effect of the gradual displacement of many native-born farmers by foreign-born farm operators? While it is difficult to give well-founded answers to these questions, the information assembled in Hardwick by Professor Walter McKain in 1938 throws some light on the situation.

The population of Hardwick has been even more unstable than one would expect from the great changes outlined in the foregoing. There were considerable out-migrations to Bennington and Barnard, Vermont, as early as 1762 and 1775. But in these early years new families were born or came in to take their places. Between 1800 and 1810, the tax lists added 29 new names; between 1850 and 1870, 91 new names; and between 1910 and 1930, 105. Of the 167 names on the tax lists in 1800, only 30 remained in 1930; and only 12 of the 30 households represented were those of farmers.

Combined with the in- and out-migrations to produce population shifts were changes in birth rates and death rates. The out-migrants were usually younger people in their child-bearing years. This tends to lower birth rates of the population group left behind. The in-migrants were likewise younger and of foreign stock besides — first generation Americans usually have larger-than-average families. This has tended to offset the first effect over the years, but not recently. A study of the families of Gilbertsville in 1934 after the closing of the mills showed only 251 children under five years per 1,000 women of child-bearing age, and only 268 for the 105 farm families of that year. The older families left on farms after a period of out-migration have few sons and daughters at home. With prevailing death rates, at least 360 children under five years of age were needed to maintain a constant population.

McKain's survey also showed that nearly one fourth of the *commercial* farmers included in the survey did not have children living at home, and twelve of the families were childless. This meant that over 20 percent of the farms would not remain in the immediate family of the present operators when they retired. Table 22 presents these and other data for the 29 foreign-born and 33 native-born separately and combined. The predictions as to whether the farm will be operated by children of the family were made by a local extension agent working closely with these families.

TABLE 22

Family Stage, and Prospect that Farm Will Be Operated by Children, by Nativity: Hardwick, 1938

	Number of families	*Stage of family**					*Will farm be operated by children?***		
		Br.	*A*	*B*	*C*	*D*	*Yes*	*No*	*Doubtful*
Foreign-born.......	29	3	0	33	3	20	11	15	3
Native-born.......	33	4	2	7	11	9	7	17	9
Total.........	62	7	2	10	14	29	18	32	12

* Stage of family: Br. — Broken family (single, widowed, etc.),
A — No children at home, husband under 31,
B — No children at home, husband over 30,
C — Eldest child under 16,
D — Eldest child over 16.

** Of the 15 foreign-born in the "no" column, 3 had no children at home; and of the 17 native-born, 12 had no children at home.

The twelve families marked "doubtful" had young children whose agricultural interests would be hard to predict. If it were assumed that the children of six of these families would not remain on the farm, a total of thirty-seven farms would not be worked by the children of the present operators.

Perhaps, however, a few of the children now living off the farm would take up farming if they inherited the farm property. Even when this factor was considered, over half of the commercial farms would either be abandoned or transferred to other families in the next generation.

The flow of foreign-born into Hardwick had about ceased in 1935. This was reflected in the ages of the foreign-born operators. None was under 40 years of age and the mean age was 55. The average age of the native-born farmers was 50, and nine were under 40 years of age. This selective factor was also revealed in the analysis of the family stages of the respective groups. Whereas twenty of the foreign-born families had children over 15 living at home, only nine of the native-born families were in the same stage. Thirteen of the native-born families, on the other hand, were either in the young married stage or had children under 16 living at home. Only three of the foreign-born families were classified in this group. The extension agent believed that the children of twelve of the foreign-born families would not remain on the farm, and was uncertain about three of the families. If he was right, the children of foreign-born parents in Hardwick were not any more disposed toward farming than the children of native-born parents.

The foregoing analysis indicated that there would be a change in the farm population of Hardwick during the years just ahead. Either there would be a period of farm abandonment in the area, or there would be an increasing number of new owners. If the farms were kept in operation, fully one half of the new owners would not be members of the present operator's family. This would be of importance in the formulation of a land-use planning program for the town.

These expectations, as will appear in detail later, were fully realized. Of the 34 full-scale farms analyzed in 1937–38, only 22 were in full operation in 1945. Six of the 34 had been absorbed in other farms. Eight of the 34 had become residential farms, with all but a few acres of the crop and pasture land rented out. Two thirds of the full-scale farm operators had "foreign-sounding" names. About 15 of the 22 farms had changed owners or were now being rented.

In addition to the 64 commercial farms, 76 residential farms and 20 part-time farms were included in the 1938 Hardwick survey.[3] The three groups taken together made up the total farm population. The average age of the part-time farmers was 56 years, and of the residential farmers, 54 years, compared with 53 for the commercial farmers. Whereas nearly half of the commercial farmers were foreign-born, only a fifth of these other two groups were. Also, 50 percent of the part-time farmers and 36 percent of the residential farmers had no children living at home, compared with 24 percent

[3] Counting 13 on land now absorbed in the Quabbin Reservoir and Reservation.

for the commercial farmers. A large fraction of the part-time and residential farmers were apparently retired or partly retired. It should be evident that fully as large a proportion of these as of the commercial farms would be abandoned or in the hands of new owners. It was even possible that such farming represented a later stage in a cycle — when the present commercial farmers retired, their farms might not be operated and soon would be classed as residential. Since in many cases their children were not interested in farming, in time the farms might be completely abandoned or sold to newcomers.

LIVING CONDITIONS

Our concern with living conditions in this chapter is with how they vary in different parts of the Town. We have already seen in Chapter 5 that Hardwick's plane of living index as measured by Hagood was 150 in 1945 as compared with the County average of 155, and 134 to 148 in the towns adjoining it, and 159 in North Brookfield, one town removed. In 1938, the more refined index devised by McKain and Norcross and applied to the eight towns as described in Chapter 5 was worked out for each of the farm families in Hardwick. As one would expect, those who lived in or on the edges of the village of Hardwick had the highest indexes — 79 percent of them had electricity, 70 percent running water in their houses, and 50 percent radios and automobiles. Of those living in the part of the Town later on in the chapter classified as unsuited for agriculture, only 15 percent had electricity and 45 percent running water. These families also lived on the poorer roads.

Since this survey in 1938, however, there has been much progress along these lines. All of the thirty-two families visited in 1954 had electricity and telephone service, a radio, an automobile, and running water in their homes, except for two without phone service and one without an automobile. In addition, twenty of them had freezers and sixteen had television.

MARKETS AND PRICES

Prices and marketing of Hardwick milk have been particularly sensitive to the market forces described in Chapter 7 because of Hardwick's location about midway between Worcester and Springfield. Before 1910, most of the milk produced in Hardwick was shipped directly to Boston over the B. & A. railroad. The Saunders Act of 1910 caused Boston dealers to buy more of their milk in Vermont and New Hampshire, and the Hood Milk Company diverted its Hardwick supply to the Springfield market. By 1935, however, the growth of its industries had increased Worcester's needs, and with improved milk trucking to help, about 45 percent of the Hardwick supply was again being sold in Worcester. The Hood Company was buying about all of the Springfield shipments, but five smaller dealers were buying most of that going to Worcester. As pointed out in Chapter 7, the period from 1935 to World War II was one of highly unsettled milk markets in this area, with the percentage of Class II milk in the Springfield market reaching 31 in 1938. The producers selling to Hood's were all members of the New England Milk Producers' Association and selling under a base-rating plan. The Springfield market had to meet competition from Vermont, Connecticut, and New York.

Also as explained in Chapter 7, both the Springfield and the Worcester markets are now operating under federal milk orders, jointly administered with the Boston and Lawrence-Lowell markets, and this has introduced more regularity and stability into the marketing and pricing of the milk. About all the milk produced in Hardwick, except that which is retailed locally, goes to a group of small dealers in Worcester. The formulas under which Class I and Class II milk are priced are the same as for the Boston market except for very minor adaptations. The percentage of Class II milk entering into the Worcester market blended price ranges from around 30 in May-June to 10 percent or less in November, and averages about 18 percent, as compared with 40–45 percent in the Boston market and 23 percent in the Springfield market. The percentages in the short season can be as low as they are because Class I milk is transferred freely from the Boston milkshed to anticipate any daily or weekly deficits, the larger distributers being the same in all three markets. Included in the Class I surplus of the Worcester and Springfield markets are regular shipments of milk from certain plants in southern Vermont which otherwise could be in the Boston milkshed. It follows from the foregoing that the Worcester County producers whose milk goes to Worcester, although receiving exactly the same Class I prices, and very nearly the same Class II prices, receive a higher blended price than those in the Boston milkshed. Part of this, at least, is compensation for more even seasonal production.

Back in 1935–1940, the disposal of surplus poultry products presented much less of a problem than was the case for milk. There were only about twenty egg producers in Hardwick who had a year-round surplus over local demand. The Economy Stores of Boston sent a truck through the area which collected about half these eggs and the rest of the local surplus was hauled to Worcester. Broilers were bought by traveling buyers from New

York. With the great expansion of poultry production during and since the war these facilities have been expanded. Also one dealer collects and handles most of the hatching eggs produced in Hardwick.

The marketing of apples has changed greatly over the years. In the 1920's, the approximately 10,000 barrels of apples produced in Hardwick in an average year were hauled in barrels to Worcester, with very little sorting, and shipped in carlots to New York City. Today the few remaining apples are sorted and graded and delivered in boxes mostly for sale in the cities near at hand.

Most of the farmers in Hardwick now buy their feed, fertilizers, sprays, seeds, and small equipment through the cooperative Farmers' Exchange in Hardwick Village, which is operated in conjunction with the extension work of Mr. Ernest Ritter. The patronage refunds over the years since the Exchange was organized have totaled around $160,000. But more important, the combination of the services of providing these supplies with regular extension work has furnished an avenue through which the farmers have been supplied promptly with that which is new in crop varieties, types of fertilizers, feeds, sprays, and the like.

PROCEDURES

At this point the reader needs to know more definitely the procedures followed in assembling the data required for the planning analysis which follows and then in the analysis itself.

First, each family living in the Town but outside a village on a piece of land big enough to have any agricultural production at all, plus any families living in the village but known to be operating farms, were interviewed by means of a short schedule. This schedule was designed partly to supply data needed about each of these units and partly to furnish a basis for selection of a group of farms to be analyzed in detail.

Many of these families merely lived on a piece of land that once was a farm and did no farming whatever. They might rent their crop and pasture land or sell some standing timber now and then. They were not even "residential" farmers in the census classification. Some of them, however, had gardens and fruit trees, and a minor fraction had a cow or two and/or some poultry. In Table 23 are listed the numbers of farms by type that were covered in the short-schedule survey and the number that were covered by the planning analysis.

Second, detailed data were obtained and plans were made for these latter farms such as outlined in Chapters 9 and 10. In general, the basis of

TABLE 23

Numbers and Types of Farms Surveyed and Planned in Hardwick in 1937–1938

Type	Short schedule	Planned in 1937–38
Dairy	53	29
Poultry	4	0
Fruit	3	2
Dairy-poultry	3	2
Dairy-poultry-fruit	1	0
Part-time	20	2
Residence on farms	76	2
	160	37*

* The woodland was mapped and analyzed on five additional residential farms.

selection was to include representatives of all different types of farms in the Town so far as enterprises and combinations were concerned, and enough of each to represent the more important and usual variants of them.

Third, a reconnaisance survey was made of the land and land use of the remaining farms and the woodland not in farms. The 37 farms surveyed in detail contained 5,110 acres of land, divided roughly into 1,300 acres of cropland, 1,370 acres of open pasture, 930 acres of brushy pasture, 940 of wooded pasture, and 570 acres of woodland. This left about 10,400 acres of land covered only by reconnaisance survey, but 4,500 acres of this was in part-time and residential farms and most of the rest in woodland, nearly all in the western part of the Town.

If the detailed surveying were to be repeated today, it would ordinarily be with the aid of aerial photographs and soil maps prepared by an S.C.S. technician. The method used in this study in Hardwick had been developed for use in forest surveying by A. C. Cline, G. H. Forster, and C. R. Lockard at the Harvard Forest for canvassing small woodlots. The boundaries of the farms were mapped out by a two-man crew using a staff, compass, and a steel tape, and the field boundaries and other divisions within the farms by a hand compass and pacing. The scale of the map was 200 feet to an inch. Cross-section paper was used for the base map. As a general base for such mapping, a map showing the network of roads, the farmsteads and buildings, and the natural features was very helpful.

The woodlands within each farm were divided into compartments or stands having fairly uniform species or combinations of species and age and density of stand, and these were classified according to the system explained in Chapter 10. Open pasture and brushland was similarly mapped into compartments. The timber in the different stands was inventoried by actual counting and measuring of the crop trees and other trees in a sample plot in each stand.

The procedure in analyzing these 37 farms was that outlined in Chapter 9 on "Planning a Farm." The planning was *with* the farmer and family rather than *for* them in the largest measure practically possible. The alternative plan chosen by the family was spelled out in written form, together with a map of the farm as then operated and another of the farm as it was to be operated under the plan, and a copy of this was left with the farm family. As will appear later, the family on some of the farms asked to have such a plan outlined because of their interest in the information even though they were unlikely to carry it out. That is, they wanted to see what such a plan would look like, and see its potentials for income, but they were not then really ready to make the required effort and investment to execute it.

These 37 farms were all visited again in 1945, and the amount of progress made was checked against the plan chosen. Also a revised plan was worked out to fit changed circumstances in the family and any new ideas of the family as well as changes outside the farm. In late 1954 and early 1955, those of the farms still in existence were visited again and their progress was again checked, but no revisions were made in the plans.

The tabulation shows the changes that took place in numbers by types of Hardwick farms in this seventeen-year period.

Type of farm	*1937–38*	*1945*	*1954*
Dairy	29	24	18
Dairy-poultry	2	2	2
Poultry	0	1	2
Fruit	3	0	0
Part-time	2	0	1
Residential	1	7	9

Only five of the farms had disappeared altogether. But five others had become only family residences, the crop and pasture land being rented or having been sold to actual farmers. In two other cases, the families had moved away and the pasture land was being rented out as pasture for heifers or dry cows. The two part-time farmers in 1938 had taken full-time employment off the farm by 1945. The three small, largely fruit farms in

1938 were not really being operated, at least independently, by 1945. Finally, it will be observed that two of the dairy farmers had given up dairying and become full-scale poultry farmers, renting the crop and pasture land to other dairy farmers. Also conspicuous in the developments in this period was the emergence of a second large dairy farm, this absorbing all or most of five of the original twenty-nine dairy farms. Also the large dairy farm already operating in 1938 was renting 155 more acres than in 1938. Together these two farms were milking around 180 cows in 1954, with an average production of 9,400 pounds per cow. These two large farms were producing in 1954 nearly a third of all the milk of this group of dairy farms. Table 24 shows the changes in number of cows milked and total milk produced on these farms from 1938 to 1954.

TABLE 24

Changes in Number of Cows Milked and Production per Cow and per Farm on the 29 Dairy Farms Planned in 1937–1938

Year	*Number of farms*	*Number of cows per farm*	*Production per farm*	*Production per cow*
1938	29	20.8	125,200	6,020
1945	24	26.0	182,000	6,500
1954	18	37.0	252,000	6,850

AGRICULTURAL POSSIBILITIES

Figure 29 maps the physical features of Hardwick Town and its villages and roads and then its land use according to six categories as the land was in use in 1937. (The land since put in the Quabbin Reservoir Reservation has been so designated.) It will be noted that only a very small fraction of the land even in the eastern part of the County was cropland or plowable pasture, and that part of the remainder even here was in woodland or swamp, although open pasture was predominant.

The map in Figure 30 classifies the land of Hardwick Town into six groupings according to its suitability for different types of agricultural and associated uses, as indicated. In addition, it designates by abbreviations, where space permits, the principal soil types for the land within each of the blocks thus classified. The soil-type abbreviation, taken directly from the Soil Survey map, are as follows:[4]

[4] See Chapter 3 for description of these soil series and types.

Class 1	Gl	Gloucester loam
	Gf	Gloucester fine sandy loam
	Pl	Paxton loam
	Sl	Sutton loam
Class 2	Ms	Merrimac sandy loam
	Mg	Merrimac gravelly sandy loam

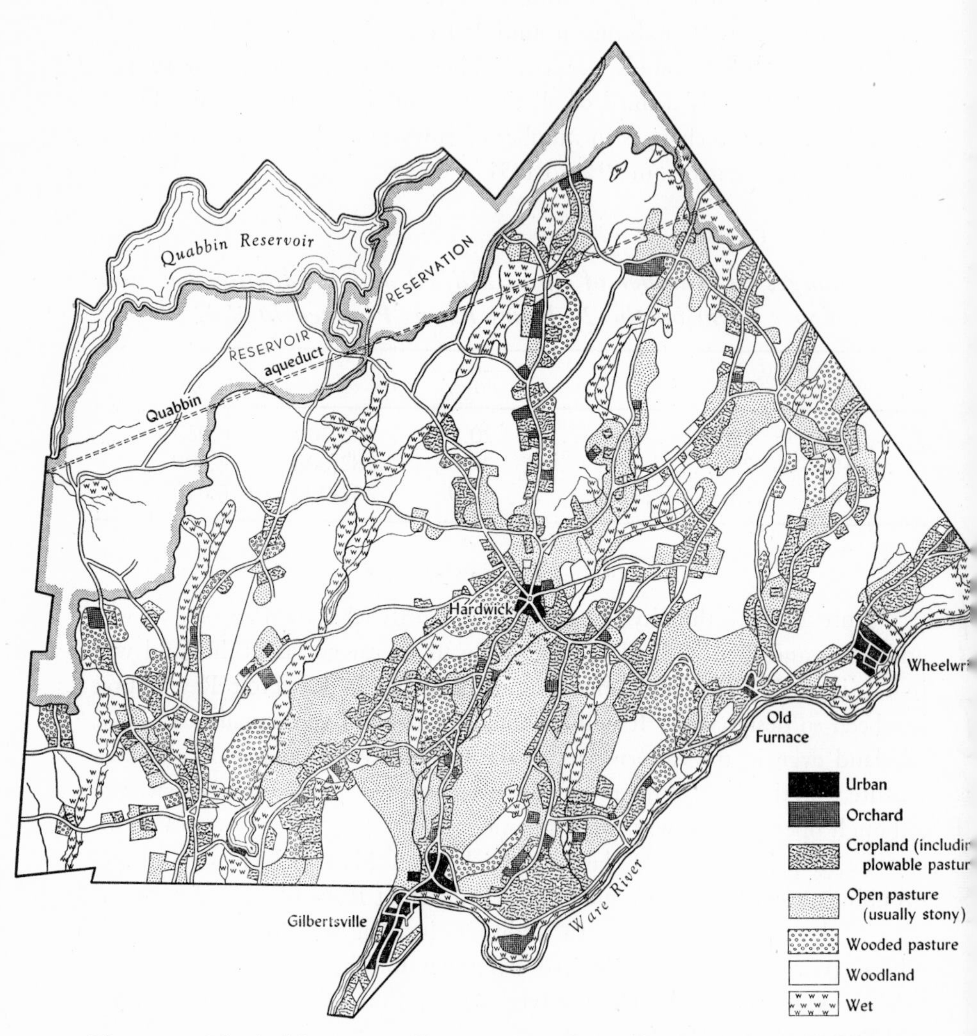

Figure 29. *Physical features, villages and roads, and land use, Hardwick Town, 1937 (based largely on land-use maps of Worcester County prepared by the Massachusetts State Planning Board in 1937).*

Class 3	Gr	Gloucester stony fine sandy loam
	Gt	Gloucester stony loam
Class 4	Hg	Hinckley gravelly sandy loam
	W	Whitman stony loam
Class 5	G	Gloucester stony sandy loam
	R	Rough
Class 6	M	Meadow
Wet	Mu	Muck

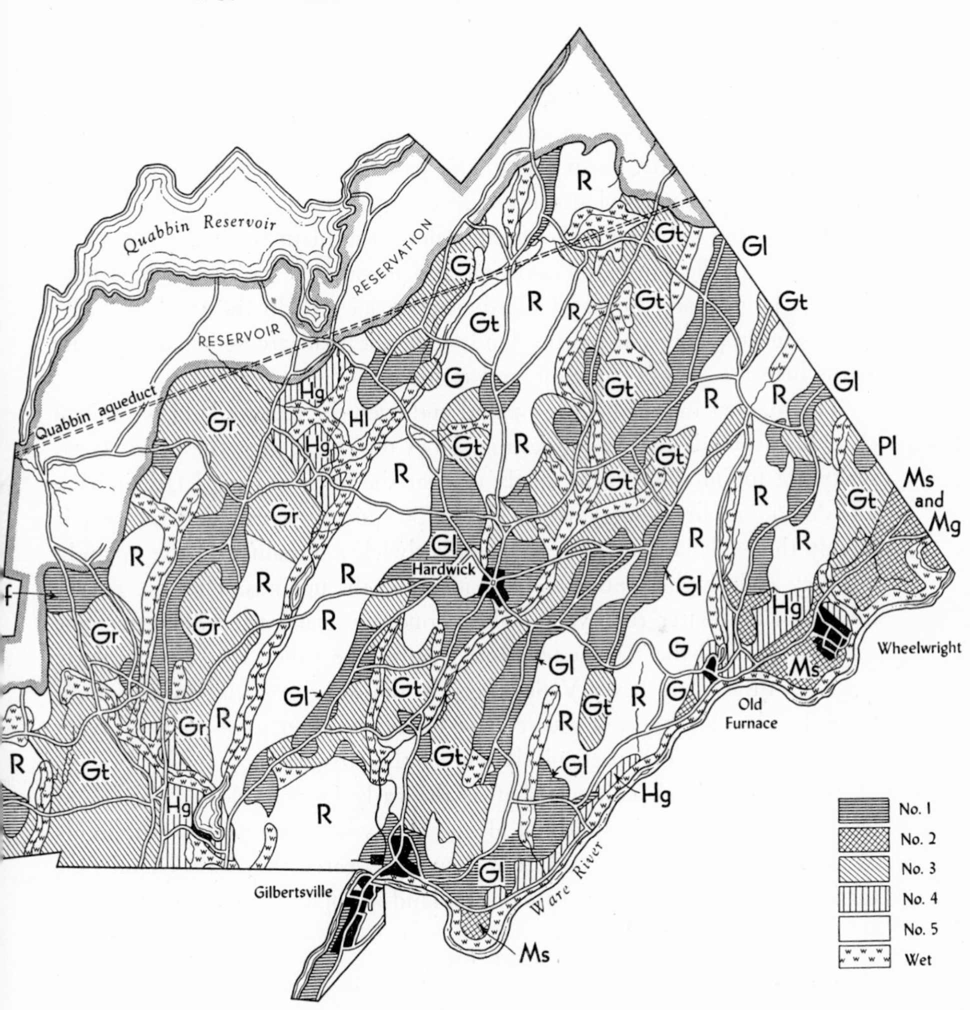

Figure 30. ***Land of Hardwick classified into six classes according to soils and use adaptability.***

This map shows clearly enough the band of Gloucester soils running through the center of the Town from northeast to southwest. These soils have enough loams and fine sandy loams to provide enough cropland to go with the intermingled and adjacent Class 3 stony Gloucester soils available for pasture, to make possible economic dairy farm units. The Merrimac soils adjacent to these in the southeast corner make possible another block of farms in this section.

A comparison of Figure 30 with Figure 29 shows to what extent soil types and land use are fitted to each other. It is true that the agriculture of Hardwick Town is mostly in the parts of the Town where the Class 1 and 2 lands are, but beyond this the correspondence is not too close. The cropland is confined mainly to narrow strips along the road, for the most part immediately adjoining farmsteads. The pasture land is mainly in narrow belts just behind the cropland, although there are some sizable pasture areas in the southern part of the Town and along the main roads leading north from Gilbertsville through Hardwick and toward the northeast. It is here that the larger dairy farms of Hardwick are located. In the southwest, the patches of cropland and pasture land along the road are very narrow. The farms here are mostly part-time and residential.

The manner in which the cropland and even the pasture land is situated close to the roads is very interesting. Does this mean that the better lands really are found close to the roads, or that the farmers have let their back lots deteriorate first? A glance at Figure 30 quickly reveals that the first is largely the explanation. The roads of Hardwick are mainly on the uplands, but they avoid higher points and elevations on the uplands. They are mostly found on the better soil types — the Gloucester loam, the Gloucester fine sandy loam, and the Gloucester sandy loam. The valley roads, particularly the one in the Ware River Valley, keep to the Merrimac soils mainly. Both upland and valley roads, of course, have to cut across strips of poor soil types here and there. This is particularly true of the crossroads.

But another explanation is that as the early farmers cleared their land back from the roads, they did not always stop when they came to the limits of the Class 1 and 2 soils, and once they had cleared the Class 3 land they tended to keep it in open pasture or cropland in rotation with pasture.

DAIRY FARMING

In 1937–38

The group of 29 dairy farms analyzed here are nearly all in the eastern half of the town where Figure 29 shows a preponderance of stony open pasture and very little woodland. The principal facts for the 29 dairy farms planned in 1937–38 were as follows. They averaged besides the 20.8 cows only 6.5 heifers and calves. They were buying an average of 1.7 cows per farm per year. Their average production as already indicated was 6,020 pounds per cow and 125,200 per farm. They were feeding an average of 1,700 of purchased concentrates per cow.

As for the land, these farms averaged 38 acres of land in crops in 1937–38, all of this in hay except for 3.3 acres in corn silage and 0.7 in potatoes. The hay was divided into 18.6 acres of red clover and timothy, 10.8 acres of the same plus alfalfa, 1.8 acres of alfalfa, 3.1 acres of oats and hay, and 1.5 acres of millet for hay.

The pasture land averaged 68.0 acres per farm, plus 8.0 acres of pastured woodland. Of the 68 acres, 28 were classified as brushy, and the rest was mostly simply open stony pasture. Very little was improved pasture. These farms averaged only 12 acres of woodland.

At the 1938 levels of prices and wages, the expenditures of these 30 farms would have averaged $2,025 with "normal" conditions, the receipts $4,565, leaving a net of $2,540. The general price level in that year was more than a half lower than now.

The averages of cows milked, given a few paragraphs back, conceal a wide range. The farms were all essentially family farms, but two of them had less than 10 milk cows, and one of them was milking 50. Twenty-four of them had between 16 and 28 cows. The labor hired averaged only 15 months per farm, but one farm, that of a producer-dealer, had three hired men the year around. The proprietor plus the family labor averaged only 14 months per farm — on five of the farms not classified as part-time and with no family help, the proprietor was working less than full time on his farm. These 29 farms therefore averaged 5 months over two-man farms. This was less than 9 cows per man. The net incomes ranged from $150 to $4,300 per farm.

There were similar differences with respect to management. Two of the farms averaged less than 4,000 pounds of milk per cow, and two over 8,000 pounds. One of the farms had improved every acre of its pasture capable of improvement and another was doing everything close to the other extreme.

The Chosen Plans

Now let us consider the changes that were written into the revised plans on these 29 farms. These were by no means the ones that would have increased the net farm incomes the most; they were instead those which the farmers were in favor of adopting after various other changes were reviewed with them. In general, they were conservative on the score of increasing milk output because most of the farmers at that time were operating under a base-rating plan which meant that all the milk produced over the base would be paid for at Class II or cream prices.[5] It is true that this base could have been raised, but only after a farmer had demonstrated higher output in the base period, and this meant lower blended prices for them for a year at least. The general emphasis in the plans was therefore on reducing purchases of concentrates and forage by producing and feeding more of the latter, as well as improving its quality by getting more protein in it through more alfalfa and ladino; also on raising more calves and heifers as replacements. The average reduction in purchases of concentrates per cow in the plans chosen by the farmers was only 640 pounds, but combined with this was an increase of 420 pounds of milk per cow, an increase in the herd size from 20.8 to 24.2 milk cows per farm, and of heifers and calves from 6.5 to 18.7 per farm. As then operating, six of the farmers were raising no replacements or practically none of them. Under the projected plans, only two would operate on this basis. These were farms with very limited pasture area. On most of the farms, the increased hay and pasture was to be produced ordinarily merely by some combination of the following:

1. Liming and fertilizing present pasture and hay land.

2. Reseeding present pasture with improved mixtures, on some farms including ladino clover.

3. Improving some poor pasture by clearing it of light brush and reseeding and liming and fertilizing. In some cases, enough stones were to be removed in addition so that the land could be worked somewhat with a bog harrow, etc.

4. Replacing old hay fields with new ones with more clover, commonly alfalfa, in a light 30-percent mixture with timothy or other grasses, and sometimes with a high alfalfa mixture.

5. Sowing rye as a winter cover crop and pasturing it in the spring before other pasture was ready, and sowing oats or millet in the spring and

[5] The base rating is an amount of milk for which the producers receive the Class I or fluid-milk price, the base rating having been determined by their individual output in the preceding years' short months, usually September-October-November.

pasturing it in the summer, these providing more nearly all-season pasture feed.

All that was proposed in these plans in the nature of bringing more land into cultivation was some inexpensive drainage of a few acres on three of the farms. The total acreage of cropland would remain about the same. The projected net incomes averaged $425 higher per farm at 1938 prices, with an average of only ten more days of hired labor per farm. The net incomes were to be increased more from a saving of expenditures for replacements and feed than from an increase of receipts.

Farm planning looks forward to more than increasing net farm incomes in the years just ahead. It has the further objective of raising the level of productivity of the land. All of the 29 plans provided for such raises. Much of the pasture land would have a closer cover of grass. The rotations proposed in most cases called for reseeding to grass and clover with oats and no tilled crop in between. In these ways along with a more liberal use of fertilizer, the land was to be made more productive.

These plans could, to be sure, have provided for more conservation than they did. But this would have called for larger expenditures and would have resulted in larger increases in output. The market for milk in the areas did not warrant such an expansion. If conservation programs are to be effective, they must adjust themselves to economic conditions in each period of time. If they do not, they do not achieve higher total use-values of products over time.

The Changes by 1945

The onset of World War II greatly changed the economic situation in Hardwick. The market was ready to take all the milk it could produce. On the other hand, hired labor became scarce and wages rose rapidly. Farm machinery prices rose less rapidly and the higher incomes enabled farmers to buy more machinery. A definite effort was made to make farm machinery available. The use of power equipment to remove brush, stones, and stone fences became a common practice. Also the value of ladino clover in pastures came to be more generally recognized by extension workers and leading farmers.

The first recognition of the impact of these changes came with the replanning done by Francis Schadegg in 1943 as part of the study of "Wartime Farm Production Adjustments in the Northeast" made by the Northeast Office of the Bureau of Agricultural Economics. The seventy farms that Schadegg replanned in Worcester County included five of the Hardwick dairy farms planned in 1938. Four of these had already increased their milking herds by 10 percent. The fifth had reduced its herd from 23 to 7 because of labor difficulties; the land was mostly being rented for pasture. The new plans that Schadegg worked out with the farmers would have increased the sizes of the four milking herds a fourth above those of 1943. For a longer-time goal, the plans called for enlarging two of the farms with 12 and 14 cows in 1943 by acquiring additional land. The long-time plans for all four of these farms called for improving a larger acreage of pasture and adding to the cropland by stone removal.

The 24 dairy farms still operating in 1945, and for which revised plans were made in 1946, were producing a total of 21 percent more milk in 1945 than they were in 1937–38, and 2 percent more than in the plans projected for them in the 1938 plans. They were doing this in part because they had acquired additional land — some of this from inside the group of 29 planned in 1938 and some from outside the group. One farm in particular, as stated earlier, had absorbed five other farms from inside the group. The total area farmed and the total cropland in dairy farms was about the same as 1937–38. The total area of improved land farmed increased 11 percent, mostly as a result of improving grass pasture by fertilization. The total area of improved pasture increased from 19 acres to 194 acres, but the latter amount was only about a third of the amount planned for improvement in 1938. The acreage of hay containing substantial amounts of alfalfa increased from 59 acres to 157, whereas two and one-half times this amount was originally planned. The amount of lime used per acre of improved land approximately doubled during the period. The applications of fertilizer (including manure) were increased by 2 pounds from 57 per acre of cropland for nitrogen (N), 10 pounds from 52 for phosphate (P_2O_5), and 5 pounds from 56 for potash (K_2O).

As already indicated, the 24 dairy farms in operation in 1945 were milking 11 percent more cows than the 29 farms in operation in 1929. In addition, they were rearing 40 percent more calves and heifers. It was in this latter way that they were using part of their increased hay and pasture output.

The increase in mechanization is indicated by the fact that the proportion of the farms using tractors had increased from 21 percent to 87 percent, of those using hayloaders from 12 to 74 percent, and of milking machines from 27 to 78 percent. Labor, on the other hand, had decreased 28 percent as measured in total man-year equivalents.

The major part of the increase in milk output had come about by the purchase of more concentrates, which was precisely the reverse of what had been planned. The average rate of concentrate feeding had risen 40 percent, to 2,500 pounds, and the 11 percent more cows they were milking were yielding 480 more pounds of milk per cow largely because of this.

There was nothing unusual about this development. Almost always when the demand for milk rises suddenly and the price of milk follows in consequence, dairy farmers meet the situation in the easiest and quickest way by increasing the grain in the ration. Unfortunately they tend strongly to continue with this rate of grain feeding after the ratio of milk to feed prices turns the other way. In the course of as few as five years in most areas, however, the dairy farms that have the highest net returns are those that keep their feed bills relatively low by producing a large part of the rations for their cows, as was planned for these farms in 1938.

Plans Chosen in 1946

With such large changes in the market demand for milk and in mechanization and labor supply as had come since 1938, it was apparent that the plans made then might need considerable revision. The farmers were no longer thinking in terms of the restrictions of base ratings, which had been abolished, and more in terms of possibilities of developing their farms and increasing their outputs. This did not mean that they would ever develop fully the potentials of their farms. Nevertheless, they were ready to talk about such possibilities.

The first decision to be made in any such planning with these farmers were the prices on which to base decisions. The parity ratios actually prevailing in 1946 were 10 to 15 above 100. It did not seem safe to assume that these would continue. What was assumed in the planning instead was a level of prices of wages, feed, and other supplies and farm machinery purchased at about 1943–1945 levels, and prices of milk around 95 percent of parity on this basis. The general level of prices has of course been somewhat higher than assumed — there was more inflation than was expected — but it is the ratio of prices received to prices paid that really counts. The national parity ratio was only 89 in 1954 when the farms were visited the third time, but it averaged well up to 95 for the 1946–1954 years.

Most important were the changes in land use which were written into the new plans for the 24 farms analyzed in 1946 as averaged in Table 25. The new plans thus called for no increase in cropland, but for removal of 1,150 feet per farm of stone walls (fences). They also called for converting to fertilized open pasture an average of 3 acres of stony pasture by boulder removal and 3 acres of brushy pasture by clearing off the brush. The addition of an average of 16 or more acres per farm of ladino pasture was also to come partly from boulder removal and partly from brush clearing. A total of 22 acres per farm was to be cleared of stone or brush. An average of 12 acres of brushy pasture was to be fenced off for woodland. This plus the fencing in of the new pasture called for 1,730 feet per farm of new fencing. Also an average of 300 feet per farm of drainage was planned on four farms.

TABLE 25

Land Use on 24 Dairy Farms in Hardwick Replanned in 1946

Land use	*1946*	*Chosen plans*
Cropland	59 acres	59 acres
Ladino pasture on noncropland	—	16
Fertilized pasture	10	16
Total improved land	69	91
Other open pasture	52	33
Total open land farmed	121	124
Brushy pasture, mostly stony	49	29
Woodland	56	68
Other	9	10
Total acres	235	231

At the same time, the rate of phosphate and potash fertilization application was to be increased by one third and two thirds respectively.

These changes combined were calculated to increase roughage by 30 percent, enough for 8 more cows than the 28 in 1945, and 8 heifers instead of 5. Milk production per cow was to rise 520 pounds per cow to 7,020 and total milk from the 24 farms by 33 percent, with a reduction of 260 pounds per cow of grain fed.

This essential enlargement of these farms was to call for an increase from 2.4 to 2.6 man-years of labor per farm. A little additional machinery would be needed, namely, milking machines on all farms not already using them, and hayloaders for all remaining farms except the two needing field hay balers and one a field forage chopper. The additional investment needed would be $4,560 per farm, a third of this in more livestock, 28 percent in buildings, 26 percent in land improvements, and 13 percent in machinery. The plans called for new barns on three farms. The maximum credit needs on any farm in any year to carry out these plans would be $2,250.

Changes by 1954–55

The 18 dairy farms out of the 24 in 1945 which were still operating in 1954 averaged 37 cows per farm in 1954, or an increase of 9 compared with 8 in the chosen plans. But the production per cow had increased only 350 pounds compared with the 520 pounds in the chosen plans. The major reason for this was that the concentrates fed per cow were only 2,250 pounds as against the 2,500 pounds planned. No doubt the relatively high price of feed in 1954 was a factor in this. Per farm milk production averaged 252,000 pounds as compared with 182,000 in 1945 and 125,200 in 1937–38. These farms had therefore doubled in size in terms of milk output since 1937–38. The output of milk from the 18 farms in 1954 was only 4 percent larger than that of the 24 farms in 1945, but 24 percent larger than that of the 29 farms in 1937–38. These 18 farms averaged 6.3 heifer calves raised per farm in 1945, and 8.5 in 1954. The ratio of replacements to cows therefore had not increased appreciably. Nine of the 18 farms reported buying a total of 45 cows during the year. Excluding the two big farms, however, the purchases averaged only 3 cows per farm.

The principal reason that the milk output did not increase more between 1945 and 1954 was that the larger farms that absorbed the smaller ones did not increase the size of their herds enough to equal the herds on the farms absorbed.

No doubt shortage of labor and high wages were also a factor in this situation. These farms averaged slightly under 24 man-months of labor per year in 1945. They were thus getting smaller in terms of average labor force in spite of the consolidation of 6 of them into larger units.

Along with the foregoing, these farms had made little headway in clearing land and improving pasture. Only 8 of them had done any of this at all, and these an average of only 4 acres per farm. The 1946 chosen plans called for ten times this much. They had, however, increased their use of fertilizer much more relatively. This added much less to the labor demands.

The easiest way of increasing output apparently was to rent land from those wanting to quit farming — 8 of the farms were renting an average of

90 acres per farm. The rented land consisted in most cases of all the land in one or more smaller farms, or all of the crop and pasture land in them.

Cases

Let us now consider briefly the varying situation on a number of individual farms.

Farm AY — This farm may be taken as one example of what is commonly referred to as a family-sized farm, the farmer himself and his relatively young family doing all the work. It contained around 150 acres of land in 1938, of which only 40 were cropland, 60 acres were woodland, and the rest was a mixture of open and brushy pasture. The herd consisted of 16 cows and 3 head of young stock started each year. The plan worked out with the family for improving this operation is outlined in Table 26.

TABLE 26

Plan for Farm AY Developed in 1938

Crops	Acres	Yield	Production
Silage corn	4.0	12.0	48 tons
Oats	4.0	2.8	38 tons of hay plus 12 tons of pasture
Alfalfa and grass	14.0	2.8	(hay equiv.)
Ladino pasture mixture	23.0	2.1	9 tons of hay plus 40 tons of pasture (hay equiv.)

The roughage production was to amount to 48 tons of corn silage, 47 tons of hay (mow dry), and 52 tons of pasture as measured in the equivalent of hay. The corn and alfalfa hay mixture was to be raised on 22 acres of land located in the larger less stony fields, while the ladino clover was to be raised on land not so well suited to cultivation and with a heavier texture. The alfalfa and grass was to be used primarily for pasture. It would be necessary to pasture some of the alfalfa in the latter part of the summer and to cut some hay from the ladino mixture in the early summer in order to balance pasture production with the needs of the livestock over the season.

In order to produce this amount of roughage on this acreage of land, fertilization would have to be considerably higher than that generally used on crop and pasture land. Annual fertilizer and lime purchases were to be approximately equal to the equivalent of the following materials:

8-24-8	1 ton
Ammonium nitrate	¾ ton
Superphosphate	7½ tons
Muriate of potash	3¾ tons
10-10-10	1 ton
Lime	9 tons

This amount of fertilizer together with the manure produced on the farm would provide 55 pounds of nitrogen (N), 100 pounds of phosphoric acid (P_2O_5), and 140 pounds of potash (K_2O) per acre of crop and pasture land. With reasonably good management of the dairy herd, a production of 7,000 pounds of milk could be expected with 2,400 pounds of grain fed per cow per year, as compared with the 6,200 pounds of milk in 1937.

The equipment used for this production included a milking machine, tractor, tractor tillage equipment, truck, hayloader, and side-delivery rake. The labor force would include about one and a half months of hired labor in addition to the operator and his fourteen-year-old son.

The accompanying summary shows the expected receipts and expenses, converted to a 1943–1945 price level.

Receipts		
1,353 cwt. of milk at $4.00	$5,412	
4 cull cows at $75.00	300	
14 calves	56	
Other	62	
Total receipts		$5,830
Expenses		
Grain (560 cwt. at $3.00)	$1,680	
Labor, 2 months	190	
Fertilizer and lime	555	
Gas and oil	200	
Taxes	180	
Other	900	
Total expenses		$3,705
NET FARM INCOME		$2,125

It will be noted in the foregoing farm organization that 2.25 acres of improved land were planned for each cow in the milking herd. This assumes that a large part of the hay would contain a substantial proportion of alfalfa and the pasture land would be reseeded every five or six years to a pasture mixture containing ladino clover. Hay yields were expected to average 2.8 tons of mow-dry hay per acre for the life of the stand and the pasture was to be seeded on areas well adapted to ladino clover.

In such planning generally in the region, where lower yields are expected, the acreage required for a herd of 20 cows and replacements may be as much as 50 or 55 acres. On the other hand, less improved land will be needed, at least for a few years, where there is a substantial acreage of reasonably open pasture not suited to improvement. Eventually the unimproved pasture, however, grows up to brush and woodland and has to be replaced with other sources of pasture.

On farms where there is not enough improved land to supply roughage for the livestock desired by the operator, whether he wants a twenty-cow unit or some larger number, several methods are used to obtain the roughage. More land may be cleared if available, which may be improved at a moderate cost, or land may be purchased. However, suitable land is frequently not for sale at the time the plans are made, but may come on the market at some later time. In such situations, although purchase of land may not be included in the plans, over a period of time many adjustments of this type will no doubt take place as they have in the past. Still another possibility is to operate a smaller dairy unit and supplement the income with other enterprises such as poultry, fruit, vegetables, or labor off the farm. Some of these possibilities will be illustrated later on.

Farm CR—The situation with respect to combining units in order to obtain a two-man dairy business may be illustrated with the following case of a farm operated by a father and his son. The farm as operated in 1938 contained approximately 300 acres of which 87 acres of crop and pasture land were being rented from a neighboring farmer who had once operated a 17-cow dairy herd on this farm. The combined units had 39 acres of cropland, 50 acres of open pasture, 120 acres of brushy pasture, and 75 acres of woodland. The barn on the home farm had tie-ups for 23 cows. Young stock were kept in the barn on what had been the other farm. All of the crop and pasture land on both farms was being used to produce roughage for a herd of 21 cows and replacements. But with stone removal on four acres of cropland and 15 acres of pasture land, enough roughage could be produced on the home farm for a herd of 20 cows and replacements, provided that good stands of alfalfa hay and ladino clover pasture mixtures were obtained. The level of fertilization would need to be as heavy as on Farm AY. With the addition of a hayloader and side-delivery rake to the present equipment, one man could operate the farm. This would mean that either the father or the son would have to find employment elsewhere. With milk production per cow at 8,800 pounds of 4.2 percent milk and 2,800 pounds of grain fed per cow per year, net farm income would be approximately $2,700 after paying interest on the cost of improvements.

If, however, the barn and the land now rented on the adjoining farm were purchased, enough land would be available to produce roughage for a 40-cow herd with replacements raised. The barn would have to be enlarged to provide tie-ups and hay storage space.

The estimated additional investment of $13,600 required to make this shift from a one-man unit to a two-man unit was analyzed at 1943–1945 prices as follows:

Land (87 acres) and barn	$5,000
Enlarging barn	4,000
Additional livestock	3,600
Clearing additional land	550
Refrigerator	450

Receipts and expenses for the two-man unit compared to the one-man unit would be as indicated in Table 27. The estimate of net farm income

TABLE 27

Comparison of Budgets for Farm CR Operated on a One-Man and Two-Man Basis (in dollars)

	One-man		*Two-man*	
Receipts				
Milk	6,990		14,145	
Livestock	360		715	
Other	60		100	
Total		7,410		14,960
Expenses				
Grain	2,240		4,110	
Labor	500		1,800	
Fertilizer	400		880	
Taxes	220		450	
Interest on add. inv.	75		690	
Other	1,265		2,180	
Total		4,700		10,110
NET FARM INCOME		2,710		4,850

allowed hired wages for the son at $1,500 per year. An increase in income of $2,140 could be expected from the larger unit, but it should be emphasized that this increase would depend upon the farmer's ability to maintain the same rates of productivity for the larger unit as for the smaller unit.

An examination of this budget will show that the increase in income would be much less if production per cow were substantially lower than that expected for this farm. The figures in Table 28 show the estimated net farm income for the two with three different rates of grain feeding and production.

TABLE 28

Projected Net Incomes of Farm CR Operated on a One-Man and a Two-Man Basis at Three Different Rates of Grain Feeding and Output per Cow

Pounds of grain per cow	*Pounds of milk produced per cow*	*Net farm income (dollars)*		*Increase over one-man unit*
		One-man	*Two-man*	
2,800	8,800	2,710	4,850	2,140
2,200	7,200	1,760	2,950	1,190
1,600	5,500	725	860	135

How important adjustments of the sort just planned for Farms AY and CR are in the town of Hardwick may be judged from the fact that of the 29 dairy units studied and being operated in 1938 or more recently operated, 3 units had less than 15 cows and 4 more had 18 or 19 cows, and the remainder had 20 cows or more. Six of the 7 farms with less than 20 cows had less than 45 acres of improved land. Two of the farms in this group were idle in 1945, although more had supplementary poultry enterprises, and the operators of 3 were working off the farm at least a part of the time. Enough land could not be improved on 2 of the 7 farms to provide roughage, particularly since the open pasture on them was not suited for improvement and would become less productive year by year. The improved land on one of these was very stony and poorly arranged so that it could hardly make a desirable unit for any size of herd. The other unit could well be operated as a combination or part-time dairy farm. There was also the possibility that a farmer might keep fewer than 20 cows, give them better care, and receive just as high an income as if he handled more cows.

Farm BF — Nothing is said in the foregoing analyses of Farms AY and CR about the base-rating problem involved in 1938. The increase in output outlined for AY would not come all at once. Each new year, the increase over the year before would receive only Class II milk prices. Farm CR acquired the base rating of the second farm when it rented it, but it too would need an increasing base rating year by year until the new level of production was reached. This was no longer a problem in 1946 since the base-rating system had been abolished during the war.

Farm BF may be taken to illustrate the impact of the base-rating system. In 1938 it had 300 acres of land and 66 acres of low-producing cropland and was keeping only 16 cows, with a base rating of less than 300 pounds per day. The farmer was well along in years and had allowed much crop and pasture land to grow up to brush. One of the alternative plans worked out for this farm in 1938 provided for establishing 23 acres of alfalfa, growing 14 acres of corn for silage, 40 acres of improved pasture, and 19 acres of oats and rye for grazing in season, and keeping 40 cows and replacements. The operator then on the farm, however, chose a plan much less ambitious and made little progress with even this before selling the farm in 1944. The new owner did not consider the 1938 plan ambitious enough, and in 1946 a plan was worked out with him that called for clearing 20 acres of pasture land of brush and seeding it to a ladino pasture mixture, and clearing 10 more acres for crops. A bog-harrow would be used with the lighter brush and a bulldozer with the heavier growths. On five fields with lighter Merrimac sandy loam soils, rotations with corn for silage, oats, and alfalfa-mixture hay would be followed. These combined with relatively heavy fertilization would provide good roughage for 75 milk cows plus 16 replacements each year. The grain ration was set at 2,000 pounds per cow in milk, and the milk output planned for was 7,500 pounds, compared with 5,200 under the former operator. The net income estimated under this plan was around $6,500 at 1943–1945 prices.

A large additional investment would be needed to carry out this plan, particularly because the present barn was in poor condition and really needed to be replaced; also an operation of this size would need a field hay and forage chopper. Assuming this, the additional investment for the proposed plan was estimated at $25,300 as follows:

Land clearing	$ 800
Field chopper	2,200
Barn	15,000
Dairy equipment	1,500
Increase in livestock inventory	5,800

The amount of credit necessary to finance this investment would depend upon the rate at which the plan was put into effect and the proportion of current income which the operator desired to put into the business. The plan could be put into effect most economically if the adoption was spread over a period of from four to six years. A large proportion of the additional cows could be raised as the roughage production was being increased. The larger barn could be built about 1950.

The schedule of new investments, borrowings, and repayments in Table 29 illustrates financing with gradual adoption of the plan and payment of part of the cost out of current earnings. Arrangements with the bank loan agency should be based on some tentative schedule of repayment such as that mentioned above. Furthermore, because of variation in prices and weather conditions from year to year, provision should be made for raising or lowering the amount of the payment according to actual income results.

TABLE 29

Suggested Schedule of New Cash Investments, Borrowings and Payments on Interest and Principal for Development of Chosen Plan for Farm BF

Date	New cash investment	Amount borrowed	Payment on interest (4½%)	Payment on principal	Balance due
April 1, 1948	$ 2,800	$ 2,500	0	0	$ 2,500
" 1949	1,200	800	$113	0	3,500
" 1950	16,600	15,600	148	0	18,900
" 1951	2,200	1,100	850	0	20,000
" 1952	500	——	900	$ 800	19,200
" 1953	——	——	864	1,500	17,700
" 1954	——	——	796	2,000	15,700
" 1955	——	——	706	2,000	13,700
" 1956	——	——	616	2,000	11,700
" 1957	——	——	526	2,000	9,700
" 1958	——	——	436	2,000	7,700
" 1959	——	——	346	2,000	5,700
" 1960	——	——	256	2,000	3,700
" 1961	——	——	166	2,000	1,700
" 1962	——	——	76	1,700	0

When this farm was visited in 1945, the herd had been increased only to 45 cows, but 35 heifers and calves were on the way to join the milking herd. Production per cow was up to 7,350 pounds. Only 13 acres of pasture land had been cleared and reseeded, but 20 acres of alfalfa were being grown. A new silo had been built and the barn had been enlarged. The hay was being baled by custom baling.

Farm MP — This farm has had the same operator since 1937 and the same land until recently. At the start it had 40 acres of cropland, 25 acres of open pasture, 40 acres of brushy pasture, and a little woodland. The plan chosen in 1938 called for no increase above the 20 cows then being milked, but for raising production per cow from 6,000 to 6,500 pounds and raising 5 replacements instead of 2, all of this with no increase above 1,300 pounds per cow in purchased feed. This was to be achieved by converting 25 acres of relatively poor mixed hay to hay with alfalfa and clover in it, seeding 4 acres of rye for late fall and early spring grazing, and 2 acres of oats to supplant the permanent pasture in July, plus improving 19 acres of the permanent pasture. These changes were expected to raise the net income from $1,600 to $2,400 in 1943–1945 dollars.

In 1945, the farm was carrying 24 cows and 3 replacements. The plans for improving the hay and pasture had been about two-thirds carried out, and production per cow had reached the 6,500 level, but with only 300 pounds more purchased feed per cow. The farm still presented some difficult problems described in the 1946 plan as follows:

> Stoniness and small size of fields present an important problem in the use of machinery. Since some of the pasture land is on lighter soil where the fields are larger than the present hay fields, it would be possible to put these pasture fields into an alfalfa hay mixture and some of the stoniest hay land into permanent pasture. This would put the pasture on land best adapted to pasture and some of the hay on fields adapted to alfalfa. The pasture fields will need heavy liming and fertilization before seeding to alfalfa. A few of the stone walls can be removed to get larger fields. By rather extensive land clearing and heavy fertilization, the farm could be made to carry 30 to 35 cows, but this would give an odd-size unit as well as requiring additional barn space. Therefore, the proposed plan is limited to growing all the pasture and roughage which the present herd with replacements will eat.

The plan chosen in 1946 called for no increase in number of cows, but for 6 replacements a year and an output per cow of 7,200 pounds, with 17 acres of alfalfa and 20 acres of ladino pasture, plus the rye and oats as before. When the farm was visited in 1954, the farm had 23 cows and 5 replacements, 9 acres of alfalfa, and only 7 more acres of improved pasture. But 50 acres of land, containing 10 acres of open pasture, was being rented; and the feed purchased had risen to 2,000 pounds per cow. Output per cow had risen about 400 pounds.

Farm GH — This farm had also been in the same family with the same land throughout. It was notable in 1938 for its low output per cow of 3,500 pounds. The chosen plan called for raising this only to 4,000 with about the same number of milkers (20), but more replacements, by improving the quality of the hay and pasture. In 1945, this farm was carrying 25 cows averaging 4,500 pounds, and in 1954 averaging around 4,800. The quality of the herd was a continuing factor in the situation. Another farm averaging 3,900 pounds per cow in 1938 was getting 6,500 from a fifth fewer cows in 1945, and 6,700 from a fourth more cows in 1954.

DAIRY-POULTRY FARMING

Only one of the farms visited in 1937–38, 1945–46, and 1954 combined poultry with dairying on a sizable scale throughout. Another stopped operating before 1945, and another added poultry to dairying at about the same time. There were 5 other dairy farms that kept about 100 layers or the equivalent.

The farm that combined these two enterprises throughout had 23 cows in 1938 and 958 layers and was raising 6,600 chicks and 1,150 turkeys. The gross poultry receipts were nearly three times as large as the gross dairy receipts. After deducting the direct purchased feed bills for the two enterprises, however, the comparison was more nearly like $2,600 for dairy and $3,800 for poultry. The chosen plan in 1938 called for keeping 3 more cows and stepping up production by 550 pounds per cow, while cutting feed inputs by a half down to 800 pounds by substituting high-quality hay and pasture for it. By 1945, the dairy herd had been enlarged to 38 cows, and the turkey enterprise had been expanded. In 1954, the number of cows had declined to 28 producing an average of 7,600 pounds of milk, and the poultry enterprise had been shifted almost entirely to laying hens. The size of the family group desiring to make a living on this farm has apparently figured largely in the expansion of its business by including poultry. No doubt the shifts in the nature of the poultry enterprise were occasioned in part by attempts to meet changes in market conditions.

The poultry enterprise on the other dairy-poultry farm in 1938 was clearly designed to supplement the income from a farm with only 20 acres of cropland. The returns above feed costs from sale of eggs and poultry were $600 in 1937. The same has been true for the other dairy farm with a supplementary poultry enterprise since 1945, with net poultry returns of about $1,600 above feed costs in recent years. The management alternatives for such a farm are pretty well indicated in Chapter 9 on "Planning One Farm" in the sections on "Poultry Farms" and "Dairy-Poultry Farms."

POULTRY FARMS

As indicated earlier, only three other towns in the County sold more farm eggs in 1950 than did Hardwick. About 60 per cent of the eggs sold in recent years, however, have been to hatcheries. This has largely been a development since the first survey in 1937–38, and the follow-up work in 1946 did not include any new farms. The two poultry farms operating in 1954 that had begun operations before 1946 had been dairy farms before this, one with 20 acres of cropland and 22 cows, and the other with 45 acres of cropland mostly in poor hay, and 20 cows. But the reasons in these particular cases for discontinuing dairying were illness, death, and drafting of sons for military service. Both were renting their land to dairy farmers in 1954. The first of these was keeping 2,400 layers in 1954 and raising 3,350 chicks. The second was keeping 3,000 layers and raising 15,000 broilers.

Special circumstances on individual farms and within individual families will go far in determining the choice between dairy or poultry or dairy-poultry farming in any area like Hardwick. But forces outside individual farms will determine the general choice for each area as a whole. Poultry farming about doubled in New England between 1940 and 1950. The sharply rising consumption and demand for eggs and poultry meat was one factor in this. Also the pattern of shifting from dairying to poultry was already better established in New England than in most potentially competing areas. Finally the rapidly developing new technologies were adopted quickly in this region.

But whether competition in this field will continue on its wartime and early postwar basis is by no means certain. The Southeast is now expanding most rapidly of all in this field. It may well have some climatic advantages. Surely it has a larger supply of cheaper labor.

FRUIT FARMING

The Census of 1945 reported 50 acres of apple trees on five farms in Hardwick Town. The field work in 1937–38 located three of these with a total acreage of 30. On one of these, the apples were supplementary to a 23-cow dairy operation and on a rented additional farm. Two of the orchard farms in 1938 had become residential farms in 1946, with all the land including the orchards being farmed by the renters.

The plan worked out for the other of these farms in 1938 called for a supplemental small dairy enterprise, since the orchard was on droughty Hinckley soils scoring only 35 to 39 out of 100 on Dr. Beaumont's rating of soils for orchard purposes, and therefore likely to yield a very uncertain crop of apples. The operator was advanced in years, however, and did not carry out the plan and had quit farming altogether by 1945. Only one of the farms visited in 1954–55 was operating an orchard, and this was a small orchard along with a 23-cow herd. Dry weather and a hurricane had much reduced the crop in 1953 and 1954. The management problems of orchards in Worcester County are also analyzed in Chapter 9 on "Planning One Farm."

The part-time and residential farming on the farms in the group of farms studied included in addition to home gardens, and small flocks of poultry on less than half of them, such things as four cows in one case and two cows on another in 1938, and three cows and six beef cattle on another in 1945. Another had a very small orchard and kept bees in 1938. The extent of these activities declined a good deal over the period as the families grew older or more employment became available.

FARM WOODLANDS

The plans worked out in 1938 provided for the future use of all of the 570 acres of woodland, 940 acres of wooded pasture, and 930 acres of brushy pasture in the 37 farms analyzed in the foregoing. The plans chosen for these farms in 1938 would have reduced the average acreage of brushy pasture from 28 to 22 and increased the acreage of woodland from 41 to 47. These plans divided the present stands of timber into compartments or stands and indicated the treatment for each in the manner indicated in Table 30. The treatments indicated by the numbers in the column under practices were such as the following:

No. 1. Fence against grazing
No. 2. Improvement cutting — that is, cut out poor trees, trees of species not favored, and sprout clumps
No. 3. Thinning
No. 4. Gypsy moth control cutting
No. 5. Pruning
No. 6. Planting
No. 7. Weeding

Practices 1 and 2 in Table 30 are the Numbers 1 and 2 in the foregoing list, plus those indicated in the footnotes to the Table.

TABLE 30

Treatment of Timber Planned for One Farm in Hardwick in 1938

Stand No.	Area (acres)	Land-use class*	Age of stand (years)	Practice No.	Volume to be cut: Cu. ft.	Volume to be cut: Cords	Man-days for stand	Left per acre: Crop trees	Left per acre: Total trees
33 & 33	26.9	Btr. Hwd. Pine	30–40	1 & 2**	7,774	97.1	146	186	371
4	3.3	Btr. Hwd.	15–30	1 & 2	808	10.1	15	350	450
6	5.3	Btr. Hwd.	30–40	1 & 2	1,960	24.5	37	125	310
8	6.0	Btr. Hwd.	20–30	1 & 2	840	10.5	16	145	310
17	2.8	Inf. Hwd.	20–60	1 & 2†	420	5.2	8	30	200
26	2.5	Btr. Hwd.	30–40	2	950	11.8	18	70	350
27	1.3	Inf. Hwd.	20–60	2‡	377	4.7	7	10	140

* Better — Btr. Inferior — Inf. Hardwood — Hwd.
** Fencing needed immediately. No. 2 can be delayed 5–10 years. Remove overtopping old culls.
† Gradual conversion to pine recommended.
‡ Open stand by removing big culls. Convert to pine.

Following are several more detailed prescriptions of treatments for different stands on *another* farm:

Stand 1 — Mixed Oak–Hickory Type — 8.4 acres

Age . . . . 20–30 years
Quality . . . . M
Stocking . . . . B

This represents the only hardwood stand on the upland soil in the entire woodland. It is in a deteriorated condition due to clear cutting for fuelwood and grazing. The stand is very spotty, with small groups of gray birch averaging one-tenth acre in size intermingled with the better hardwoods. Large scrubby pasture-grown oaks are also scattered throughout the stand suppressing better formed valuable species. The stand is understocked in quality trees. Of the 446 stems per acre, there are but 59 crop trees, representing one sixth of the total volume of the stand.

A heavy improvement cutting is needed to reduce the quantity of oaks, especially the slower growing oaks such as white and scarlet, as a gypsy moth control measure and in order to free the well-formed red maple, hickory, white and yellow birch, elm, and red oak. The gray birch groups should be clear-cut and the openings planted to white pine, using 5 x 5 spacing. The large pasture-grown oaks should be girdled because they are too large to cut.

Stand 2 — Gray Birch Type — 6.0 acres

Age..................20–30 years
Quality...............—
Stocking..............B

The present stand averages 4.5 cords of gray birch per acre or a total of 23 cords for the stand. There are approximately 25 white pine seedlings per acre, which owe their origin to two or three nearby large seed trees.

Since the stand contains suitable seed trees and is favorably located in respect to compartment 3 for an additional source of seed, natural reproduction of pine should be favored as the start of a new stand. This can be done by gradually removing the gray birch as the density of the white pine increases. A light overstory of gray birch should be maintained to suppress partly the pine and thus reduce weevil damage. If natural reproduction is inadequate, supplementary planting of white pine may be resorted to.

Stand 3 — Red Maple Swale Type, 2.7 acres

Age..................40 years
Site..................Wet
Quality...............M
Stocking..............B

This stand is badly deteriorated through grazing and cutting. Out of 360 trees per acre there are but 70 of crop-tree quality. Multiple-stemmed red maples compose the largest proportion of the stand, interspersed with a few single-stemmed red maples, elms, and white pines. There are not enough good quality stems in the present mixture to form a complete stocking at maturity, but with treatment sufficient reproduction can be secured to make up this deficiency.

An improvement cutting is recommended removing one fifth of the total volume of the stand. There is no reproduction at the present time, but with elimination of grazing it is expected that natural reproduction will become established. Spot planting with white ash may be necessary if satisfactory reproduction is not secured naturally.

Stand 4 — White Pine Type, 2.3 acres

Age..................40–60 years
Quality...............M
Stocking..............B

This is a small area removed from other woodland areas and already fenced in with contiguous pasture land. Since it affords the only shade in the pasture, it should be retained for that purpose. There is no reproduction or underbrush for browse to attract the cattle, and it is believed that the cattle will use the area only during very hot days. Such a light degree of occupancy probably will not damage the present crop.

Stand 5 — Recent Cutover, 2.7 acres.

The previous stand of red maple and gray birch was recently cut over, and it is recommended that a new stand be established by planting. Since there is a shortage of softwood trees on the farm, white pine may be used to advantage. The presence of hardwood stumps sprouts, which will act as fillers, makes advisable a 6- to 7-foot spacing.

Compartment 6 — Brushy Pasture, 16.2 acres

This is deteriorated brushy pasture that is in excess of the land needed for pasture under the reorganization plan. This area will be needed for supplementary pasture for about five years, or until such time as the reduced area of pasture is capable of supporting the herd. A resort to natural tree reproduction to fully stock the area would be a long-time process because of its unfavorable position in respect to possible seed trees. Therefore in order that the land be made productive as soon as possible, it is recommended that it be planted to a mixture of white pine, Norway spruce and European larch. If needed, larch can be grown on short rotations for posts and poles to take the place of chestnut. White pine and spruce will be useful in supplying home needs for construction materials, as well as a cash crop for sale as lumber or pulpwood.

Compartment 7 — Brushy Pasture, 12.8 acres

This is brushy pastures in excess of the needs under the reorganization plan, and is recommended for conversion to woodland when the selected areas have been improved to support the herd. Since the moister portion of this area is favorably adapted to reproduction by natural means, only the drier places will have to be planted. Planting will be needed in the southern tip of the compartment on about 2.0 acres. White pine is recommended for planting using 5 x 5 spacing. Scarifying the surface is recommended on the remainder of the area, with a mixture of moisture-loving species such as red maple, white ash, elm, and yellow birch favored.

This farm therefore had 51 acres of potential woodland in 1938 of which less than half was already classified as woodland. During the past few years, about 8 cords of cordwood per year had been cut to supply the farm needs, and in addition 8 cords for cash sale at approximately $7.00 per cord. This cutting was not being done in such a way as to improve the quality and productivity of the existing woodland, nor to enhance the control of gypsy moth. Grazing had also prevented normal reproduction and thus there was no undergrowth to improve the quality of growing timber. Eventually the reproductive stock of desired species would be depleted. It was suggested that the improvement cuttings be made on the present 22 acres of woodland as rapidly as labor was available and the market would absorb the product. It was estimated that 135 cords should be removed, this requiring 130 man-days of labor. The current cordwood price was $6.00 per cord at the farm; hence these improvement cuttings would net approximately $800, less any labor which might be hired.

Plantings should be made on the portions of the 29 acres of pasture and recently cut-over land that would not seed in immediately by natural means. This would require a cash outlay of approximately $10 per acre and could be carried out as rapidly as funds were available to invest in future woodland.

After the initial improvement cuttings, the weeding, thinning, and improvement cuttings were to be made from time to time with unutilized farm labor. Probably these practices would yield enough cordwood to supply the needs for home use with possibly small amounts for sale.

Most of the existing stands averaged about 40 years of age. Hence in about 30 years, mature timber would be ready for cutting and approximately the equivalent of one half-acre could be cut every other year. Thus it would take 44 years to cut the present stand of 22 acres; by that time the 29 acres of new stands would be ready to harvest and thus the 51 acres would be on a sustained-yield basis.

This woodland, if properly managed, would at maturity yield on an average of 3,000 board feet per acre. A study of lumber prices during the past 40 years gave justification for assuming a net price of $22 per thousand; thus the woodlot would yield $310 of sawtimber every other year. This was equivalent to approximately $3.00 per acre per year for the 51 acres of woodland on this farm.

If instead of the foregoing grazing were continued on these woodlands, reproduction would be hindered and the woodlands would progressively deteriorate to the point where sawtimber yields would be negligible.

On the other hand, if the woodlots were fenced out, but no woodlot practices carried out, the income from salable sawtimber could be expected to be cut in half because of reduced yields and poorer quality.

Not only was a plan of woodland management worked out for each of these farms in 1938 before the hurricane, but projections were made as to the *volume* and *value* of the *mean annual growth* of each stand over its rotation period and the stand per acre at the end of the rotation period. Table 31 is a summary of these projections for the 37 farms planned in detail and 5 others, all residential farms, for which woodland plans were made, with a classification by type of stand. Of course, the price per thousand and per cord assumed piled at the roadside in 1938 were low according to present values. This analysis was done jointly with men then on the staff of the Harvard Forest under the direction of A. C. Cline, now of the U.S. Forest Service. The cruising and other field work on the woodlands was mostly done by Gordon Chute and Mace Raymond.

TABLE 31

Summary of Projections as to Volume and Value of Mean Annual Growth for the 42 Farms

Item	Volume / rate	Per acre	Total
BETTER HARDWOODS TYPE: 984 acres			
Average volume per acre	2,195 cu. ft. (at end of 80-year rotation, all-aged stand)		
Mean annual growth	55 cu. ft.		
Value per acre:			
70% industrial wood			
40% sawlogs	22.0 cu. ft. @ $25 per M	$3.30	
20% bolts	11.0 cu. ft. @ $25 per M	1.65	
10% pulpwood	5.5 cu. ft. @ $ 8 per Cd.	.55	
Total industrial		5.50	
30% fuelwood	16.5 cu. ft. @ $ 4 per Cd.	.82	
Total per acre		6.32	
Total annual value for 984 acres			$6,219
SOFTWOOD – BETTER HARDWOODS TYPE: 299 acres (25–75 mixture)			
Average volume per acre	2,897 cu. ft. (at end of 80-year rotation, all-aged stand)		
Mean annual growth	72 cu. ft.		
Value per acre:			
80% industrial wood			
50% sawlogs	36.0 cu. ft. @ $22.50 per M	$4.66	
30% bolts, posts, pulpwood, etc.	21.6 cu. ft. @ $15 per M	1.94	
Total industrial		6.80	
20% fuelwood	14.4 cu. ft. @ $ 3.50 per Cd.	.63	
Total per acre		7.43	
Total annual value for 299 acres			$2,220
SOFTWOOD: 571 acres			
Average volume per acre	4,000 cu. ft. (at end of 70-year rotation, all-aged stand)		
Mean annual growth	114 cu. ft.		
Value per acre:			
90% industrial wood			
70% sawlogs	80.0 cu. ft. @ $15 per M	$7.20	
20% bolts, posts, pulpwood, etc.	23.0 cu. ft. @ $10 per Cd.	2.87	
Total industrial		10.07	
10% fuelwood	11.0 cu. ft. @ $ 3 per Cd.	.41	
Total per acre		10.48	
Total annual value for 571 acres			$5,983
INFERIOR HARDWOOD (swamp): 44 acres			
Average volume per acre	1,200 cu. ft. (at end of 40-year rotation, even-aged stand)		
Mean annual growth	30 cu. ft.		
Value per acre	30 cu. ft. @ $4 per Cd.	$1.50	
Total per acre		$1.50	
Total annual value for 44 acres			$66.00
Total annual income, all stands			$14,488

Planning in 1945

The woodland planning just described was virtually completed before the hurricane of 1938. Much of the timber was blown down; and all of most of the white pine stands like that of Stand 4 above. This of course disrupted the schedule of treatments laid out and spoiled the estimates of returns from improvements cuttings. Nevertheless, the planning has been reported here exactly as it was done, since any future planning in this and other areas will need to take the stands as they are at the time just as was done in this case. Accordingly, when the 34 farms were visited and replanned in 1945 the woodland possibilities of each of them was again analyzed in terms of the stands. Following is an example of the planning done at that time.

Farm T.

The following outline indicates the present condition of the woodland areas of this farm together with the suggestions for a reasonable forest management plan. More specific recommendations on suggested practices and cuttings will be made available as needed.

Plot	*Acres*	*Present condition*	*Suggested treatment*
1	27.0	This was heavily damaged by hurricane, so that the residual stand is a scattered overstory of oak and maple 20–40 years old. The understory is 0–20-year-old hardwoods of fair to poor density. A steep northwest slope has an older stand of better hardwoods.	Fence out cattle. Make improvement cutting every 10 years to take out the overstory. Cordwood and a few logs will be the chief products for 40 years. Gradually harvest better trees at 16″–18″ diameter breast high, with improvement cuttings.
2	8.0	Even-aged 20–40 year stand with some older groups. Predominantly hardwoods with some hemlock. Medium density and poor reproduction.	Fence out cattle to help reproduction. Make improvement cuttings every ten years starting within 5 years. The chief product will be cordwood for 25 years; then trees with 16″ or more d.b.h. will be harvested gradually along with improvement cuttings.
20	7.5	Even-aged, 20–40 year stand of mixed oaks, partly burned. Medium density, poor reproduction.	Keep cattle out. Salvage dead trees for fuelwood. Make improvement cuttings every 10 years, then trees 16″–18″ d.b.h. will be harvested gradually as the improvement cuttings are made.

With frequent partial cuttings covering the entire areas every 8 to 10 years, the annual yield during the initial period will be from 10 to 15 cords of fuelwood. This will require 15 to 20 man-days of labor. As the stands mature under good management, the yearly cut should reach about 50 cords of fuelwood or its equivalent in other products. There will be an increasing proportion of sawtimber after 10 to 15 years. As most of the material cut during the early improvement operations will be cordwood, it is essential that a market be found for the amount in excess of farm requirements.

A system of clear-cutting every 40 years or so wastes trees that die prior to that time, does not encourage reproduction of valuable species of good form, and produces few if any good sawlogs. Therefore it is estimated that the proposed system of cutting will about double the returns from woodland products. There will also be a long-term, gradual increase in the productivity and value of the woodlands which will add to the value of the farm.

Results in 1954

No detailed checking of the woodland development was made at the time that the 32 farms were visited in 1954. These farms averaged 217 acres of which 40 acres were woodland, 9 acres were improved pasture as compared with none in 1938, and 55 acres were cropland as compared with 35 in 1938. As explained earlier, the farms had grown larger in acres by absorbing others of the original 37, but by no means entirely in this way. Too much weight therefore must not be given to the fact that 33 percent of the land in the 32 farms was in woodland compared to 8 percent in 1938. These 32 farms were renting or had bought, more largely the former, 1,630 acres additional land in 1954 as compared with 1938, and some of this was woodland not in the original 37 farms. More of the increase had come about as a result of fencing cattle out of the woodland.

CHAPTER 12

Section A, West Central Section

This chapter and the five following will each undertake a planning analysis of land use in one of the six sections into which Worcester County has been divided, as explained in the first chapter. The preceding chapters have first given a general description of the land in the County and its use, with historical background and related factors such as the people and their relationship to the land, urban industry, and markets. Then Chapters 9 and 10 have outlined the method of analysis of the individual operating units in which most of the land is used. Finally, Chapter 11 has described in detail the land and its use in the one town of Hardwick and made a planning analysis much as had already been done for the town of Petersham in the separate publication described earlier.[1] The actual planning job for the remaining fifty-eight towns in the County therefore is still to be done. This is the task of Chapters 12 to 17.

Of course it will not be feasible or necessary to work out this planning analysis for all these fifty-eight towns in the same detail as has been done for Hardwick and Petersham. In fact, to do so would call for a vast amount of repetition of the same operations town by town. The towns themselves and their people may indeed want to have such detailed plans made. The objective of this book is not to supply them with such plans, however, but to show them the way and the results of such planning on the different types of land and in the different land-use situations in the County. They will find, it is hoped, somewhere in the six chapters an analysis that will fit most of the situations in any of their towns.

[1] John D. Black and Ayers Brinser, *Planning One Town — Petersham, A Hill Town in Massachusetts,* Cambridge, Mass., Harvard University Press, 1952.

To meet the objective just defined, it has been deemed necessary to do a fairly detailed job of planning analysis for one of the towns in each of the other five sections, as was indicated in Figure 1, and a much more general analysis of the remaining towns, except for those of them that were analyzed in somewhat more detail, and with a somewhat different approach, by the Country Life Committees.

Finally, care has been taken in the writing of these chapters to present only in general outline the results of any planning by towns and sections that are of the same pattern as that outlined in Chapters 9 and 10 which dealt with planning individual farms and forest operating units, or in the preceding chapters by sections. It thus follows that the particular emphasis in each of the succeeding chapters is on planning situations special to that section. For each section, however, much more detailed outline of land types, forest cover, and land use is needed than anything presented in Chapters 2 and 7.

Also it needs to be restated lest it be overlooked that the 1952–53 Seminar on Land Use and Conservation assisted much at one stage in this planning operation. In that year, the Seminar group was divided into groups of three or four, each of which prepared a report on one of the six sections. Thus the group that helped in this way on Section A consisted of William Jenkins of the Agricultural Extension Service of Nova Scotia, a graduate student, Joseph Zaremba, trained in forestry at Syracuse University and now teaching there, and A. J. Klingelhoets, now assistant state soil scientist in Wisconsin.

Country Life Committees prepared first-draft reports for the towns of Oakham and Rutland in Section A.

Figure 20 in Chapter 6 shows that Section A was next to the most agricultural Section of the County in 1925 but that its agriculture has declined steadily and substantially since. Figure 31 in this chapter shows that wide differences exist among the eight towns in this respect. Cropland and open pasture make up a sizable fraction of the land in Barre, New Braintree, Oakham, and eastern Hardwick, but only a small part of that of the other towns. The detailed analysis for Hardwick fits the other three agricultural towns very well. Like Hardwick their commercial agriculture is mostly dairying. The detailed analysis for Petersham in the separate publication for that town fits fairly well the other three towns, Hubbardston, Rutland, and Princeton. This similarity will be particularly apparent in analysis of part-time and residential farming on pages 29 to 34 of that report. There are no cities in this Section, but Hubbardston, Princeton, and Rutland are near enough to Gardner, Fitchburg, Leominster, and even Worcester to make part-time and residential farming in them entirely practicable. The manufac-

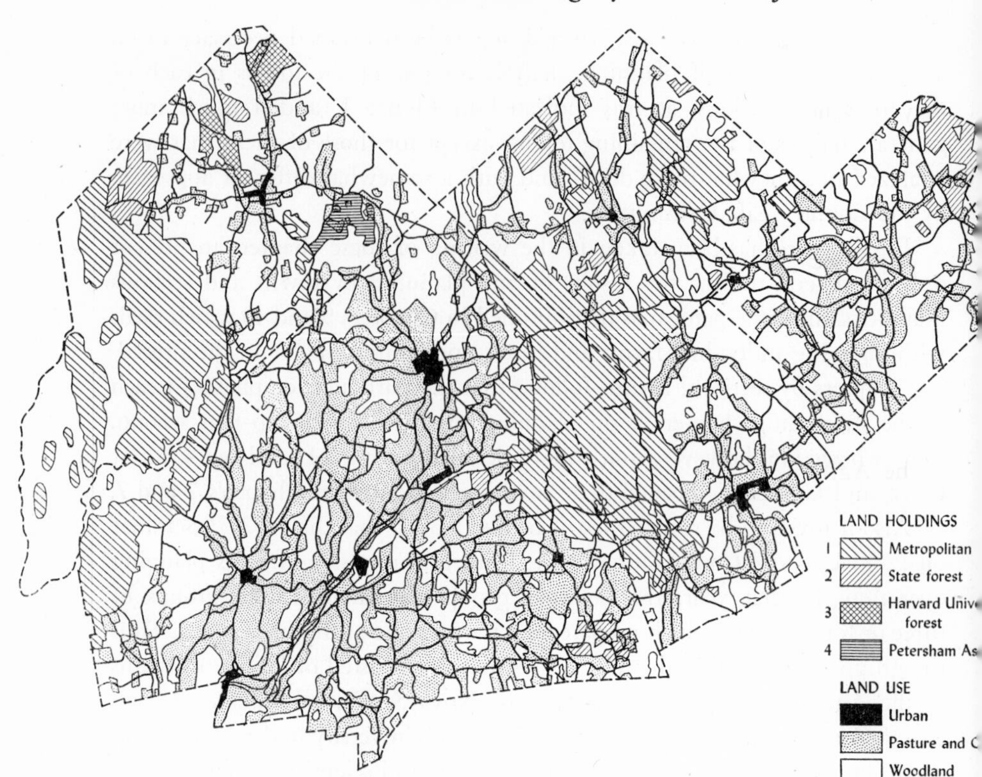

Figure 31. ***Land holdings and major land use and roads, West Central Section of Worcester County (Section A).***

turing firms of Gardner furnish employment for about 5,300, those of Leominster for about 5,700, and those of Fitchburg for over 10,000. Finally, Barre has 6 small plants employing 500 or more.

LAND USE

The most striking feature of the land use of the West Central Section as shown in Figure 31 is the large area in public or other noncommercial ownership. The Quabbin tract includes 30,600 acres in Petersham and Hardwick Towns, besides 41,540 in the adjoining counties of Franklin and Hampden on the west. The Ware River tract covers 16,475 acres in the adjoining corners of four towns, Barre, Rutland, Oakham, and Hubbardston, plus a 2,000-acre tract in eastern Hubbardston. These are all under the control of the Metropolitan District Water Commission, MDWC. The State Forests occupy 4,600 acres and the Harvard University Forest 2,100 acres. Most of this land in noncommercial ownership has soils not suited to agriculture. The eastern tracts, however, include areas of potentially cultivable soils. Apparently settlement never reached these and no roads were built into them, so that they remained in timber. They are mainly surrounded by No. 4 and No. 3 land.

It was not possible in a map of this scale to show cropland separately from open pasture land, but if it had been, most of the cropland would have appeared, as in Figure 29 in Chapter 11 on Hardwick Town, as fields abutting on the network of roads. The topography of the area is the main reason for this. All of the towns in this section occur on a topographic formation referred to as the Central Upland of southern New England. Elevation above sea level for this section ranges from 700 to Mount Wachusett's 2,015 feet in the town of Princeton. The topography of this Upland consists in the main of large areas of comparatively smooth ridges with steep valley slopes, small areas of nearly level terraces along the major streams, and the elongated, rounded hills called drumlins. The roads, as in Hardwick Town, follow the ridges with good soils or the stream terraces.

Table 32 not only indicates in definite figures the differences among these eight towns in major land use, but the differences in the rate of decline of their farming. The three towns of Barre, Hardwick, and New Braintree have declined approximately only 2, 7, and 6 percents respectively, whereas some of the other towns have suffered better than a 50-percent loss in agricultural land in this 25-year period. For the Section as a whole, from a total of 995 farms containing 111,077 acres in 1925, agriculture has declined to 545 farms with approximately 77,908 acres. This means there has been a decline of 43 percent in the number of farms and a 30-percent decrease in acreage. The land not in farms is nearly all in woodland. Census figures for 1950 show that approximately 53 percent of the farm land was still in woodland or woodland pasture. If one were to add this 53 percent of farm woodland to the other woodland, approximately 115,403 acres or 59 percent of the total area of this Section of Worcester County would be in woodland.

SOILS

The major soils of this whole Section are the same as those described for Hardwick Town in Chapter 11, but in the western third of it the Gloucester and Rough Stony types are preponderant with Charlton third, whereas in the central portion the Brookfield and Paxton series so dominant in the four Brookfield towns to the south are dominant. In the eastern part of this Sec-

TABLE 32

Percentage of All Land in Farms and in Cropland by Towns of the West Central Section of Worcester County, 1925–1950

Towns	1925		1935		1945		1950	
	Farms	Cropland	Farms	Cropland	Farms	Cropland	Farms	Cropland
Barre	58	14	62	14	64	15	56	10
Hardwick	71	21	60	16	57	13	64	12
Hubbardston	62	11	51	8	22	6	31	5
New Braintree	89	30	95	29	83	28	83	21
Oakham	59	17	59	12	54	16	40	9
Petersham	34	5	17	3	29	4	20	2
Princeton	61	12	46	8	45	9	27	4
Rutland	60	11	54	11	24	8	27	5

tion, the combination is Charlton, Paxton, and Sutton. In Figure 32, these soils are grouped into four classes according to the use to which they are best adapted.

The soils in Group One are suitable for general farming and dairying, and selected areas are favorable for orchards, small fruits, truck gardening, and special crops. Little or no remedial action from the standpoint of physical factors is needed. However, analysis may show that further economic gains may be had by adjustments in type of farming, cropping system, management, and the like. The soils placed in this category are medium to moderately coarse textured, are well drained, and comparatively free of stones. Charlton loam (Cl), Gloucester loam (Gl), fine sandy loam (Gfs), Paxton loam (Pl), and Merrimac fine sandy loam (Mfs) are soil types of this group.

The soils in the second group, although suitable for general farming, dairying, poultry raising, and in favorable cases for orcharding, small fruits, and truck crops, need more intensive adjustments of the physical factors to bring them up to the same level of production as the soils in Group One. In some cases this may not be physically possible. The soils in this group range from medium to moderately coarse textured, and from moderately well drained to somewhat droughty. Some of them contain enough stones or rock ledges to interfere with cultivation. Gloucester (Gsl) and Merrimac sandy loams (Msl), and Charlton (Csl) and Sutton (Srl) stony loams are typical soils in this group.

The soils included in the third category are not suited for tilled crops in most cases unless drastic changes can be made in their physical make-up.

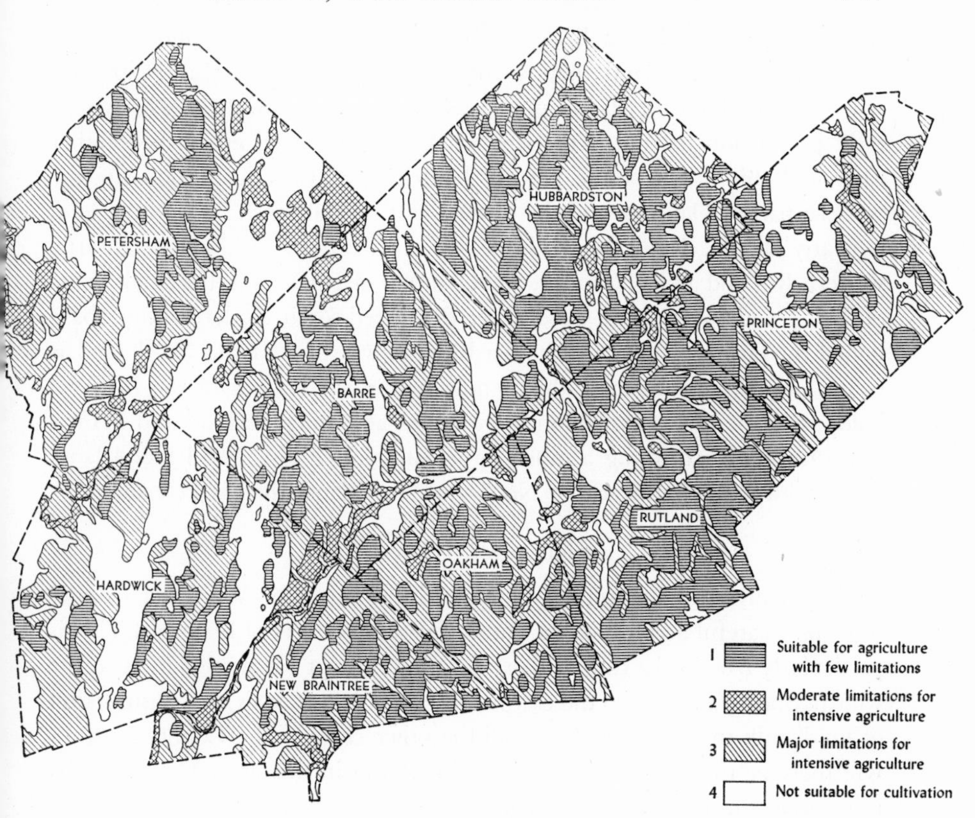

Figure 32. *Classification of the land of the West Central Section of Worcester County into four classes according to adaptability to agriculture.*

They may be more economically suitable for forage production, poultry farming, or forestry. Textures of soils in this group range from medium to moderately coarse. They may grade from droughty to very poorly drained and be shallow, ledgy, or very stony. Rumney and Scarboro fine sandy loams, Gloucester stony loam, and Merrimac loamy sand are examples of this group.

The fourth group is comprised of those soils and classes of land types which it is not economically feasible to improve for intensive agriculture. They are used most economically for forestry, wildlife preserves, recreation, reservoir locations, residential purposes, or other urban developments. They consist of very poorly drained, rough and stony or very droughty soils and classes of land types. Areas of Rough Stony land (R) and Gloucester very stony loam were placed in this category.

Closer study of Figure 32 reveals some wide differences among the towns.

In most of Barre and New Braintree, a good part of the No. 3 land and even some of the No. 4 land that is adjacent to No. 1 land was in pasture when the land use of the County was surveyed around 1940. Here fresh milk production for the Worcester market became well established rather early and this has kept the pasture land in use. This description fits the western part of Oakham and the eastern part of Hardwick. Where the land is nearly all No. 3 and No. 4, however, as in eastern Oakham and Barre, western Rutland and Hardwick, and about all of Petersham, the small tracts of No. 1 and No. 2 land were never developed, or if so, have been abandoned for farming since. In Hubbardston, only a little of the No. 1 land is being farmed, and much of this is now within the bounds of the MDWC holdings. This same description fits some of adjoining Rutland and Princeton. Princeton is farming a much larger amount of No. 3 and No. 4 land, along with its limited tracts of No. 1 and No. 2 land, than is Petersham.

AGRICULTURAL POSSIBILITIES

Any analysis of agricultural potential in an area like Worcester County must take careful account of the future for the products of its farms. This is particularly true in the case of dairy farming. Except for some outlets to the west in Springfield and to the east in Boston, only as fast as the consumption of fluid milk in Worcester City and the other cities of the County expands will there be room for an expansion of dairying in this area. Moreover, the milk dealers in these cities will continue to be on the alert for cheaper milk from Vermont and New York. And who knows when new technology may not bring to eastern markets from the Midwest some substitute for locally produced fluid milk?

We shall, in this analysis, however, ignore this last possibility and plan the use of land in dairying in Worcester County in terms of a demand growing with local population and purchasing power. If the disposable income of the families of Worcester County rises at the average rate projected for the nation in the P.M.P.C. Commission report, and the consuming population of this market area increases in its usual proportion to the national average, there will be a local market demand for about 30 percent more fluid milk in 1975 than now.[2]

The analysis of individual dairy farms in Chapter 9 on "Planning One Farm," and in Hardwick in Chapter 11, make very clear that 30 percent more milk in this area could be produced very easily. The results on the Hardwick

[2] *Resources for the Future,* Vol. II, pp. 63 ff., President's Materials Policy Commission, June 1952.

farms are reinforced by those on 25 farms scattered over the County that were included in the Charles H. Hood Foundation project.[3] These 25 were keeping 34 percent more cows per farm in 1946 than in 1938, raising a half more replacements, and producing 38 percent more milk with only 23 percent more purchased feed.

More purchased feed alone would give the 30 percent more milk prospectively needed in 1975. But this is not the most economical way to obtain it. Let us consider first the central part of Section A where farming is at present most intensive. Most of the dairy farms in this area have additional land, either within the farm itself or adjacent to it, which could be improved economically. Many of the dairy farms in this area need more cropland and improved pasture land to take care of their present livestock. Other units may desire still more for expansion of their present enterprise. On the better soils in this area, approximately two acres of cropland and/or improved pasture are needed to support each animal unit such as a dairy cow. If some of this better land were improved, much of the No. 3 and No. 4 land could be devoted to timber production. For example, Barre, which had a total population of 1,697 cattle in 1950, had nearly three acres per animal unit or 5,569 acres in pasture alone. The same situation prevails in Hardwick, New Braintree, and Oakham, which have respectively 3.7, nearly 3.0, and better than 5 acres per animal unit in all types of pasture.

Many of the unimproved pastures in this area are on stony phases or wooded areas of the deeper and better soils in Worcester County such as Gloucester and Charlton. A good pasture improvement program would allow at least half of the present acreage used for pasture, or some 5,000 acres, to be converted back into timber production. It would also release some of the cropland being used for pasture at the present time. This cropland is needed in many cases for the production of winter roughage and would result in savings to the farmers by enabling them to grow more of their own livestock feed.

If at some future time, not now in prospect, this nation needs more dairy products in this region, much of the No. 3 and No. 4 land can be brought into use for pasture and hay. Stone removal at present prices would cost between $50 and $75 per acre. The clearing of land covered with trees would cost approximately $100 per acre, while clearing land which is both stony and wooded would cost around $150. Some soils areas may lend themselves to drainage, but much of the experience here with drainage has been discouraging. In most cases it has proven more profitable to clear new land

[3] R. G. Wheeler and J. D. Black, *Planning for Successful Dairying in New England*.

than to spend large sums for drainage works. Even in the case of seepage spots, tiling may or may not be practical in this area, depending upon the cost in relation to the benefits which will be derived from it. The stone removal on the No. 3 and No. 4 lands now in pasture was done by the early farmers gradually over the years from 1750 to 1830, at times of the year with little other work to do. But now that it has been done, it may well be advantageous to keep part of this land in pasture and for hay by methods now known — liming, fertilization, and reseeding with good grasses occasionally.

Along with increasing the productivity of the land now within the farms in this central part of Section A, there will be needed some further increase in the acreage within part of them. Only in this way will the returns per farm family keep up with the advancing returns to workers in industry and trade. The most strategic way for this increase in size to be achieved is for the farms firmly established but with not enough land to buy the land of those quitting farming because of age or other reasons. Credit may be needed to enable them to do this. Assistance in planning farm reorganizations and such enlargements will help greatly in promoting such a development.

Part-time farming also has a place in this area. The principal centers of it in this area are: a small section located around the center of the town of Hardwick, a rectangular area surrounding the more thickly settled section of the city of Barre, and a long narrow area in the southern part of the town of Barre which includes Barre Plains, South Barre, and White Village. These part-time farms located along main roads offer no problem from the standpoint of servicing. However, some of those in the town of Barre are located in areas which are questionable because they are on No. 3 and No. 4 land. In cases where land may be best suited for forestry and other extensive use, it may be in the best interest of the town to zone them against further increases in part-time farming units.

For the parts of the West Central Section with only a little farming, like Petersham and Princeton, and many similar areas elsewhere in the County, the analysis for Petersham in *Planning One Town — Petersham* serves present purposes pretty well. So far as full-time farming is concerned, the conclusion is that few if any new full-time farms have a place in the picture even as far off as 1975, but that there is still place for making the few existing full-time farms more productive by land improvement and by enlargement. The zoning map in Figure 33 does, however, show one small tract, marked F F B, where existing part-time farms could be developed into full-time farms. To quote exactly:

There are four types of situations in which this is feasible. The first is one in which the land now in crops and pasture is badly run down but will support a full-time farming operation if its productivity is restored. The second situation is where the farm has within its boundaries some old fields and pastures that have only recently been abandoned and hence are easily rehabilitated. The third situation is one in which a part-time farm can be enlarged by adding fields from other farms being abandoned, or part-time farms can be combined. An expansion of dairying is clearly indicated in all these three cases. The fourth situation is one in which the land base cannot be enlarged to advantage, but a poultry enterprise can be added, or possibly even a vegetable or small fruit enterprise. Market outlets will be important in both these cases, but especially in the latter.

The analysis in the Petersham report also fits part-time farming elsewhere in Section A and in the County. The following is therefore quoted from this report:

More important, especially in terms of numbers of families and population, will be changes within the part-time farming group; first, in the form of expanding somewhat the agriculture on existing part-time farms, and second in the form of developing some new ones. A large fraction of present part-time farms can readily increase their output by the same general type of improvements as indicated for the three part-time farms analyzed. Others can do it by adding a poultry enterprise of a few hundred hens. The reasons that present part-time farmers may expand their farming at this time are as follows:

1. The work week has been shortened.
2. New equipment suited to small operations is being developed.
3. More custom hiring is now possible.
4. New technologies increase the output with less labor — for example, the prepared feeds and sexed chickens available to poultrymen, and use of artificial insemination in dairying.
5. Part-time farmers are in a position of comparative advantage because of being able to operate farms as a supplement to off-the-farm work.

The factors that may work against an expansion of part-time farming operations are the following:

1. Workers with off-farm jobs have divided interests and do not give enough attention to their farms.
2. They are less likely to have the requisite farming skills.
3. They are less likely to keep informed as to new technologies.
4. They may be handicapped by the small scale of their operations.

These four reasons against expansion of part-time farming have always operated and have not acquired any new force of late. The reasons for expansion nearly all represent new developments favoring part-time farming. Hence, there seems to be reason to expect somewhat larger-scale part-time farming operations.

Most of the part-time farms, however, are considerably smaller than the three analyzed, and after expansion will still have no large volume of output for sale — less than $500 gross in a majority of cases.

The Symbol P F A on the Zoning Map indicates locations of part-time farms that may reasonably enlarge their operations. The Symbol P F B represents good locations for new part-time farms. Any new farms established in these latter locations are likely to have to content themselves with a few acres of already open land, or of land made available by clearing. They will tend, therefore, to be small-scale part-time farms, with the family living, including use of the dwelling, being clearly the larger part of the enterprise. Commonly one line of production only will be expanded to commercial scale.

The amount of part-time farming that develops in a community is dependent somewhat upon marketing and other facilities. Hence there are definite advantages in concentrating part-time farms on certain roads.

The zoning map in Figure 33 also singles out the present residential farming sites, marked R F A, and the potential ones, marked R F B. The R E S on the map indicates purely residential areas. The term residential farming covers a wide range in production;

at one extreme, families with only a small garden, and at the other those who grow their own potatoes, cut much of their own fuel-wood, and keep some chickens, a few pigs, and a cow, and perhaps even raise a heifer now and then. A few of these farms may have attached to them two or three hundred acres of woodland. Most of them, however, if they have any appreciable woodland at all, have only the amount that one would have found on a small farm 50 to 100 years ago, for many of these residential farms are nothing more or less than what has become of a farm too small to give a family a decent living after 1840. The remains of the old barn may have been made over into a garage. In some cases, the cropland was added to near-by farms sometime between 1840 and 1920, and the woodland may or may not have been bought along with the cropland. Many of the residential farms of today, however, have only one to two or three acres of land. The new ones established in the future will tend to have no more than an acre.

The future of residential farming in Petersham, and, for that matter, Worcester County generally, depends upon several major factors, which the Petersham report states as follows:

1. How many of our city families come to prefer having plenty of space, and rural surroundings, with a car to get them to town and back, to living on a city lot nearer to jobs, stores, movies, and so on.

2. How much industry and trade spreads out into the suburbs and smaller cities. Workers living five or ten miles out from Athol or Gardner are likely to be nearer to their jobs in time spent in travel than those living in Arlington or similar towns in Greater Boston.

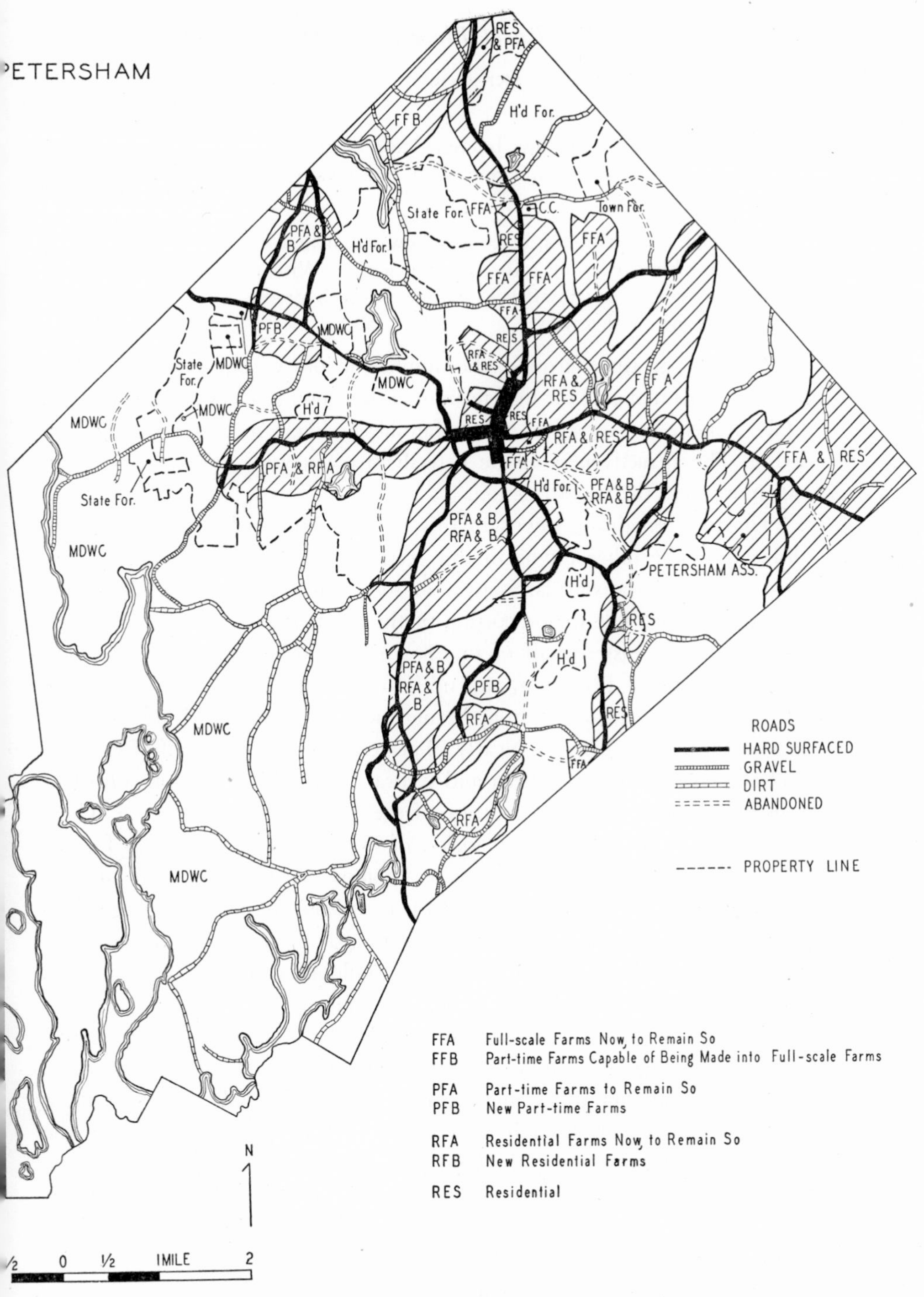

Figure 33. *Zoning map of the Town of Petersham.*

3. The public utilities and other facilities that rural towns make available to rural residential districts.

4. Most important of all, how interested the particular family is in producing fresh food for its own use, and commonly much more of it than it would think it could afford to buy.

5. Associated with No. 4 is, of course, how much time the family is willing to put into this kind of living rather than in leisure. With present working hours, most families have an abundance of time for such production for home use if they care to use it that way.

As with part-time farming, the number of jobs within easy driving distance is also a major factor in determining the amount of residential farming. Only a small percentage of urban families is likely to prefer this way of living. The attractiveness of the Petersham countryside, however, may call out more than the usual fraction.

The two remaining towns in this Section, Hubbardston and Rutland, differ from the other towns in this section of Worcester County in that they still have relatively large areas of soils which could be developed for agricultural use. The major portion of these better soils occur in an extensive belt in the eastern half of the Town of Rutland, extending over into the western tip of Princeton, and up into the southern and central part of Hubbardston. Charlton, Paxton, Bernardston, and Brookfield are the most prominent soils in this area. Nearly 70 percent of the eastern half of Rutland and 60 percent of the southern and central part of Hubbardston consist of soils in Group 1. The major portion of the remainder is in Group 3. There is ample land available for expansion of existing farms as well as for the development of new units in this area. Another alternative for better utilization of the land resources in this area is to expand the part-time farms into full-time operating units. There are many poultry farms in the town of Hubbardston. On the better soils, these could be combined with a dairy enterprise to make fuller use of the land resource.

Part of these lands in Hubbardston and Rutland, however, are in the MDWC holdings. Although these would be suitable for farming use from a physical standpoint, it does not seem economically feasible to develop them for such at this time even if these lands were to be relinquished by the MDWC. In the first place, the land pattern of these areas is such that the farming units would be isolated or scattered. Scattered farm units in this area certainly would add greatly to the cost of supporting services such as roads, electric power lines, and schools.

The forestry uses of these lands will be analyzed in the section following.

Little has been said in this chapter about the place of poultry farming in Section A. Figure 16 in Chapter 6 shows that Hubbardston produced 62,300 chickens in 1950 and 461,000 dozen eggs. It is, in fact, one of the three leading poultry towns of the County. There is no apparent reason for this except that probably a few enterprising poultrymen showed the way. As others followed their lead, they had the advantage that an area of concentrated poultry production has in buying and selling. There is a measure of this same concentration of poultry farming in New Braintree, Hardwick, and Oakham. Arable land which is scarce here is not a limiting factor in poultry farming. Instead, it tends to grow in locations where there is too little good land for other types of farming and where there are good roads to market.

WOODLAND POSSIBILITIES

Of the 196,132 acres in Section A, 115,406 acres or 59 percent is in woodland. Of this 43,029, or 37 percent, is in farms. Of the 73,200 acres remaining, about half is in public ownership and the rest mainly in relatively small nonfarming holdings. As compared with New England generally, and the rest of Worcester County, this creates a situation so far as ownership is concerned that is unusually favorable to the development of productive forestry. Tracts of the size of those in MDWC ownership, especially when combined with those in the Franklin and Hampshire County parts of the Quabbin Reservation, making a total of 72,000 acres of publicly owned forest in close proximity, provide an opportunity for combining good silvicultural management which is rarely equaled in this part of the nation.

Timber Resources

On the other side of the picture is the destruction of growing stands wrought by the 1938 hurricane. The woodlands in five of the eight towns were sample-cruised by the staff of the Harvard Forest as part of this project shortly after the hurricane. Estimates have been made for the other three towns on the basis of the data for the adjoining towns. Table 33 shows the percentage distribution by woodland land-use classes and estimated cubic volume of timber for the eight towns combined, excluding the MDWC holdings in Petersham and Hardwick, for which no volume estimates were available, in the volume columns, and all the MDWC holdings in the area columns. Basic to this distribution is the over-all situation that the forests of Worcester County are of the white-pine transition-hardwood type. A great proportion of the growing stock consists of hardwood species and the hurricane destroyed a large part of the standing timber, so that Worcester County like much of southern New England is in a condition in which it can contribute most to national needs by increasing its output of pulpwood, especially hardwood pulpwood, in the near future while increasing at the same time the capacity of the land to produce sawtimber.

TABLE 33

Distribution of the Woodland in West Central Worcester County According to Woodland Land-Use Classes in Terms of Acres and Cubic Volume

	Acres*	Percentage	Cubic feet** (thousands)	Percentage
Better Hardwood	24,890	29	16,166	23
Softwood-Better Hardwood	9,350	11	8,872	13
Softwood	5,435	6	5,913	9
Inferior Hardwood	12,240	15	7,551	11
Softwood-Inferior Hardwood	31,330	27	28,899	41
Indeterminate	1,300	2	153	2
Totals	84,540	100	70,400	100

* Excluding all MDWC lands.
** Excluding MDWC lands in the Quabbin Reservoir.

The softwood and mixed softwood stands average more volume per acre than the hardwood stands in spite of the fact that the hurricane destroyed most of the merchantable white pine. Approximately 40 percent of the estimated 70 million cubic feet is in Better Hardwoods or Softwood-Better Hardwoods, while somewhat over half of the volume is in the inferior woodland land-use classes. The large proportion of volume in inferior types is further evidence of the deteriorated condition of the woodlands in this area.

Although the distribution of stands according to age classes is not summarized in this analysis, the available data indicate that about 70 percent of the forested area supports forest growth less than 40 years old, about 10 percent in the 40 to 60 age class, and the remaining 20 percent in uneven-aged stands.

There are wide differences among the towns in the types of stands that are most prevalent. To the west in Barre, Hardwick, New Braintree, the Better Hardwood is most common; in Hubbardston, Oakham, and Rutland to the east, the Softwood-Inferior Hardwood type prevails. The better agricultural towns also have more than average amounts of Inferior Hardwoods.

The woodlands in the eight towns can also be grouped into three broad forest land-use areas. The groundwork for this classification are the results of the work of the Worcester County Land Use Planning Committee studies in 1938. Using the classification of existing forest cover types and general condition of growing stock, the entire County was divided into eight broad forest land areas. The eight towns fit into three of these as shown in Table 34.

TABLE 34

Classification of Forest Cover Types (in acres) by Towns in West Central Worcester County in 1938, by the Staff of the Harvard Forest

Land-use class	*Area No. 1* Hubbardston, Petersham	*Area No. 2* Princeton	*Area No. 6* Barre, Hardwick, Oakham, New Braintree, Rutland
Better Hardwood	15,756	3,890	24,663
Softwood-Better Hardwood	10,159	9,769	6,040
Softwood	5,769	1,400	6,461
Inferior Hardwood	281	465	153
Grand totals	31,965	15,524	37,317

Petersham and Hardwick are grouped in Forest Land-Use Area 1 in the table. Close to 70 percent of the area is in woodlands, and the soils are of those types which are primarily suitable for supporting better hardwoods. The present hardwood stands consist mainly of oak, maple, ash, and birch, which is a typical combination of species. This growing stock is largely transitional in character, midway between the northern hardwood forests of birch, beech, and maple and the central hardwood complex of oak and hickory. There also remain stands of almost pure white pine which grew on the abandoned farm lands. It was in these stands that the hurricane damage was heaviest.

Most of the woodlands in Princeton are typical of those in Forest Land-Use Area 4. Pine and northern hardwoods are not so common as in Area 1. A higher percentage of Princeton is in woodland than is the case in any other town in West Central Worcester County. Woodland grazing is not a problem in either Area 1 or Area 4.

The woodlands in Hardwick, New Braintree, Oakham, and most of Barre and Rutland are characteristic of those in Forest Land-Use Area No. 6.

This area also lies between the northern and central hardwood forests, and thus contains an intermingling of species characteristic of both areas. The better hardwoods include hard maple, white ash, red, black, and white oak, and hickory. The inferior hardwood species are largely gray birch, aspen, cherry, and oak stump sprouts. Most of the woodlands not in MDWC ownership are in farms and are heavily grazed, with the result that reproduction has been retarded. The soils are the type which will support better hardwoods and a greater proportion of softwood than in either Areas No. 1 or No. 4.

Oakham was one of a group of towns whose woodlands were analyzed more intensively in the early years of this project. After the hurricane, its woodland was classified as follows:

Better Hardwoods	811 acres
Inferior Hardwood	1,422
Softwood	430
Softwood-Inferior Hardwood	2,153
Recent cutover	111
Hurricane destroyed	571
Total	5,498 acres

By age classes, 18 percent of this woodland, including 160 acres of pine plantations, was put in the 1-to-20-year class, 60 percent in the 21-to-40-year class, 18 percent in the uneven-age class, and only 52 acres in the 41-to-60-year class. The Better Hardwoods were nearly all in the 20-to-40-year class.

A similar analysis for the woodlands of Rutland showed a larger proportion of Softwoods and Inferior Hardwoods, and less of the Better Hardwoods. The recommended treatments included the following for these inferior stands:

Pine is seeding in well beneath inferior hardwood species, particularly in the northern part of the town. This pine should be encouraged on the lighter soils; growing the pine for a time under partial shade of the inferior hardwoods may be advisable for protection against the white pine weevil.

The Hubbardston analysis classified all but 20 percent of its woodland as Softwood-Inferior Hardwood and concluded the following:

White pine occurs frequently, particularly in mixture with inferior hardwoods. Most of the groups of pine which were in the older age classes were destroyed by the hurricane. Damage from the storm was severe and widespread throughout the town; most of the merchantable timber has been salvaged.

Pine is seeding in well on abandoned pastures and fields. The sandy Brookfield soils seem to grow white pine better than good hardwood species.

Markets

Nothing needs to be said about markets for the woodland products in Section A beyond what has already been said for the County as a whole in Chapter 7, except to point out that a tract as large as that of the MDWC could have its own processing facilities and go further in developing its own outlets than is possible with many small independent holdings.

Management Alternatives

The management alternatives for woodland in farms, and for nonfarm holdings ranging in size from small acreages in residential farms up to tracts of several thousand acres, have already been analyzed sufficiently in the chapters "Planning One Forest" and "Planning One Town," Chapters 10 and 11, so that little specific needs to be said at this point. Attention here will be given mainly to three alternatives for the MDWC forest lands.

Excluding the MDWC lands, about 80 percent of the woodland in the towns of Barre, Hardwick, Oakham, and New Braintree is in farm ownerships averaging 80 acres of woodland per farm. Expansion of farming in this area is likely to be in the form of more intensive use of existing farm land, as very little of the woodland area is suitable for farming. The needed adjustments will probably involve shifting some of the poorer agricultural land to woodland use while converting some of the pastured woodland areas to more intensive farming. At any rate, the area in woodlands is not expected to change appreciably in the future. The management plans for the farm woodlands will involve the integration of forestry with other farm enterprises. An extension forester is available to provide technical information relating to cutting and marketing. Cooperative units similar in size to the 1,900-acre unit proposed for Petersham could be organized for more efficient use of equipment and skilled labor. However, it should be pointed out that successful operation of such units can be expected only through voluntary participation of the members and it is probable that only a small percentage of the farmers in a given area will accept this obligation. Assuming that one third of the farmers would respond to farm planning, a cooperative unit of 1,900 acres would require tracts scattered over an area as large as New Braintree or Oakham.

In the towns of Petersham and Princeton, only one third of the woodland area is in farm ownership and this fraction is likely to decrease as the needed adjustments in agriculture are made. Conditions in these towns more nearly favor the consolidation of adjacent ownerships into larger tracts than in the agricultural towns. Units up to 5,000 acres may be found to be the most efficient depending, of course, on ownership, access to roads, topography, and condition of the growing stock.

The soils in north Rutland and southeast Hubbardston favor the expansion of farming in this area. For this reason, some woodland area may in time be converted to farm land. On the other hand, continued purchasing of land by the MDWC may more than offset the acreage that is likely to be converted to agriculture. The proposals for management units are similar to those suggested for the towns of Petersham and Princeton.

Let us now turn to the MDWC tracts. These were acquired for the protection of the watershed which supplies water to the towns in the Boston area. Originally about 10,000 acres consisted of arable land, pasture, and brushland. The Commission organized a reforestation program to plant most of it to conifers. The planting period extended from 1926 to 1941, with approximately 9,000 acres planted mostly to red and white pine at a density of 1,200 trees per acre. Other species included some Norway spruce and hemlock. Early survival was about 90 percent, but hardwoods have now overtopped part of the stands.

Prior to purchase by the Commission, the Quabbin Area was the center of an active white pine lumbering industry. Some landowners managed their woodlands with a view to sustained-yield forestry. Evidence of this activity is the fact that the Commission sold 50,000,000 board feet of timber, mostly pine, from the area later inundated by the reservoir. Another 20,000,000 board feet of white pine is still standing. This is being used at the rate of 200,000 board feet a year to supply the lumber necessary for the maintenance and operation of the Commission's water supply operations. Of the 30,590 acres of MDWC land in Worcester County, 12 percent is in pine plantations, 17 percent is classed as Better Hardwoods, 20 percent as Inferior Hardwoods, 33 percent as Softwood-Inferior Hardwoods and the remaining 16 percent as Softwood and Softwood-Better Hardwood.

One obvious alternative open to the Commission is to continue its present intensity of management, which is about the equivalent of Intensity B as defined in Chapter 10. Improvement cuttings, thinnings, or other cultural treatment which require actual monetary investments are not contemplated except in limited amounts along roadsides or when labor is available in off-season in other departments. It may be that harvesting will be planned, under the supervision of the Commission's forester, in a manner that will insure prompt and valuable reproduction. If, in the future, markets were to become established for small timber so that thinnings and improvement cuttings would pay for the costs of harvesting them, an intensity even approaching that of Intensity A could be practiced. Even the existing intensity of management is considerably higher than the average for Worcester County.

It has been estimated that if an Intensity B program were continued, the gross annual income per acre would average as follows, given the same values per acre as in Table 11 in the Petersham report, though these values now seem somewhat high.

Better Hardwoods — 64 percent of full stocking............	$4.00
Softwood — Better Hardwoods — 57 percent of full stocking.	5.20
Softwoods (including pine plantations) — 52 percent of full stocking....................................	9.30
Inferior Hardwoods — 44 percent of full stocking.........	4.70

For the total acreage in the Quabbin and Worcester County tracts, the annual income will be $151,000 plus $42,000 from the pine plantations.

Intensity A is an obvious alternative. With estimating done in the same way as that by the Harvard Forest Staff for this intensity, the MDWC tracts will yield a gross annual income of $740,000 including $60,000 revenue from the pine plantations. But it is not likely that the Commission, nor for that matter any private owner, will embark on a program of such intensity at this time. For one thing, in the absence of a market for low-grade material a considerable long-range investment is involved. The Commission seems to look upon investments in forestry with disfavor unless they are necessary to maintain the value of the land for watershed purposes. Fortunately, in this area the management of land for timber production is compatible with management for watershed protection, so that past watershed improvement projects have also improved the capacity of the land for timber production. Another factor in achieving better forest management is the efficiency of the labor employed by the Commission.

The third alternative is to lease the cutting rights to a pulp company for a raw material base. The advantages of such a lease would accrue to both the Commission and nearby landowners as well as to the pulp company. The Commission and other owners of woodland would be provided with a market for small timber, thus making it feasible for them to practice better forest management, while the pulp company would be sure of at least a part of the raw material base necessary for continuous operation.

Under the existing form of management the annual pulpwood volume available from the MDWC lands, exclusive of pine, has been estimated to be 14,000 cords. Also about 8,000 cords have been estimated as available annually from intermediate cuttings in the pine plantations. This 22,000 cords would be about 20 percent of the total volume necessary for continuous operation of a 250-ton pulp mill. Concurrent with this pulpwood output would be a much larger volume of sawtimber to provide for a substantial sawmill industry.

OAKHAM TOWN

The report of the Oakham Country Life Committee does not present any mapping of the Town into areas needing similar adjustment, nor does it outline these readjustments. It was only a first-stage report. It does describe the natural features and resources of the Town, its land-use pattern and agriculture, and its people and institutions; and it traces the history of these. It reports the State Planning Board's classification of the land into 38 percent of "good adaptability" to agriculture, 46 percent of "limited adaptability," and 14 percent "unsuitable." The historical review points out two events that led to a decline in the number of farms, a temporary loss of market outlet for milk in Worcester City in 1923–1925, and the absorption of farm lands within the MDWC reservation. But these losses have been partly made up by the enlarging of dairy herds and poultry flocks.

As in this group of towns generally, around three fourths of what was open pasture has been allowed to grow up to brushy pasture, with the result that the cows and replacements are not getting more than a third of the pasture feed that could be economically provided. The town has never had any industry and the population is still 70 percent farm-rural. Only a fifth of the farm operators do any off-farm work. But summer homes are increasing in number, Worcester City being only nine miles away.

RUTLAND TOWN

The Country Life Committee report for Rutland was likewise a first-stage report. It brings out clearly the difference in the degree of development of the land resources of Rutland and the towns west of it. Fully half of Rutland's land was classified as of good adaptability to agriculture, yet only 14 percent of it was in crops or plowable pasture. Most of the commercial farming is concentrated in the southeastern part of the Town. The number of cows on farms has held up pretty well since 1925, and poultry farming has increased, but nothing like as much as in Hubbardston. It is broiler production that has increased most. Many of the farm operators or members of their families are employed in the sanitariums and health institutions located in the Town.

HUBBARDSTON

The agriculture and land use of Hubbardston have been briefly indicated at several points in the chapter. A few things about them are worthy of more particular attention, even though no Country Life Committee prepared any kind of a report for this town. The census data show a more pronounced decline in the percentage of cropland than in the adjacent towns, and in the number of cows on farms. The number of farms has fallen off two thirds since 1925, about the same as in Princeton, but much more than in Westminster adjoining to the northeast. As we shall observe in Chapter 16, the farmers in Westminster are largely Finnish, and work off the farm in Fitchburg and Leominster a good deal. Still, they do a good bit of farming along with their off-farm work. Very many of the Hubbardston farm families are Finns also, but they have shifted strongly to poultry farming. Two thirds of the family income in 1950 was still from farming. This shift to poultry means less growing of forage for livestock and the use of more cropland as poultry range.

It is also of interest that some of the abandoned former pasture land in this town, as in Westminster, is now growing blueberries in the same way as in Washington County, Maine. The birch and other light-seeded species are kept mown and the blueberry fields are usually burned over every third year to start new clusters of fruit-bearing stems.

Cooperative marketing of the blueberries along with the buying of feed and selling of eggs and poultry, through the United Farmers' Cooperative with headquarters in Fitchburg, has been an important factor in these developments.

CHAPTER 13

Section E, Southwest Section

The Southwest Section of Worcester County, Section E, is chosen for analysis next because it is adjoining the West Central, and because it is also very largely agricultural. In fact, it is the most agricultural section of Worcester County, with 50 percent of its land in farms in 1954, as compared with 36 percent in Section A. Not only this, but since 1925 less of its land has been retired from farming than has been the case in any other section.

This relatively stable use of land for farming is, however, not distributed uniformly throughout Section E. In the north and west, North Brookfield and Warren had over 30 percent of their total land area in crops in 1954; Spencer, West Brookfield, and Charlton had between 20 and 30 percent; and Sturbridge and Dudley in the south had less than 10 percent.

Two of the eleven towns in this southwest section, Charlton and North Brookfield, were in the group of ten studied intensively in this project. These two, along with Oxford and Spencer, were also reported upon by Country Life Committees.

The farming in this Section is predominantly dairying and poultry raising, but in no town is the dairying quite as important as in New Braintree and Hardwick in Section A. North Brookfield, Spencer, Warren, and Charlton come nearest to it. Spencer, North Brookfield, and East Brookfield are the leading poultry towns. Oxford, situated nearest to Worcester City, has by far the most apples and vegetables, with Warren next in apples and Dudley next in vegetables.

SECTION E. GENERAL

A good part of the analysis of this chapter will be confined to the individual towns receiving special attention, but some general treatment is needed to provide the setting.

Population and Industry

Although the Southwest Section has more agriculture than Section A, it also has more industry. The four manufacturing enterprises of Barre largely gave that town a population of 3,590 in 1955 with factory payrolls of $3,000,-000; the twenty-seven in Southbridge Town gave it a population of 17,300 with payrolls of $21,600,000. Southbridge is one of the centers of the manufacture of optical goods in the nation. Spencer's population was 7,600 and Dudley's 5,600. Charlton's was about the same as Barre's, however, and likewise those of North Brookfield and Warren.

In Table 35 are assembled the available data for the 11 towns on present population and changes since 1850, on population on farms in 1950, and on the principal industries and the range in number employed. These towns have a highly diversified set of industries with, however, more dependence on textiles, and especially woolens, than is good in view of the general movement of these lines of manufacturing to the South. Figure 5 in Chapter 5 showed that the industry of some of these towns has had setbacks in the past — Spencer, Warren, and North Brookfield, for example.

The towns with very little industry, like the Brookfields, Sturbridge, and Charlton, have gained little in population over the years. In general the farm population of the towns is about proportional to the area of the town, as is shown in the outline maps of the town in the figures in Chapter 6.

Some of the population of these towns is supported by recreation, mainly in the form of summer residence and camping on the numerous lakes, several of which are quite large: Quaboag Pond in Brookfield, Wickaboag Pond in West Brookfield, Lake Lashaway in North and East Brookfield, and Cedar and Long Ponds in Sturbridge.

Plane of Living

According to Figure 9 in Chapter 5, the indexes of the plane of living for the eleven towns in Section E averaged 4 points above the County average of 155 in 1945. But the indexes of Warren and its two adjoining towns averaged only 132. The high indexes are those for Sturbridge, 173, and the towns nearest Worcester City.

The Land

The topography and soils of this Section of Worcester County are much like those of Section A. But the Brookfield and Charlton series replace the

TABLE 35

Population and Industry, Southwest Section of Worcester County

Town	Population (1955)	People on farms (1950)	Population (1850)	Principal industries	Range in employment
Spencer..........	7,611	421	2,000	Shoes	800–1,350
N. Brookfield....	3,455	306	1,400	Rubber soles	150– 350
W. Brookfield....	1,935	179	1,100	Small	——
E. Brookfield....	1,391	129	——*	Small	——
Brookfield.......	1,774	156	1,300	Wire, gummed	100– 250
				paper, and tape	100– 250
Warren..........	3,509	319	1,200	Clothing,	250– 500
				pumps,	100– 250
				other	150– 300
Sturbridge.......	3,411	239	2,000	Textiles,	100– 250
				tools	100– 250
Southbridge.....	17,271	133	2,000	Optical goods,	2,500–5,000
				worsted	750–1,000
				textiles,	300– 750
				cutlery	200– 500
Dudley..........	5,596	414	1,100	Woolens,	250– 500
				towels,	250– 500
				other	200– 450
Charlton........	3,466	609	1,900	Woolens	150– 350
Oxford..........	7,777	231	2,106	Wooden boxes,	100– 250
				woolens	100– 250

* Included in Brookfield.

Gloucester except in western West Brookfield and West Warren Towns, and there is less Rough Stony land except in these two areas and toward the southern border of the Section. This means that except on the outward edges, the topography is slightly less broken and the elevation a little lower. This accounts in part for the lakes along the stream courses, and more swampy land and dark-colored Hinckley and Merrimac soils. The Charlton soils are dominant in Charlton Town and southern Spencer. Of course, it was in Charlton that this series was first identified and named. The Sutton series is dominant in Dudley.

In Figure 34, these soils are grouped into the same four classes as in Figure 32 for Section A. It is very easy to see from this map why the agriculture of this section continues to flourish, most of all in North Brookfield and Charlton, but also in Dudley, Spencer, and Oxford, and why there is

Figure 34. ***Classification of the land of the Southwest Section of Worcester County (Section E) into four classes according to adaptability to agriculture.***

so much less of it in the rest of the towns except Warren. The figures in Chapter 6, however, show Warren with about as much agriculture as the five first named, although all but the southeast third of the town has mostly rough stony Gloucester and Brookfield soils. Other evidence indicates that enough of this land has been kept in sufficiently productive pasture to support a sizable and continuing dairy industry. One explanation of the use of these less favorable soils for agriculture is that the early settlers chose their farm lands either without knowing which were the better soils or with their eye on defense from the Indians or nearness to roads and to the established towns. Once they had finished the back-breaking toil of moving the stones off the land into fences or "walls," they

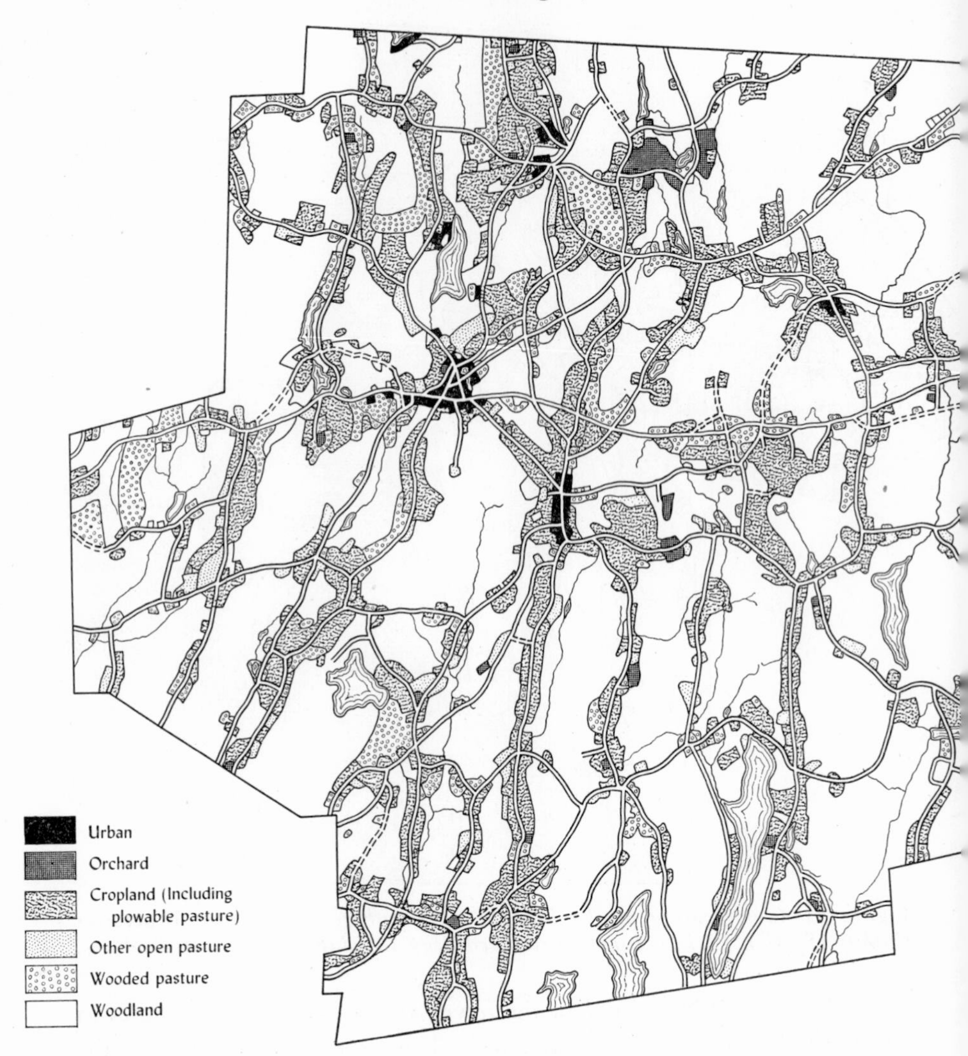

Figure 35. ***Physical features, villages and roads, and land use, Charlton Town, 1937.***

continued to farm it. Under proper methods of management, much of the Gloucester stony loam will give satisfactory yields if enough stones are removed to permit mechanized equipment to be used.

Full planning analyses were made of 15 farms in Charlton and North Brookfield in 1938, all dairy farms except one poultry farm in Charlton, one poultry and one poultry-dairy in North Brookfield, and one fruit and one vegetable farm in North Brookfield. One of the dairy farms was essentially part time. All but one of these farms, a dairy farm, was operating in 1945, and only one more had ceased operating a decade later. The dairy herds in Charlton averaged 21 cows in 1938, 28 in 1945, and 26 in 1954—one of the farms no longer renting a second farm and hiring a helper. The dairy herds in North Brookfield averaged 24 in 1938, 26 in 1945, and 44 in 1954—two of them had bought or rented other farms and had become large-scale operations. Of the 15 farms, 11 were still being operated by the same families.

In addition, a small group of the part-time and residential farms included in the short-schedule survey were studied much less intensively to discover what the nature of their problems were and what might be done to help them.

CHARLTON TOWN

Figure 35 shows in the same detail as Figure 29 for Hardwick Town the physical features, land use, and so forth for Charlton Town, except that no separation is made of "open pasture, usually stony," and "wooded pasture." They are combined as "other pasture" in this map. Open and wooded pasture merge into each other in a hardwood area like this and the State Planning Board field surveyors were unable to distinguish the two clearly.

Figure 35 can be matched with Figure 36, which shows in much more detail the classification of soils than does Figure 34. Unfortunately, the State Planning Board's map upon which this is based does not use quite the same classification as that used in Figure 34. The No. 1 and No. 3 classifications are closely the same. All land classed as No. 3 in this map would be classed as No. 3 in Figure 34. No. 5 is included as No. 4 in Figure 34. Most of No. 2 on this map is classed as No. 1 in Figure 34, but the droughtier and the sandy and gravelly parts of it are put in No. 4 in Figure 34.

Such matching shows that for the most part only narrow strips of Class 1 land along the roads were cleared for farming and left in crops and plowable pasture. The "other pasture" usually adjoining it along the same road in the area was mostly not cleared of stones and much of it had grown up to brush and trees. It thus appears that a large area of even Class 1 land in Charlton is not now being used either for crops or pasture, and probably never was for the most part. This is particularly true in the southern half of the Town.

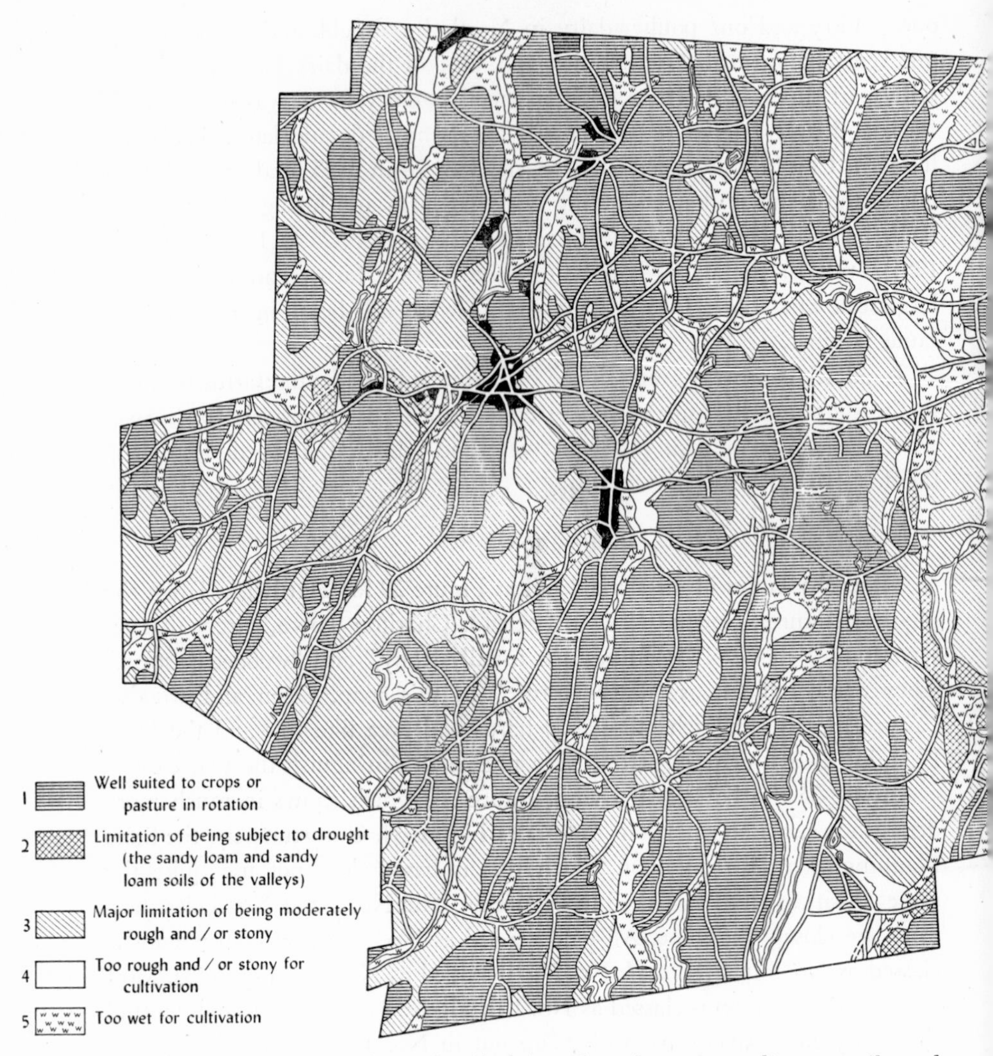

Figure 36. ***Land of Charlton classified into five classes according to soils and use adaptability.***

Another thing which shows up in Figure 36 is the network of small valley streams which thread this area. The streams are sluggish, leaving the land in these valleys mostly too wet for cultivation. This of course is a phenomenon resulting from the geologically recent settling of the earth's surface along the coast of New England and as far inland as parts of Worcester County.

Agriculture

The initial 1937 short-schedule survey of the farms of Charlton identified a large sample of 23 dairy farms, 2 fruit farms, 20 part-time farms, and 80 residential farms. Following were the principal facts about these farms at that time:

Dairy farms (23)

Size — from 9 to 70 cows; 6 with 10 or under. Average, 20.
— from 40 to 460 acres; 9 with 100 or less. Average, 178.
— from 20 to 145 crop acres, 7 with 30 or less. Average, 50.
— total pasture, 6 to 226 acres, 9 with 40 or less. Average, 84.
(only 2 reported woodland pasture separately).

Woodland — 15 farms had woodland, an average of 69 acres per farm, of which only 3 acres were pastured.

Crops — 16 had an average of 6.5 acres of silage corn, 18 an average of 5 acres of oats, 13 an average of 3 acres of millet, 5 an average of 7.4 acres of alfalfa, 10 an average of 10 acres of mixed clover hay, and 21 an average of 40 acres of mixed grass hay.

Working force — 8 of the operators worked off the farm some part of the year, 16 of the farms hired a total of 29 different laborers part-time or full-time, and 7 percent of the farms had 10 sons sixteen years or older. Only 6 had milking machines and 4 were operating retail routes.

Housing — It will be of interest to outsiders that 13 of the farm dwellings were 100 years or older (oldest 160), yet only one house was reported in poor condition.

Fruit farms (2)

The 2 fruit farmers each had around 30 acres of apples and nothing else.

Part-time farms (20)

Size — from 1 to 200 total acres, 6 with 20 or less. Average, 40.
— crop acres from ½ to 44 acres, 5 with 10 or less. Average, 14.
— pasture, 14 with an average of 16.5 acres.

Woodland — 7 with an average of 36 acres.

Livestock — 17 with a total of 37 cows, 14 with 21 heifers; 15 averaging 70 hens (one with 300, another with 200, one raising 900 chicks and another 750). The one-acre part-time farm kept 300 hens and the 2-acre farm kept 2 cows and had 60 hens and raised 170 chicks.

Working force — 10 of the farm families had boys sixteen or over, 3 hired some labor.

Residential farms (80)

Size — from 4 to 430 total acres, 12 with 10 or less. Average, 38.
— crop acres from 0.1 to 85 acres, 23 with 2 or less. Average, 11.
— pasture, 28 with an average of 35 acres, but 700 acres of this was on 5 farms renting out pasture land.
— livestock — 18 farms had a total of 24 cows, 31 averaged 26 hens, and 24 averaged 63 chicks.

The averages for these residential farms mean very little because at one extreme are several families living on large holdings and renting out the pasture and hayland and keeping no livestock themselves, and at the other are a large number of workingmen's families with a few chickens and a garden.

Case Studies

Several of the individual farms that were analyzed in detail at that time can be used to illustrate the type of problems they faced and ways of meeting them.

Dairy Farms

Farm AB — This was one of the larger dairy farms. It was operated by the family with little outside help. Its main problem was to increase the productivity of the land so as to support a larger herd and earn a larger family income. A secondary problem was the considerable erosion under way on its sloping Paxton and Sutton soils. Its dairy herd was already being well managed with a production of over 7,000 pounds of milk per cow and adequate replacements being raised. The revised plan worked out with the family called for improving 25 acres of pasture partly with ladino clover so as not to have to feed silage in the summer, and keeping ten more cows; also for substituting clover and timothy for mixed grasses on 30 acres, and growing 9 more acres of millet for silage. The farm was already growing 13 acres of corn silage and 18 acres of alfalfa. The erosion problem was to be solved mostly by not growing corn on the steeper slopes of the drumlin and using longer rotations with reseeding with oats, hay, or silage without an intervening corn crop. If corn was to be grown on any too sloping land, strip cropping was to be practiced. A question left open was whether to keep on renting pasture for the young stock or improve still more pasture. The farm had 80 acres of brushy pasture that could be improved.

Farm ML—The main problem on this farm was that only 25 acres of its present 90 was cropland and the rest was mostly brushy pasture. This did not provide an adequate income. The situation was being met in part by renting the land of another 80-acre farm not too far away, but this arrangement was only on a year-to-year basis. The cropland on the home farm was mostly of Merrimac soil. The remainder on the two farms was Charlton. The herd consisted of twenty-one milk cows and only three replacements. Production per cow was below 5,000 pounds. A supplementary source of income was 3.5 acres of sweet corn. The farmer had used little fertilizer in the past. The revised plan called for improving 10 acres of improved pasture and substituting clover and timothy for mixed grass hay on the home farm; using more fertilizer; feeding 800 more pounds of the improved roughage per cow but less purchased concentrates and still getting more milk per cow; keeping ten head of replacements instead of three and building up the quality of the herd.

Farm KL—This was also a small dairy farm of 80 acres of land and none rented, with nine cows and no replacements, and production below 4,500 pounds per cow. The problem was to increase the income of this family from the farm, and, if this could not be done adequately, to buy more land or find more employment off the farm. The older of the young sons was working full-time off the farm at the time. It was decided first to test out the possibilities of the first alternative. Only 25 acres of the land was in crops and none of the pasture was improved. The revised plan called for keeping twelve cows, raising three heifers a year, as a result of improving 10 acres of pasture, growing 8 acres of alfalfa instead of none, 3 acres of clover and timothy instead of none, and fertilizing freely. Feed bills would be reduced and production per cow raised 1,000 pounds. Net farm income would be expected to be doubled. But there would still be need for some off-farm work by the farmer or his younger son as well as by the older son, if this family was to live as well as those on full-time commercial family farms in the area.

Part-time Farms

The main question for most of the part-time families was how much farming they wished to do. Many of them had land or buildings enough to support more farming than they were then doing. In fact, many of the farms had formerly been operated as full-time family farms, but their land had been partly or largely abandoned to brush and trees when they found off-farm work that paid them better than farming on their inadequate farms. With a shorter week in prospect, many of these part-time farmers could bring some of this land back into use if they cared enough for the additional income. Or they could expand their poultry enterprise. Indeed, even with the technology known at the time when their land was allowed to revert to brush, some of these farms could have been made to yield adequate incomes.

Farm WH illustrates these possibilities for a part-time dairy farm. It had 15 acres of cropland in 1937, 17 of open pasture, and 25 acres of brushy pasture and carried three cows and a small flock of hens. Replacing the mixed-grass hay crop with an alfalfa mixture and improving the open pasture by fertilizing and liming and reseeding with a ladino clover mixture would have made this farm support at least six cows and replacements.

In similar manner, a somewhat smaller part-time dairy-poultry farm with 10 acres of cropland and 15 acres of poor open pasture could have been made to support four cows and replacements in place of two, and could have used the full capacity of the poultry house — 400 hens, plus 1,500 chicks — instead of the 75 hens, plus 150 chicks raised in 1937.

A third part-time farm was combining two cows with 4 acres of sweet corn and other vegetables in 1937. It had crop and pasture land enough for five cows and replacements with the same or less vegetables as desired.

Residential Farms

Of the four residential farms briefly investigated, two of them had land-use possibilities of producing as much as the part-time farms just described, but the heads of the household had full-time off-farm jobs and restricted their farming to the family vegetables and small fruit plus 15 hens in one case and one cow in the other. Another was a 200-acre farm six miles from town with the hay sold standing and the pasture rented. The only farming activity was a family garden. The fourth, that of a retired skilled tradesman, had only two acres, a family garden, a half-acre orchard, and a few hens.

Woodland

Counting both farm and nonfarm woodlands, Charlton had 18,400 acres of woodland in 1941, of which about one half was Better Hardwoods and one fourth each Inferior Hardwoods and Softwoods-Inferior Hardwoods. The description written at this time was as follows:

> Clear-cutting has been quite common in the hardwood stands before they reach saw-timber size. Most of the stands contain small-sized trees, a large percentage of which are of stump-sprout origin. Oak and hickory are the predominating hardwood types. Red, black and white oak are also quite common. Favored gypsy moth food trees are prevalent. There is some grazing of the farm woodlots. The better stands occur on the upland areas of large tracts that are not grazed as heavily or cut as frequently as the more accessible areas. Softwood is quite scarce. Nearly all the older trees were blown down or severely damaged by the hurricane. There are a few white pine trees scattered through the woodland areas. These white pines generally mix with inferior hardwoods rather than occur in pure stands. Probably not over 10 percent of the timber is softwood. The woodland soils are mostly Charlton sandy and stony loams capable of producing a good growth of better hardwood saw-timber species.

The general management recommended by Raymond and Chute was as follows:

(1) Improvement cuttings should be made to favor the best formed trees of good species.
(2) Weedings should be made on the younger stands to improve the composition and quality by the control of inferior elements.
(3) The gypsy moth food trees, particularly the oaks and the gray birch, should be reduced materially.
(4) No treatment is recommended for the areas of very low stocking. The greatest need in these sections is the discontinuance of cutting in order to provide time for the woodland to be built up to better stocking.
(5) A few small areas should be planted where the present stands are entirely inferior or where conversion to a valuable crop can be made only by planting, as in abandoned pastures.
(6) Grazing should be eliminated to permit reproduction to become established.

Almost needless to state, these recommendations, like those of the Harvard Forest staff for Section A, are somewhat in advance of their time — the holders of timberland are for the most part not ready for this level of management.

For each of the six farms for which case analyses were made in Charlton in 1939, the woodlands were mapped out in stands and treatments were prescribed for each stand in the manner described in Chapter 11 on Hardwick Town. Only 35 percent of these woodlands were Better Hardwoods, but 12 percent were Softwoods. Also 18 percent were classified as Indeterminate because of the hurricane destruction of 1938. An estimate was made of the annual income from these stands if managed as they had been, and if managed as recommended. The comparison was $1.40 per acre as against $4.60 per acre, these in terms of future timber values as anticipated before the war.

Sub-area Units

The Country Life Committee classified the land of Charlton Town as follows: 2 area units, making up 25 percent of the Town land then in farms, as needing only "minor agricultural adjustments"; 5 area units, making up 9 percent of the Town then in farms, as needing "major agricultural adjustments"; 1 area unit making up 2 percent of the Town then in farms as "suited only to poultry and residential use"; 7 area units making up 61 percent of the Town as land not then in farms and not immediately suited to agriculture except poultry, part-time, and residential farming; and finally 7 urban and industrial areas each making up less than 1 percent of the Town.

Only the land in the first 7 of these area units, or 34 percent of it, was classified as agricultural. The farms outside these units were mostly part-time or residential. The report made scarcely any land-use recommendations by area units, and those made of a general nature were much like those in the revised plans for the case study farms and the previous woodland suggestions. The principal exception was a small area in the northern part of the County that was designated as dairy-fruit. This was proposed as an extension of a larger dairy-fruit area in Spencer to the north. The land is rolling to hilly and the orchards in Spencer were on carefully selected slopes and in sufficiently open country to give good air drainage. Keeping the ground covered with a good growth of mixed hay with mulching under the trees had kept the soil in good condition.

Off-farm Work

The sample survey of this Town included a canvass of the off-farm workers that may well serve as a good case study of off-farm work.

8 dairy farmers — 4 in textile mills, and 1 each in shoes, metal, highway work, and WPA. But these 8 farm families had 12 other members working off the farm, in factories, stores, garages, etc.

14 part-time farmers — 4 in textile mills, and 1 each of the following — postmaster, town officer, storekeeper, truck driver, printer, house wrecker, road worker, shoe factory worker, and wire maker. The farm families had 8 other members working off the farm.

50 residential farms — in 22 different occupations ranging from 10 in

textiles, and 8 in metals, 6 in stores or restaurants, and 3 on WPA., to 2 firemen, a contractor, and a college professor. And 20 sons and daughters worked in town.

Erosion

A final word is needed on the subject of erosion. Mr. N. P. Tedrow reported on this as follows:

The most sheet erosion in this Town occurs on the Paxton soils. When this soil becomes saturated with water above the hardpan layer, it erodes very easily. The most serious erosion occurs in the spring on fields that were plowed the previous fall. It is a general custom to plow all fields in the fall that are to be planted to corn the following spring. Cover crops are not often used. Some sheet erosion also occurs on the steeper slopes of other soil types.

The fields in this town are larger than those of many of the neighboring towns. As a general rule the slopes are fairly uniform. Contour strip cropping is practical on slopes over 5 percent. By alternating sod strips with cultivated strips the amount of erosion can be greatly reduced. Strips should not exceed 100 feet in width. The width of strip should be decreased as the slope increases. Long rotations such as are used at the present time, with hay occupying six to ten years in the rotation, aid in controlling erosion. Winter cover crops should be used whenever possible. The pasture land responds well to fertilizer treatment. However, very little erosion is observed on pastures. The shortage of cropland in this town makes it very difficult to convert even the steepest cropland into pasture or woodland.

NORTH BROOKFIELD

The agriculture and land use of North Brookfield is enough like that of Charlton so that to report upon it in the same detail would be repetitious. The town is only about half the size of Charlton, but in 1950 it had about 60 percent as many farms. More of the land was in crops — in 1950 the comparison was 37 percent and 20 percent, as is clear from Figure 37. The reason for this is apparent in Figure 34, which shows almost 70 percent of the land classed as No. 1, suitable for agriculture without limitations. Figure 15 in Chapter 6 shows more cows and more milk production in North Brookfield than in Charlton, and Figure 6 also more poultry.

The soils of North Brookfield are mainly of the Brookfield and Paxton series, with no Charlton. The central 60 percent of the Town is Brookfield loam with about fifteen drumlins of Paxton soil. East and west from this center the land is rougher and largely Brookfield stony loam. There is strong relief, however, in the central portion — several rounded hills of 1,000 feet or over, with a network of brooks with muck land in their valleys and

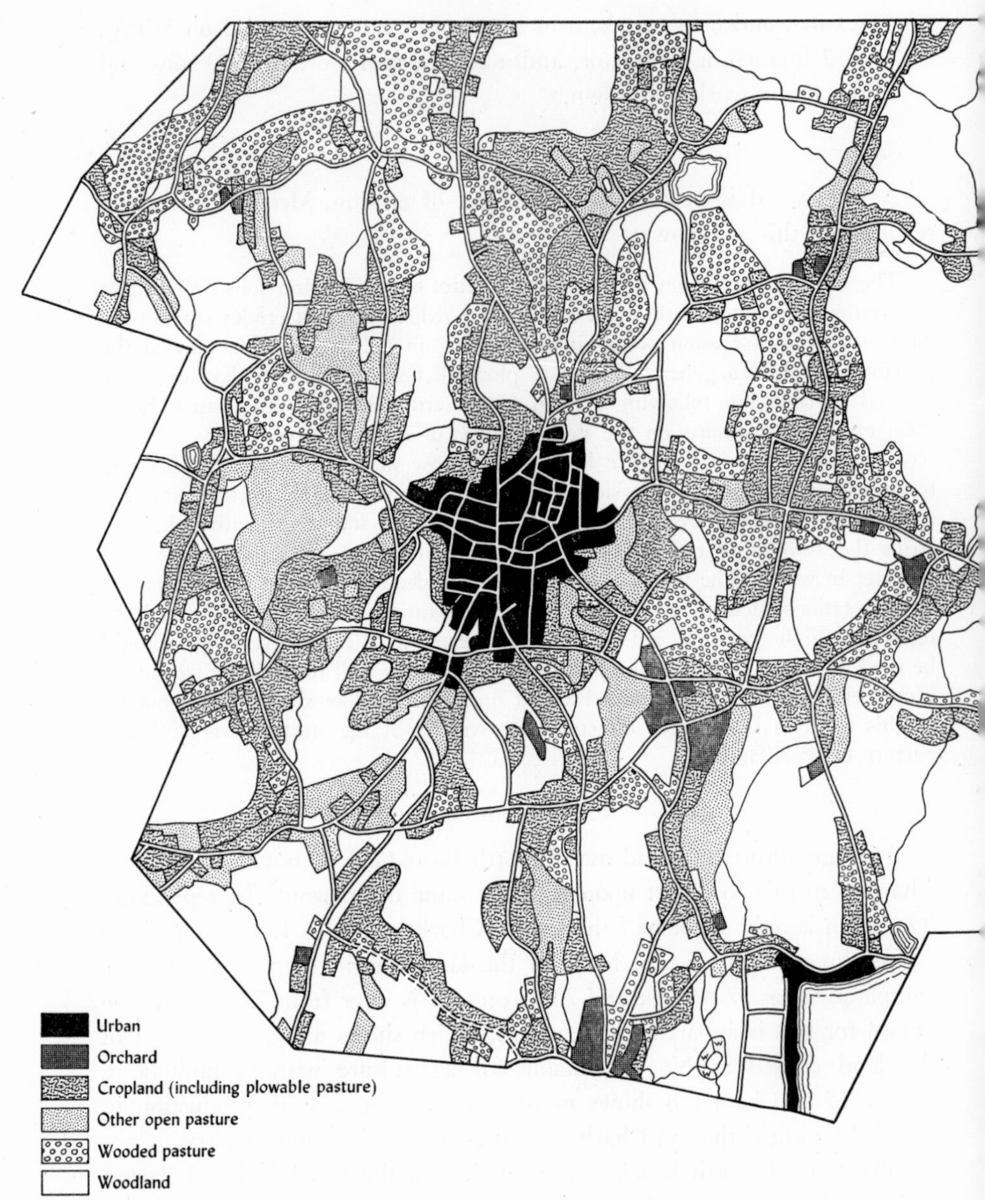

Figure 37. *Physical features, villages and roads, and land use, North Brookfield Town, 1937.*

swales. Horse Pond in northern North Brookfield has a water level elevation of 918 feet; Lake Lashaway at the southeastern corner, of 618 feet. The Country Life Committee of North Brookfield classified 74 percent of the land as "agricultural," that is, suited to agriculture.

The initial 1937 short-schedule survey identified a total of 178 farms, divided by acreage as in Table 36, and analyzed as follows: dairy, 49; poultry, 7; dairy-poultry, 4; fruit, 3; part-time, 29; residential, 81. This is clearly a larger proportion of commercial farms than in Charlton.

TABLE 36

Average Acreages in Each Land Use by Type of Farm in North Brookfield in 1937

Type of farm	*All land*	*Cropland*	*Pasture*	*Woodland*
Dairy	115	36	65	7
Poultry	34	4	24	3
Dairy-poultry	143	52	77	10
Fruit	53	47	2	2
Part-time	42	19	12	8
Residential	23	7	5	8

Case Studies

It is obvious from the foregoing that the agriculture of North Brookfield was considerably diversified. The case studies involved 4 dairy farms, 1 poultry farm, 1 dairy-poultry farm, 1 fruit farm, and 1 vegetable farm. All that will be reported here for the dairy farms are special situations not considered elsewhere in this study. One of these dairy farms was a fairly large one that was carrying too many milk cows for its present output of forage and pasture feed. As a result it was raising only part of its replacements and production per cow was not high enough. It would have paid the farmer to cull out a fifth or more of his poorer cows and improve his herd by raising more of the replacements for it. But the full solution would have included raising more forage of a better quality and improving his pasture. A large part of his pasture, however, was on sloping fields not lending themselves easily to reseeding in a long rotation. A better alternative would have been to increase greatly the yields on his level, somewhat moist land by using a mixture including alsike and ladino clover, and a light alfalfa mixture on the nearly level land.

The problem of a small dairy farm was that half of the cropland was of

Rumney soil that is too wet for rotations including corn. A rotation of millet, oats, and hay for six years was chosen for this land, and, in order to increase the output of the rest and also of the better pasture land, heavier fertilization, planting more legumes, and other measures were recommended.

The problem of another farm in 1937 was that it had found no good wholesale outlet for its milk. Surely this has been solved by this time.

The dairy-poultry farm in 1937 was a good example of an adequate income built up on a small acreage, first, by getting a good output from the crop and pasture land and high output per cow, and, second, by adding as much poultry as the family could find time to care for — 550 layers and 1,200 chicks. The only improvement considered was to include more legumes in the hay and pasture and reduce the concentrate feeding from 2,300 to 1,700 pounds per cow.

The revised plan for the poultry farm called for doubling its size to increase the family income. This called for improving five acres more land for poultry range.

The large apple orchard whose management was analyzed had suffered greatly from the hurricane. The new plan called for a more rigorous program of replacements and more careful handling of the removal of fillers and replacements at the right time.

The vegetable farm studied was growing seven different vegetables on 25 acres of Merrimac sandy loam and other level low-lying soils. The major question considered was whether or not the family would expand this enterprise to provide an occupation for two sons coming along. Part of the land needed could be provided by reclaiming additional wet land. The rest would have to be bought or rented. Plans were worked out for the two alternatives. The vegetables grown were principally beans, squash, cabbage, carrots, beets, and tomatoes. The balance of these from year to year to fit the demands of the market was a difficult problem.

Erosion

Tedrow's comments on erosion in North Brookfield contain the following statements: "Much of the crop and pastureland is located on the drumlins or smooth rounded hills. Alfalfa has not been successful with most farmers. The soils are very acid and lime has not been used in large quantities. This may be one reason for so many failures with alfalfa." "The pastureland should be treated with lime and fertilizer to maintain a heavy sod.

Continued neglect of the pastures will result in a large percentage of the present pastureland returning to woodland."

Woodlands

The 56 percent of North Brookfield that was in woodland was 45 percent Better Hardwoods, dominantly oak-hickory. Nearly 70 percent of the woodland was in farms. Gray birch was the dominant Inferior Hardwood. Clear-cutting of the young hardwoods for fuelwood had resulted in prolific sprouting of the oaks, maple, and gray birch on much of this land. It would therefore take four or five decades before really merchantable sawtimber could be produced.

The careful analysis by Raymond and Chute of all the 94 stands in the Town came out with the conclusion that if the recommended treatments were more fully carried out on all of these stands, they would eventually yield, at future values for timber products as anticipated in 1940, an average of $5.40 per acre annually, as compared with $1.50 with the present practices continued — $4.50 for the Better Hardwoods, $9.00 for the small acreage of Softwoods, and $6.00 for the mixed stands.

Country Life Committee Report

The recommendations of this Committee stressed the following:

1. Getting three empty factory buildings occupied again so as to provide more off-farm employment.
2. Correcting the small size of many dairy farms and the smallness of many of the fields enclosed by stone walls.
3. Improving the quality of the hay.
4. Pasture improvement.
5. Raising more replacements.
6. Investigation of practical methods of farm woodlot management.

SPENCER

The Country Life Committee for Spencer put 40 percent of its land in the class of "good adaptability" and 40 percent in the class of "limited adaptability," but did not get to the stage of marking out sub-unit areas and making recommendations for each. Figure 34 indicates, however, that half the land is in Classes 3 and 4, and only 35 percent was in cropland and open pasture in 1937. The soil survey map indicates that the soils of the northern half of the Town are like those of North Brookfield and those of the southern half like those of Charlton. The State Planning Board's maps show the good soils more fully utilized in farming in the northern half than in the south.

Figure 16 in Chapter 6 indicates that Spencer is one of the leading poultry towns in the County, having produced 345,200 dozens of eggs in 1950. It also sold 569,600 chickens in that year. It is thus outstandingly a broiler-producing area. It is nearer to North Brookfield than to Charlton in dairy output per unit of area. The number of cows has remained about constant since 1920.

Spencer's population in 1955 was 7,611 as compared with 8,750 in 1800, 6,000 in 1850, and 6,500 in 1935, and has fluctuated mainly since 1850 with the prosperity of the shoe industry in its central city, Spencer.

The Raymond-Chute woodland analysis for Spencer summarizes the situation as follows: the Spencer woodlands resemble those of North Brookfield and Charlton more nearly than those of other towns studied in the project. The northern part of the town is similar to North Brookfield while the southern part is comparable to Charlton. There are extensive areas of young, even-aged, coppice hardwood. The numerous stump sprouts and the even-aged character of the stands are indicators of the past practice of clear-cutting. There has been some softwood planting in the Spencer State Forest. White pine, red pine, and spruce were most widely used. The farm woodlands are heavily grazed. The stocking has been reduced by preventing the establishment of adequate reproduction; the soils have been compacted, lowering their fertility.

OXFORD

The only facts in the report of Oxford's Country Life Committee that differentiate this town importantly from adjoining Charlton are brought out in the following statements:

Approximately 75 percent of the people engaged in industrial employment in Oxford work out of town. Many people have moved into or built homes in Oxford during the past year or two who work in Worcester or Webster. It is of great importance to people and agencies in considering future policies for the town to know whether the trend in Oxford is toward a residential suburb of Worcester and Webster, toward a small industrial and agricultural center in its own right, or both . . . People who may establish residence in Oxford would help to support the town and strengthen the community as long as they are satisfactorily employed. If they should become unemployed, then the tables would be turned and the town would have to assist in supporting them. The present trend seems to be in the direction of further residential development.

This should be recognized and local policies adopted which will make for maximum utilization of this development and lessen the possible potential difficulties which could develop under adverse conditions.

This is much the same problem that confronts Petersham and is analyzed in the report on that town by Black and Brinser. Given such a residential or "bedroom town" development, some important questions arise as to the need for concentrating these workers' homes in parts of the town in order to provide facilities; also as to how much space they will occupy. Properly planned, such developments need not encroach severely on agricultural land use.

CHAPTER 14

Section F, Southeast Section

This Southeast Section of Worcester County is much less agricultural and more urbanized than the Southwest Section of the County. The center of the Section is only 35 miles from Boston, in a southeasterly direction, and on a line between Worcester City and Providence, Rhode Island. It has eleven towns, but four of them are very small and four others relatively so. The total land area is 131,300 acres compared with 172,700 in the Southwest Section, and only 26 percent of its land was in farms in 1954 compared with 50 in the Southwest Section. However, it has half as many farms since its farms average only 82 acres as compared with 115. This is because more of the farms are part-time and residential. There are four urban areas in this Section. These four towns with urban areas had populations as follows in 1955: Milford, 15,600; Webster, 13,900; Northbridge, 10,630; Uxbridge, 7,600. The urban influences of the city of Webster, of course, reach into Dudley in Section E.

In terms of trends, Section F has lost 20 percent in land in farms since 1925 and 53 percent in number of farms. The comparable figures for Section E are 16 percent and 46 percent. Sutton and Mendon have about as much agriculture per unit of area as Charlton and Spencer in Section E. These were the two chosen for intensive study in this project. They, along with Upton, were also analyzed by Country Life Committees.

POPULATION AND INDUSTRY

The part that industrial and urban development has played in the different towns is indicated in Table 37. Changes in town boundaries have affected development since 1950 in one case at least. Only Sutton, Douglas, Upton, Mendon, and Millville have remained largely farming towns since 1850. The towns showing a sizable population increase in 1945 to 1955 — Mendon, Upton, Sutton, Blackstone — gained by in-migration as well as by holding part at least of their gains by births. More urban workers are apparently moving farther out into the country.

TABLE 37

Population and Relevant Data by Towns in Section F of Worcester County

Town	Population		Percentage increase 1955 over 1945†	Average number employed in town's industries in 1955†	Number of farms††	
	1850*	1950**			1925	1950
Webster	2,000	13,190	3	3,450	39	22
Sutton	2,300	3,100	31	——*	196	128
Douglas	1,400	2,620	0	640	108	47
Northbridge	2,100	14,480	4	——*	64	38
Uxbridge	2,300	7,010	14	1,370	104	66
Upton	2,000	2,640	23	50	105	45
Milford	2,000	15,440	−1	2,030	77	29
Hopedale	1,000	3,480	14	2,880	30	12
Mendon	1,300	1,620	28	——*	114	52
Millville	——*	1,690	−2	——*	19	7
Blackstone	4,100	4,968	15	30	63	31

——* = No data available.
* See Figure 7 in Chapter 5.
** Federal Census.
† Massachusetts Department of Commerce.
†† Federal Census.

LAND USE AND SOILS

Figures 38 and 39 show the patterns of land use and soil classes in the eleven towns. The elevation of most of the Section is the lowest in the county. Most of the area is drained by the Blackstone River which flows into Narragansett Bay. But this does not mean that the land is not much broken and stony. The No. 4 land occupying about two thirds of Douglas and a good part of the rest of the Section is dominantly Gloucester stony fine sandy loam that would appear in Figure 38 to have been for the most part too difficult to clear of stones in the first place, or not rewarding enough in more recent decades to keep clear of brush and trees. The No. 1 soils are Sutton loam in the rest of Sutton, and mostly Gloucester loam and Gloucester fine sandy loam elsewhere. The No. 2 land is mostly Gloucester sandy loam. The Merrimac soils along the Blackstone River flowing southwestwardly through this Section — through Northbridge, Uxbridge, and Millville — are classed as No. 1 land, but not the Hinckley and Ondawa interspaced with it. There is very little Charlton soil in this Section and there are virtually no drumlins with their Paxton soils.

Matching of these two charts shows that in this Section as in A and E, some of the No. 1 and No. 2 lands back from the roads are not now in crops

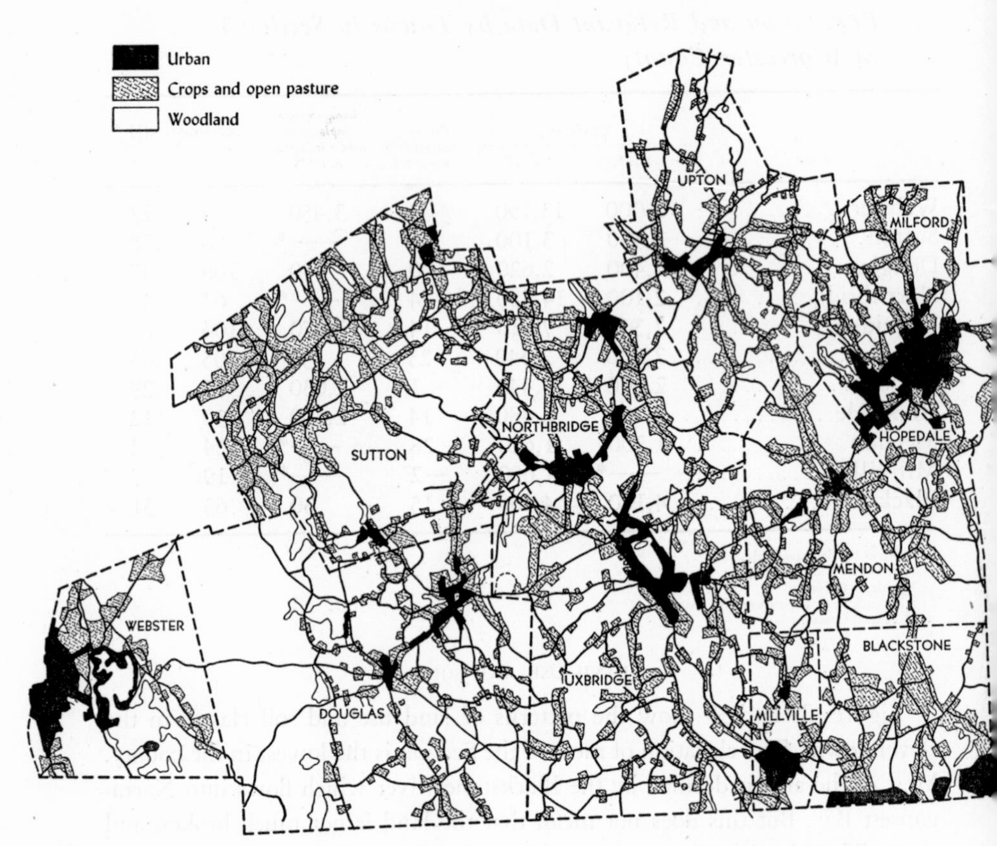

Figure 38. *Major land use in Section F of Worcester County.*

or pasture. It is clear that the lands of this Section have not been so well suited to agricultural use as those in the preceding Sections, and easy to see why only half as large a fraction of the land is now being farmed. The range in proportion of agricultural land (Class 1 and Class 2) is from 18 percent in Douglas and 23 percent in Millville, to 38 in Uxbridge and Milford and 50 in Sutton.

AGRICULTURE

For the Section as a whole, the 38,770 acres of land in farms in 1950 was divided into 37 percent cropland (including cropland pastured and idle), 43 percent woodland, 11 percent pasture, and 9 percent all other. Only 8

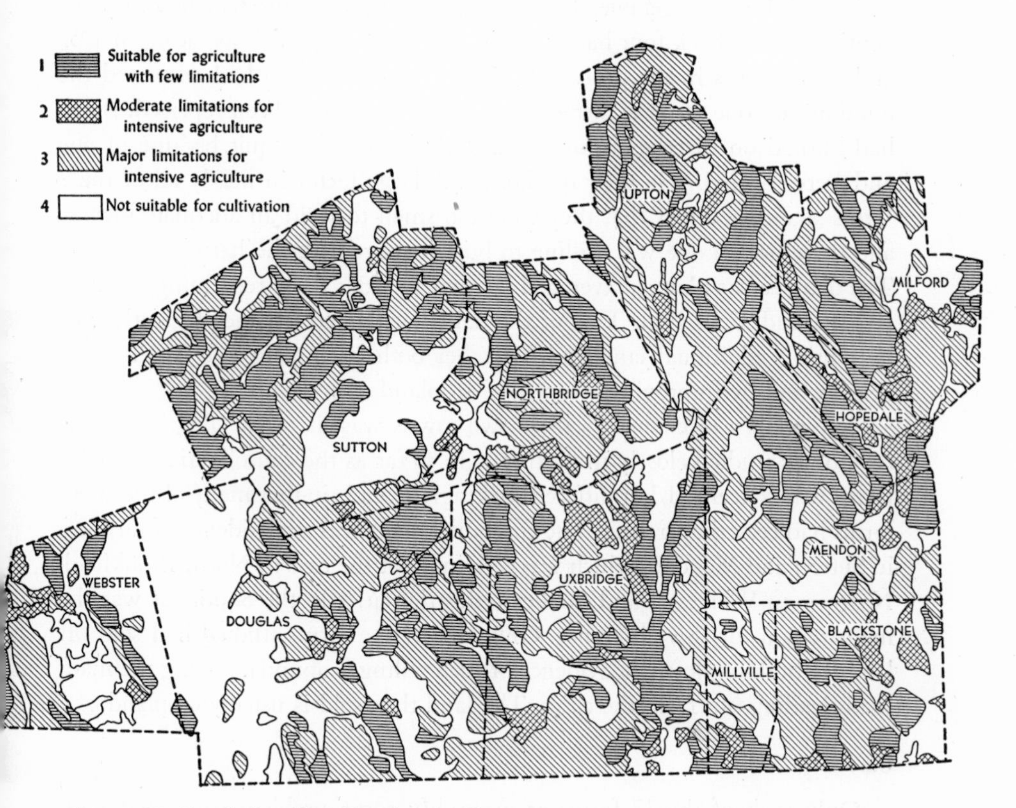

Figure 39. ***Land classified into four soil groups, Section F of Worcester County.***

of the 43 percent of woodland was pastured. This means 3 acres less cropland per farm, 8 acres less open pasture, and 4 acres less woodland pasture than the average farm of the County, and the same amount of woodland not pastured. But of course the County averages are well below those of Sections A and E. Figure 20 in Chapter 6 shows a very wide difference among the eleven towns in this distribution, in keeping with the distribution of soils and land classes in Figures 39 and 40 in this chapter. The number of dairy herds (counting one-cow herds) declined 62 percent between 1925 and 1952, but the number of cows only 22 percent. In 1952, nearly a fourth of the herds had twenty cows or more, and they contained two thirds of the cows milked.

A total of 16 farms were analyzed and planned in the two towns of Sutton and Mendon in 1938, of which 11 were dairy farms, 3 were poultry, 1 was fruit, and 1 was vegetable. By 1945, two of these farms had become residential, and by 1954, four had done so. Still another ceased operating in 1955 and another was in the process of selling out. A tornado had destroyed the buildings on one of these farms and only the house had been replaced. Barns had burned on three more of them. Two farmers had quit because of age and were still living in their old homes. A large factor in nearly all of the 7 farms abandoned was that they were too small to yield an adequate income and therefore no one was willing to buy them, replace the barns, and so on. The dairy farms planned averaged 18 cows in 1938; those remaining, 21 cows in 1945, and 32 in 1954. Two of the dairy farms had expanded greatly, one by renting additional land and the other both by buying two small farms near by and by improving 30 acres of cropland and pasture.

The pattern of change in these two towns was therefore like that in the two towns studied closely in Section E in so far as the consolidation of dairy farms was concerned, but differed strikingly from it in that many of the small farms had ceased operating. The combined effect was a subsidence of farming in Sutton and Mendon, which was certainly not the case in North Brookfield. Nearness to Worcester and smaller industrial cities in the Southeast was the main reason for this difference. Only two of the farms studied had sold off land for building lots, but evidence of such selling is abundant along the main roads leading out from the cities. The land thus sold is usually cropland.

Case Studies

Only such of the 17 farms as exemplify some problem connected with farming in this area will be analyzed here, and these only briefly in terms of their particular problems. The problem on Farm A in this group was whether to make it into a full-time farm some time in the near future when the father quits farming, or to operate it as a part-time farm, and if the latter, how much farming would be done. The farm had fewer than 30 acres of cropland and less than 10 of open pasture. At the time, the herd included 14 cows plus replacements, but concentrate feeding was heavy and 20 acres of not very good pasture was being rented. The farm, however, had 40 acres of brushy pasture which could be converted to cropland and pasture in rotation. Fifteen acres of light alfalfa mixture was already being grown.

Three alternative plans were worked out. The full-time plan promised as much as the others, but only assuming that no more remunerative off-farm work would become available than the job held by the son at that time. Furthermore, credit would be necessary to finance the land improvement and build up the herd to 20 cows even though this was spread over four years or more. Under the full-time plan the farm would increase significantly in value; under the least intensive plan, it would deteriorate and lose value.

The problem of Farm B was to raise enough good roughage to supply abundantly the herd of 20 milk cows that the farmer insisted he must have to yield him an adequate income. He had only 18 acres of land on his farm that was not too stony to cultivate, and even with the intensive corn, oats, and alfalfa rotation he was using this did not provide enough feed, particularly since he was doing some supplementary feeding in the summer and raising his own replacements in order to keep his production per cow up to 7,000 pounds. The plan worked out with him in 1946 called for using a bog-harrow and liming, fertilizing, and reseeding the part of his pasture that was least stony, and for stepping up the yields still further on his cropland. Another plan was worked out that would call for his buying an 80-acre run-down farm nearby and keeping his dry cows and young stock on this farm. Some rehabilitation of the land and buildings would be needed.

Farm C was a thirty-cow farm with a year-round hired man, on which milk production was maintained at 8,000 pounds per cow by a combination of 3,000 pounds of purchased concentrates per cow, ladino-mixture pasture, and alfalfa hay, with no replacements raised. The problem was the droughtiness and stoniness of the fine sandy loam soils. The farmer was in 1946, nevertheless, still hard at work improving more pasture and selecting patches of the less stony land to grow more corn silage and alfalfa.

Farm D had been struggling with the problems of trying to grow silage corn on Sutton and Leicester loam soils too wet for corn in some seasons, and of too little pasture feed in the summer months. The plan worked out for it called for a shift to grass silage, more alsike in the clover, more alfalfa on the drier soils, with rye and vetch for early pasture, and heavier fertilization. This would provide feed for 35 cows instead of the 25 then kept.

Farm E was a small retail dairy unit with 9 cows and no replacements; it bought about half the milk sold. The problem was to increase the size of the milk route to enable the son to remain on the farm. To achieve this really effectively, more land would need to be bought, since it would not be safe to enlarge the barn on the assumption that land could always be rented.

Farm F was a rather large orchard farm bought several years earlier. It had been neglected for six or eight years, and getting it back into full production was the principal problem. This meant careful attention to pruning, fertilization, and spraying. Furthermore, the owner had to be in a position to finance sizable operating loans on top of the purchase loan.

Farm G was a farm combining 22 cows and 15 acres of fifteen-year-old orchard being operated by an elderly farmer and his son with occasional hired labor. Its main dairy problem was poor pasture and its dependence on rented pasture; its main orchard problem, too low yields. Even with improvement of any land on the home farm worth it, there would not be enough pasture feed. Heavier fertilization of the orchard and using the orchard hay as mulch would solve the orchard problem.

On Farm H, the hurricane had so damaged the 12-acre orchard that part of it was to be converted to cropland to grow part of the additional corn silage and alfalfa needed to provide winter forage for the twenty-cow dairy herd. Pasture improvement was to solve the rest of the dairy problem.

Farm I was relying for income on a poultry flock of 1,200 hens and sale of the male chicks raised to roaster size. But it had started an 8-acre orchard on a tract of Merrimac sandy loam soil that was proving to be a frost pocket. The practical solution seemed to be to enlarge the poultry enterprise and abandon the orchard.

The average size of the poultry flocks was largest by a wide margin in 1950 in Milford and Blackstone. As for fruits and vegetables generally, about 600 acres were reported in fruit, mostly apples, on 85 farms in the eleven towns. Half the apple trees were in Sutton. Of the 120 acres on 49 farms of vegetables grown for sale, half were in Sutton and Upton.

Part-time and residential farming is common everywhere in these towns except in Douglas and most of Sutton. They are most prevalent in Hopedale, Milford, and Uxbridge, in the southern part of Blackstone, and in parts of Upton.

The special survey of off-farm work, usually 100 days or more, on a large sample of farms in Sutton reported as follows:

14 dairy farms	5 operators plus	13 other members of the families
8 dairy-fruit or vegetable	2 operators plus	8 other members of the families
6 other commercial	4 operators plus	3 other members of the families
24 part-time	24 operators plus	2 other members of the families
57 residential	34 operators plus	13 other members of the families

Of the residential farms, 29 had 5 acres of land or less and most of these had less than 3 acres. The part-time farms averaged 30 acres. Relatively more of the farms were residential in Mendon.

It is interesting to note that more members of commercial farm families were engaged in off-farm work than of part-time families. This was true in Charlton too, it will be remembered from the last chapter. This could only be true if the families were larger in terms of persons of working age.

WOODLAND

With only 26 percent of the land in these eleven towns in farms, it follows that nonfarm woodland must occupy a large fraction of the land. The range in percentage of woodland not on farms in 1950 was from 74 percent in Northbridge to 91 percent in Douglas and 99 percent in Millville. Let us first, however, consider the woodland in farms. Woodland plans were worked out for each of the 17 for which case studies were made in Sutton and Mendon. Thus one of the farms had 92 acres of woodland divided as follows: Better Hardwoods, 52 acres; Red Maple Swamp, 25 acres; Softwood-Inferior Hardwood, 10 acres; Softwood Swamp, 5 acres. The treatments proposed were as follows:

Improvement cuttings are recommended on 62 acres, removing a total of 130 cords of inferior elements such as gray birch, poorly formed oaks, and large, overtopping individuals. Grazing should be eliminated from Stand No. 21 before any improvement work is undertaken. It would require about 1,000 feet of wire to fence this area. No treatments are recommended on the swamp areas because it is impossible to grow enough saw-timber material on such areas to warrant the expense of treatments.

There is sufficient red maple swamp, which is considered permanent cordwood, to supply the farm fuelwood and posts during the build-up period without having to sacrifice the stocking on areas such as Stand No. 38 that will produce saw-timber materials. However, timely treatments should be made in the better stands to keep them vigorous and the selected trees growing at a good rate. The percentage of oak should be reduced and an effort made to better the composition and prevent the gypsy moth food species from becoming too prevalent.

The present stands capable of producing sawtimber range in age from 6 to 60 years; hence in about 20 years mature trees will be ready to harvest. At an average growth rate of 30 cu. ft. per acre per year, the entire woodland area would produce an average of 2,770 cu. ft. annually. This would supply 1,200 cu. ft. for fuelwood, 200 cu. ft. for building materials and 50 cu. ft. for posts, with about 1,300 cu. ft. of better materials for sale each year. To harvest these products would require about 55 man-days of labor, which is 20 man-days more than is spent on the woodland at present to cut the fuelwood and posts.

With the entire woodland under good forestry practice, the average value per acre of growth would be $4.21 yearly; in comparison, if the trees are cut at middle age for cordwood, the average value per acre of growth would be $1.20 annually. These values are at postwar levels of price as anticipated in 1940.

On a farm with 40 acres of woodland, improvement cutting was proposed in place of the clear-cutting of the past on 25 acres. This would furnish enough fuelwood for the family indefinitely, later some fenceposts, and eventually sawtimber worth $4.70 per acre. For the rest, no immediate treatment was proposed.

For a one-man dairy farm with 16 acres of woodland, the program was as follows:

Improvement cuttings are recommended on 11.2 acres, removing a total of 16 cords of inferior elements, such as red maple sprout stems, gray birch, and poorly formed trees interfering with the development of selected "crop" trees. The cuttings on Stand No. 2 should be limited to the drier portions, particularly where good ash occur, since the wetter portions of the heavy muck soil would not produce good sawtimber. The value of these cuttings would be about $64 at the farm. To harvest the materials would require about 24 man-days of labor. Area No. 21, now used as pasture, is recommended for conversion to woodland. This area has been heavily grazed and since there are no seed trees in the vicinity, in order to make the land immediately productive, planting with mixed conifers is advisable. The planting stock for the 4.6 acres would cost about $70 and would require 9 man-days of labor to plant. About 700 feet of single-wire fencing would be required to keep the cows out of this plantation and also woodlot No. 20. The income from this woodland enterprise was estimated at $90 a year.

As part of the Worcester County Land-Use Planning project, all the woodland — 30,300 acres — in the three towns of Sutton, Mendon, and Upton was cruised. About half of this was Better Hardwood and the rest mostly Better Softwood or Inferior Hardwood.

However, there were wide differences among these three towns. The condition of the Upton woodlands was an outstanding example of what exploitive forest practices can do. Large areas had been clear-cut, both for sawtimber and for cordwood. Fires had swept over many of the cuttings recently, causing further depletion of the young growing stock, and reduction in soil fertility. The oaks, including white, red, black, and scarlet, mostly of coppice origin, were the dominant species. But gray birch and red maple combined with scrub oak made up over 5,000 acres of Inferior Hardwood. The State Conservation Department had acquired large tracts of this cut-over area, particularly in the northern part of the town. Conifers, mostly white and red pine, and spruce recently, have been planted on much of the state land. The soils of Upton are better adapted to conifers than to good hardwoods.

It would be several decades before any large amount of sawtimber could be harvested in Upton. However, under good forest management and with time enough to build up the depleted growing stock, valuable wood products could be produced. Of utmost importance in the rehabilitation of many stands was a "resting period" of a number of years to allow the growing stock and forest soils to recover in part from the degradation resulting from the past injurious practices. In a few stands, improvement cuttings needed to be made to remove inferior elements such as the gray birch and scrub oak that was interfering with the proper development of better formed trees of good species. On the light, shallow soils, the conifers needed to be encouraged. Planting would be required where the existing stands were wholly inferior, and on some open areas, such as abandoned pastures, where conversion to a valuable crop could be made only by planting.

In Sutton at the other extreme, three fourths of the woodland was Better Hardwood. The Sutton woodlands had not been cut as heavily nor grazed as extensively as those of the nearby towns. A considerable area in the southern part of the town, known as Purgatory, was in State forest and game preserve, and consequently was not available for exploitive cuttings. However, there had been clear-cutting in the northern part on the farm woodlots and in the southern part on areas adjacent to land recently acquired by the State. The growth on such areas was dominantly sprout hardwood. The softwoods were in mixtures with hardwoods rather than in pure stands. Most of the older softwoods, both pine and hemlock, were blown down in 1938; it was estimated that not over 5 percent of the total area was then occupied by softwoods.

The most needed silvicultural treatment was improvement cutting, to favor the better formed trees of good species, such as the pines, ash, some oak, hickory, and at the same time to reduce the quantity of favored gypsy moth food. Planting with mixed conifers was needed only on areas that would not restock naturally with valuable species within a reasonable length of time.

The Gloucester soils of Mendon are not as well adapted to the growth of Better Hardwoods as are the soils of Sutton. The Mendon woodlands had also suffered from many years of heavy cutting for sawtimber and, more recently, from repeated clear-cutting for fuelwood. Little or no effort had been made to insure the future production of any high-quality materials. As a result of the repeated clear-cuttings, the woodlands were understocked, especially so with respect to good species; the stands were young, and most of the trees of sprout origin. The hurricane of 1938 had reduced the softwood element, mainly white and pitch pine, to less than 10 percent of the total growing stock.

EROSION

Two of N. P. Tedrow's statements on erosion cover the aspects of it that are peculiar to this Section. Erosion is not a serious problem in the town of Sutton. As a general rule the steeper slopes are forested or used for permanent pasture. The farming land is located on the more level areas. On Sutton soils it is often not advisable to follow the contour in all tillage operations because of the poor surface drainage. A small acreage of corn was being grown each year for silage on the better drained Paxton and Charlton loams, and this in a long rotation including six to ten years of hay. This practice alone is a good method of erosion control. The pastures should be treated with lime and fertilizer to maintain a good sod cover.

Erosion had been a factor in lowering the productivity of the cultivated land in Upton. The light textured Hinckley and Merrimac soils erode very rapidly under clean cultivation. The shallow till soils support a sparse vegetative cover and as a result are subject to erosion. Cover crops of rye or vetch should be seeded on all "open" fields on these soils as early in the fall as possible. This aids in decreasing erosion and increases the organic content of the soil. By increasing the organic content of the soil, its water-holding capacity is also enhanced.

The cropland of Mendon is divided into small fields separated by stone walls. In the majority of cases, the farmers run the rows of cultivated crops so as to get the longest rows with little thought of conserving the soil and moisture. The steeper slopes should be maintained in permanent hay as much of the time as possible. When it is necessary to reseed steep slopes, all tillage operations should be on the contour and not more than one year of clean-tilled crops should be included in a rotation. The numerous stone walls and small fields often make strip-cropping impossible. If the steeper land is not needed for cropland, it could be more economically used for pasture.

COUNTRY LIFE COMMITTEE REPORTS

Mendon

What is included from these reports are selected statements that supplement significantly the information, mostly of a later date, from other sources already presented for the towns of Mendon, Sutton, and Upton. Mendon is set forth clearly in its Country Life Committee report as a town with much of its population employed in factories and trade in the neighboring towns of Hopedale, Milford, and Uxbridge. Its population has been increasing in recent decades with the flourishing of the industries of these towns — from 961 in 1920 to 1,315 in 1940 to 1,905 in 1955. It was 1,300 in 1850 and fell off to 880 in 1910. The number of dairy cows has gained markedly since 1925 through an enlargement of its herds. The Census of 1954 reported 820 cows as compared with 565 reported by the Animal Inspectors in 1936. The pastures, however, are still retrograding. The Census of 1940 reported 28 dairy farms, 1 each of poultry, fruit and vegetable farms, and 7 combination farms, besides 96 residential and 14 part-time farms. The dairy farms contained half of the farmland and cropland.

Most of the 13,300 chickens and 52,000 dozen eggs sold in 1950 were from commercial farms. The residential farms in 1940 had only 670 chickens, and the part-time farmers only 980. They had a total of 10 and 16 cows respectively, 24 and 15 acres of fruit, and 50 and 27 acres of vegetables.

The Country Life Committee classified the land of the Town as 14 percent IA, that is, needing only minor adjustments, this being mostly the land on the broad tops and gentle slopes of the ridge running from northwest to southeast through the center of the Town. It put 13 percent in two sub-unit areas classed as IB, that is, requiring major adjustments. The rest of the Town, except the urban and recreational areas, was put in four sub-unit areas classed as suitable for forest only except for small residential and part-time farms along the roads. A tract of 190 acres including Nipmuck Pond was an area of summer camps and cottages tending to become year-round homes.

The Committee recommended a more systematic development of the part-time and rural residence areas, and the Nipmuck Pond area, so as to provide the homes with modern facilities, and improvement of pasture and the quality of the hay on the dairy farms.

Upton

This Town got its name because of its elevation above that of the surrounding towns. The Committee classified none of its land as IA, but 42 percent of it in three sub-areas as IB. This is nearly all in the southeastern part of the Town. The difficulty with this land is that its soils are droughty sandy loams. Agriculture has been declining uninterruptedly to a point where less than half as much milk was produced as in Mendon in 1950. The woodland is predominantly of Inferior Hardwoods. The State now owns over 2,000 acres of these woodlands in scattered small patches in the western part of the Town. The population of the Town has been increasing from its low point of 1,700 in 1920 to 2,920 in 1955. This is because its sole industry, hat-making in West Upton, has been prospering. Originally this firm made only straw hats. It now makes felt hats as well. The Committee's two principal land-use recommendations were for more and better home gardens in the rural residential farms and better grass and forest cover on the slopes to check the damage from floods suffered in two recent years.

Sutton

In sharp contrast with Upton is Sutton with 53 percent of its land classified by the Committee as IA and none as IB. The remainder of it except the urban and recreational land was classified as forest land, of which 75 percent was Better Hardwoods. Soils account for this difference, those of the agricultural part of Sutton being dominantly Sutton, Paxton, and Charlton, and the rest Rough Stony. As already pointed out, the agriculture of Sutton has been holding its own until recently.

About 5 percent of the Town is State forest. Included in this are the public recreation facilities at Purgatory Chasm. Summer cottages and summer camp facilities have also been developed around three other ponds.

The Committee's recommendations for dairy farming included pasture improvement and raising more replacements. They made two recommendations for the apple orcharding as follows:

> On a large number of farms there are small acreages of orchard (less than 5 acres) which are not receiving proper care because of lack of equipment. It is not economical to buy and maintain equipment for these small orchards. Cooperative effort in caring for some of these small orchards and perhaps in marketing the product might be worthwhile, particularly in view of the need for increased cash income and the recommendation for diversification.
>
> The commercial orchards in Sutton in the northeastern corner of town are dominated by five large orchards, and are mostly of trees under 25 or 30 years of age. The present rate of planting will not maintain the present orchard acreage or production. Within 15 years, more acreage will be going out of production than is coming in unless the present rate of planting is increased.

The population of Sutton increased from 2,400 to 3,400 between 1935 and 1955. This is to be accounted for by the prospering of the industries in the surrounding towns of Millbury, Grafton, and Northbridge rather than of its own or of the small industrial center of Manchaug near its southern border.

CHAPTER 15

Section D, East Central Section

This is a section with twelve towns surrounding the big city of Worcester. Not only this, but in addition the towns to the east of Worcester are in the orbit of influence of Greater Boston and Framingham. For this reason the urban effects are stronger here than in any of the other five sections. These are manifest primarily in three forms. First, in the towns near the urban centers there are large numbers of rural residences of city workers. Second, the concentration of urban populations creates a market for locally produced fresh foods, and in addition, Worcester, which is a major distribution center for central New England, is a receiving market for local products to be sold in the larger market area. Finally, the city is a center in which funds and services are available for the nearby rural communities.

This chapter will give somewhat more attention to urban factors than do the other chapters, but still very much less than did the Seminar group working on this section, since the scope of this book is restricted to rural land use. The two towns chosen for special study were Grafton and Northboro. These were also reported upon by Country Life Committees.

POPULATION AND INDUSTRY

Let us first of all get a picture of the industrial patterns and population growth of this Section. Table 38 gives the population of 1950 and 100 years earlier. None of these towns lost population over the century — rather, they participated in the rapid growth of Worcester. In the first part of these 100 years, they grew because the demand for their milk and eggs and fresh vegetables and fruit expanded. In the latter part of the 100 years, more and more of the milk and eggs came from farther away and it was the increase in rural residence of persons employed in Worcester that had the most influence.

TABLE 38

Population and Manufacturing, and Number of Farms, Section E, Worcester County

Town	Number of firms*	Annual payroll (thousands of dollars)*	Average number of employees	Population**		Population increase, 1945–55 (percent)	Number of farms, 1950
				1850	1950		
Worcester City...	603	189,047	45,000	8,000	203,480	2	51
Northboro.......	9	326	140	1,300	3,120	67	77
Southboro.......	3	679	215	1,700	2,760	36	41
Westboro........	21	4,749	1,050	2,100	7,400	22	76
West Boylston...	5	82	34	1,670	2,570	74	29
Shrewsbury......	12	461	160	1,250	10,590	41	81
Holden..........	7	382	135	1,600	5,975	78	63
Auburn..........	13	850	205	500	8,840	72	49
Boylston........	2	13	6	600	1,700	44	49
Grafton.........	20	2,068	670	3,700	8,280	23	81
Leicester........	15	3,687	760	2,000	6,030	42	63
Millbury........	29	4,957	1,070	2,900	8,350	21	45
Paxton..........	1	5	2	600	1,070	84	53

* Massachusetts Department of Commerce, 1955.
** Figure 7 in Chapter 5 and the Federal Census.

Still there are wide differences in the growth of the different towns. Boylston, West Boylston, Southboro, Northboro, and Paxton, farthest out from Worcester, had rather small populations in 1850 and have multiplied only two or three times since. Grafton and Millbury already had some industries in 1850. Auburn started as highly rural, but has had a large growth since; so too in lesser measure have Holden and Shrewsbury. The fastest growing towns in the past two years have been Paxton, Holden, and West Boylston. The greater metropolitan area of Worcester is now pushing most strongly northward. Throughout these towns, the roads out from the city are being lined farther and farther out with new dwellings of urban workers' families, or closer in on the urban fringe, with new building developments.

The differences in rate of growth since 1900 can be summarized as follows: the four towns with a population of over 8,000 in 1950 — Grafton, Millbury, Shrewsbury, and Auburn — had grown from an average of around 3,200 to around 9,200 in 1955, or 290 percent. The five more rural towns at the other extreme had grown only from about 1,900 to about 2,500, or 30 percent. The three intermediate towns — Holden, Leicester, and Westboro — had grown from 2,800 to 6,600, or 230 percent.

In Figure 8 in Chapter 5, eight of the twelve towns are shown as having "urban" area within their boundaries in 1950. The Census of 1950 also reports Northboro as having an unincorporated village of 1,142. The urban populations of these nine towns made up 43 percent of their total in 1950. Excluding the City of Worcester, this Section had 52 percent of rural, that is, nonurban population, in 1950. But far from all of these were part of the farm population, including even the residential farms category. Even allowing five members per family for the 665 farms of all descriptions reported in this Section in 1954 would make up only 3,225 out of the total *rural* population of 32,100 in the twelve towns. Thus the great bulk even of the so-called rural population consisted of families making little or no use of the land except perhaps to do a little gardening.

Now look at the picture of change in 1945–1955 in next to the last column of the table. These data are from the Massachusetts State Census and differ from the Federal Census in that they count everybody living in each city or town at the time of the enumeration; but they should be comparable between censuses. The row of towns north of Worcester City from Paxton to Northboro increased about three fourths in population in this single decade. Apparently the towns nearer to Worcester — Shrewsbury, Grafton, Millbury, and Leicester — had had their suburban growth more largely before 1945. Auburn was the only close-in town that kept on growing very rapidly after 1945.

Part of the rapid increase in population of these towns is of course due to the nationwide stepping up of birth rates. Out-migration of population into the outlying towns principally accounts for the differences in percentage growth. The Massachusetts Department of Commerce has calculated from its enumeration that Worcester City would have gained 10 percent instead of 2 percent in 1945–55 except for the migration of 13,760 to areas outside its boundaries. About two thirds of Auburn's large gain was due to in-migration, and likewise that of Holden and the other towns in the row of towns north of Worcester.

Something needs to be said about the industrial pattern of this area. It is highly diversified, which is something in favor of its stability in the aggregate. Worcester City itself exemplifies this situation. Its major payrolls are in machinery and metal working, but it has several large firms making abrasives, and stone, glass, paper, and allied products. There are some thirty firms making leather and textile goods. Auburn's thirteen plants turn out that number of products and Northboro's nine firms make seven different products.

This is probably the best time at which to point out also that the number of farms in 1950, shown in the last column of Table 38, was still roughly proportional to the area of the towns, Holden, West Boylston, and Southboro being a little on the low side, and Shrewsbury a little on the high side. Figure 14 in Chapter 6 indicates that this has probably been true historically since 1925 if allowance is made for the erratic nature of the census counts. We may be sure that Millbury did not have 50 farms in 1925 and 166 in 1945, then 45 in 1950 and 94 in 1954. Perhaps it had 100 in 1925 and 50 in 1954. For the Section as a whole, the number of farms fell off over 60 percent from 1925 to 1954, the most for any Section of the County, as one would expect around a big growing city. Land in farms fell off exactly one half.

PUBLIC FINANCE AND SERVICES

An area with a population growing as much as this one in the past fifty years is almost certain to be beset with difficult problems of financing roads, streets, water supply, sewage disposal, and other public utilities. The demand for these in such a situation runs ahead of the current income upon which to draw to pay for them. The same is true also for the services of education and health. In New England the villages and smaller cities are not incorporated separately, but are part of the "town," which in the terminology of other parts of the United States is the township. As a consequence a large part of the cost of providing new and expanded services falls on owners of rural land who often do not benefit from the rising land values in the urban centers; nor do they benefit to the same extent as the urban population from the added utilities and services. In this Section, five of the twelve towns include unincorporated villages with populations in 1950 ranging from 1,760 to 3,440. Three others are largely urban over their whole area even though the census reported respectively 45, 49, and 81 farms of some description for them.

What follows under this head draws heavily upon an analysis of Massachusetts town financing made by Professor Morris Lambie of the Department of Government of Harvard University. The base year for most of his analysis was 1951. In that year, 32 percent of the revenues of the local governments of Massachusetts came from higher up, and 60 percent of them were collected from local property taxes.

The towns have alternative ways of financing provision for their rising public needs. First of all, they can either borrow or pay for them currently. Half of the twelve towns had debts outstanding equaling 70 percent or more of the assessed valuation of their property, and in only two was this ratio under 40 percent of assessed valuations. Borrowing had increased rapidly in recent years in several of the towns.

Other alternatives are to raise the assessed value of the property, or raise the tax rate instead, or make some combination of these. In a time of rapid inflation such as that following the war, assessed values are almost certain to lag far behind the prices and costs of public services, so that tax rates almost inevitably rise even if there is no increase in services. But there will be sharp differences among towns in the amount of this lag. Professor Lambie ranked the towns and cities in Massachusetts from 1 to 351 according to the assessed value of their property per capita, their tax rates, and the direct property taxes per capita. Table 39 reports his results for the twelve towns in Section D.

Taking the twelve towns as a whole, the direct property taxes increased 126 percent between 1945 and 1952 while the general price level was rising only 65 percent. The 126-percent rise was divided between a rise in assessed value and a rise in the tax rates in the ratio of 13 to 10. A considerable part of this 13 was of course the value of new property added to the tax rolls.

Wide differences among the towns are evident. At one extreme, Grafton

TABLE 39

Property Taxation in the 12 Towns of Section D in 1950; Amounts and Rank Order among the Towns of Massachusetts

Town	Direct taxes per capita		Assessed valuation per capita		Tax rate	
	Amount	Rank order	Amount	Rank order	Amount	Rank order
Grafton	$45.55	22	$ 760	12	$60.00	310
Westboro	47.46	30	949	46	50.00	180
Leicester	50.50	46	779	17	64.80	329
Millbury	53.14	66	770	14	69.00	346
Auburn	61.34	121	1,207	125	50.80	201
Boylston	61.65	124	1,233	131	50.00	176
Paxton	65.21	155	1,918	259	34.00	25
Southboro	69.92	183	1,227	130	57.00	275
Holden	70.61	187	1,124	97	62.80	322
Shrewsbury	71.93	194	1,352	164	52.80	229
West Boylston	71.41	195	1,488	194	48.00	160
Northboro	77.34	222	1,045	75	74.00	350

ranked only 12 in assessed valuation and 310 in tax rate. After 1946, Paxton had raised its assessed valuation 91 percent and actually lowered its tax rate 3 percent. Northboro in this period had raised its property taxes 221 percent, largely by means of a 111-percent increase in the tax rate. Holden had followed a similar policy.

In terms of tax burden per capita, Table 39 indicates that the slow-growing towns — like Boylston, Paxton, Northboro, and Southboro — generally had higher property taxes per capita than the fast-growing ones like Grafton and Millbury, with Shrewsbury an important exception to this statement. The middle column suggests that differences in per capita wealth accounted for much of this.

After reviewing these and other materials and analyses assembled by Professor Lambie, the Seminar group working on Section D wrote out a brief summary of the public finance situation in each of the twelve towns. A few of the more significant of these are quoted following:

Shrewsbury: An expanding residential town with some rural character, closely tied to Worcester. Good financial condition, though recent demands have put an increased burden on the tax rate. But past experience as well as the availability of property to assess point to no danger in responding to new needs and demands for additional services.

West Boylston: Residential town with strong rural character providing preferred residence for those who work in Worcester. Continues to improve in good fiscal base and has balanced a large demand for revenue by greater reliance on valuation.

Holden: Residential town for Worcester with increased strains put upon its fiscal base due to a large growth in population, having the largest index-of-growth ratio of the twelve towns. Resultant demand on the revenue caused the direct taxes to rise 240 percent in the last seven years with the tax rate sharing the biggest part of the increase. Definite strains are apparent and serious thought is necessary to meet present and future demands.

Millbury: Industrial and residential, part of the Worcester metropolitan core with about 38 percent of its population considered urban. Strains are quite apparent with the tax rate carrying the ball for increased demands on revenue. In a period when most of the towns increased their direct taxes by a large percentage, Millbury found this difficult to do and its increase of 77 percent was put on to valuation to a considerable extent. Millbury appears to be in serious financial difficulties.

Boylston: Residential and rural, Boylston has a small rural economy with many of its residents finding employment in Worcester and

> Clinton. Though its past experience has put it in a low and tight economy, it has shown great flexibility over the last seven years. This improvement has given it a 1952 standing of a median level in the Commonwealth, and if this development can be maintained it will put Boylston in good condition.

The three public services particularly analyzed by Professor Lambie were welfare, education, and health, constituting in 1951 respectively 24.0 percent, 23.7 percent, and 6.2 percent of the then current charges against the town revenues of Massachusetts. The national averages to be compared with these are 21, 48, and 3.

The general problems facing public education in this country at this time need no discussion here. All that will be done is to indicate a few that grow out of special situations in the twelve towns. One of these is providing a good quality of high school education at reasonable cost in rural towns that are expanding very little. The best way to do this is, perhaps, to have the pupils enroll in a large high school nearby; or if one is not available, for several adjoining towns to take advantage of the state law providing for joint operation of a consolidated school. A difficulty with this latter is that if no one of the towns takes the lead nothing happens. The larger high schools are getting overcrowded in some cases and do not want enrollment from neighboring towns. The high school situation in some of the towns that have been growing moderately is that the old school building is now proving too small — shall the old building be made over and enlarged? or shall it be replaced? The major problem of the grade schools other than the general problem of adjustment to recently higher birth rates is fitting their pattern to the pattern of urban and urban-fringe growth.

As compared in 1951 with the rest of the towns in Massachusetts, the school expenditures in Section D were relatively high per $1,000 of assessed valuation, eight of the towns being among the seventy-five highest. Holden's were sixth from the top.

A special survey recently made of health conditions and health provisions in the Town of Auburn showed the children far from adequately protected from communicable diseases, and other deficiencies. It was spending only $2.13 per capita or 3 percent of its total budget on health. Other of the twelve towns were well below similar towns in the same size group. A 1948 Commission set up by the legislature of Massachusetts had reported as follows:

> Massachusetts lags behind many other sections of the country in providing adequate local health services for its citizens, especially in small communities . . . the individual town is not, in the very great majority of cases, a feasible

unit for the establishment of good local health departments in Massachusetts because the great majority of towns do not have sufficient area and population to allow for economic and efficient administration of a balanced full-time local health department.

None of the towns at that time had any coordinated sewage disposal system, each resident using either a cesspool or a filter system, although the towns of Leicester and Westboro had small sand filter systems which discharged into the Town Meadowbrook and the Assabet River respectively. The magnitude of the problem was shown in the 1945 Town Report of Grafton. A study had been authorized by the town meeting and the results of the survey underlined not only the basic needs but the high cost. Grafton has three main settlements: Grafton Center, North Grafton and South Grafton. Each needed its own system because of distance, and the total cost of adequate units was estimated to be in the neighborhood of $700,000. The report recommended that because of the unsanitary conditions prevailing in Grafton Center immediate construction of a sewage system should begin.

The welfare assistance consisted of aid to dependent children, old-age assistance, and general relief. In 1952, the town governments were bearing 29 percent of the first, 18 percent of the second, and 73 percent of the third. Among the twelve towns, the case load was heaviest in the more industrial towns like Millbury and Grafton, and lowest in the more rural residential towns like Shrewsbury, West Boylston, and the "boro" towns.

AGRICULTURE

Land and Soils

It will be remembered from our early discussion of the topography of Worcester County that the eastern border of the central plateau that covers most of the County is a line running south through the Town of Worcester and Douglas on the southern boundary of Section F. The land drops off sharply from a level of around 800 feet along this line eastwardly to 200 feet at the eastern boundary of the County and of course somewhat southwestwardly too. The drainage is mostly through the small headwater streams of the Blackstone River into Narragansett Bay. Dams were built on some of these streams to furnish waterpower for the early industries of Grafton and the other towns that had an early industrial growth. These, plus the sluggishness of the streams, produce a large amount of land marked "W" for "wet" in the soil map in the towns south and especially east of Worcester. Figure 40 shows that while relatively little of the land is classified as No. 4, this is counterbalanced by an unusually large fraction of No. 3 land, amounting to almost half of Shrewsbury and Northbridge. The slopes are nearly as long and steep in much of this area as in the central plateau even though the hills are not so far above the sea. The towns with the most No. 1 soil are Paxton, Leicester, and Worcester. The Wachusett Reservoir that supplied a good part of Boston's water before the Quabbin was developed covers as much as 10 percent of the two Boylstons. Quinsigamond is a large lake along the border of Worcester and Shrewsbury.

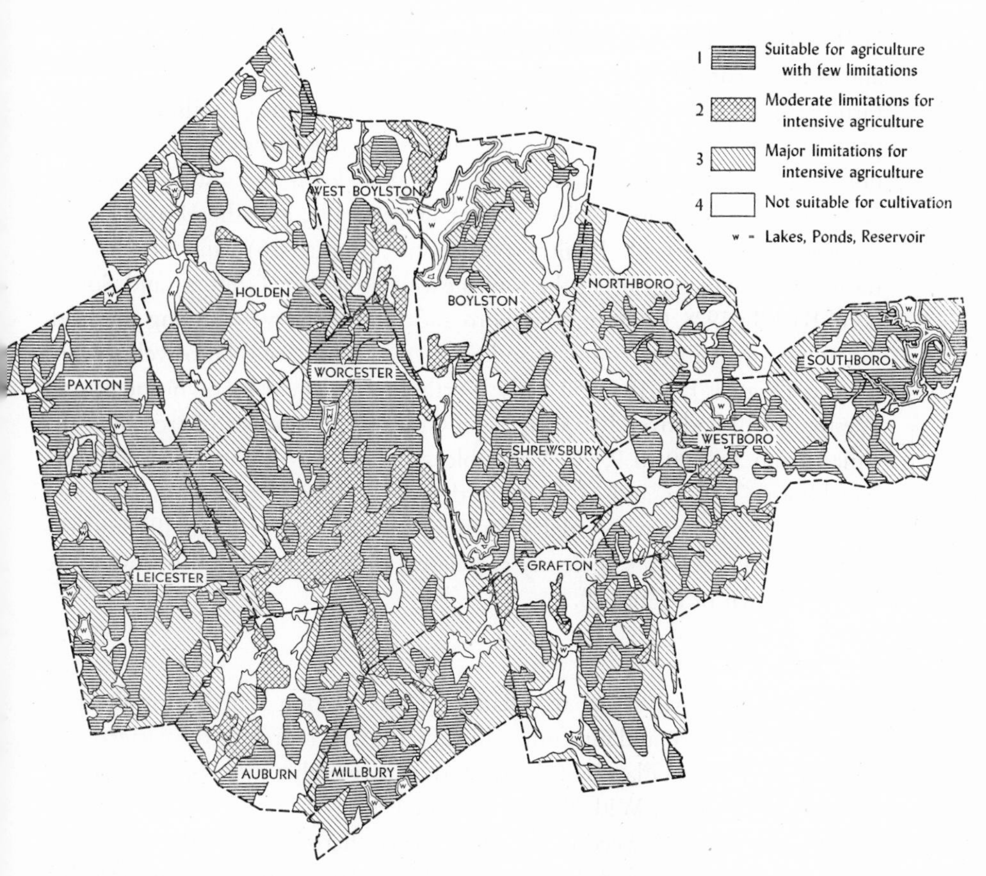

Figure 40. ***Classification of the land of the East Central Section of Worcester County into four classes according to adaptability to agriculture.***

The No. 3 soils in Figure 40 are primarily Gloucester in the eastern part of the Section — either stony fine sandy loam (Gr) or fine sandy loam (Gf). The No. 4 soils are mostly Gloucester stony loam (Gt). The No. 1 soils are generally either Merrimac fine sandy loam (My) or Sutton loam (Sl). From Worcester west, the No. 1 soils are largely Charlton loam, Paxton loam, or Sutton loam. The No. 3 soils are rough stony. There are a good many stretches of gravelly Hinckley soils interspersed with the Merrimac, Rumney, and Muck in the stream valleys and around the ponds.

Farms and Farming

Let us now review what Figures 13 to 20 in Chapter 6 show about the agriculture and land use of this Section. The decline in percentage of cropland in Figure 13 was much less than in the number of farms in Figure 14, and is fairly consistent among the towns except Millbury. Perhaps, after all, farming has been on the upgrade in Millbury? In terms of soils, one is surprised to see Westboro with the highest percentage of cropland with Millbury second and Paxton and Holden as far down the list. Paxton and Leicester have held up best in dairying (Figure 15), and the Boylstons and Auburn the least well. Poultry production (Figure 16) runs strongly to meat rather than eggs in all the towns except Leicester, Grafton, and Southboro. Back in 1928, Grafton, Westboro and Northboro were among the leading apple towns in the country, and Shrewsbury and Southboro well toward the top (Figure 17). By 1950, only Northboro had held its own and it and Westboro still had over 10,000 trees. In Grafton the number of trees had declined from 154,700 to 9,400. Vegetable growing was highest in Westboro, Northboro, Grafton, and Millbury in that order. Size of farms has increased a little in the towns where dairy farming is dominant (Figure 19) and decreased elsewhere. This is closely correlated with cropland and open-pasture acreage shown in Figure 20.

Woodland

Most of the analysis of woodlands in this Section will be for the two towns of Northboro and Grafton, which pretty well represent the eastern part of the area. The woodlands of the western part resemble those of Spencer and Rutland to the west. With the increase in 1925–54 from 48 to 74 percent of the land listed in this Section as not in farms, there has been a considerable expansion of woodland. A large part of this woodland is young growth that has come up in abandoned pastures. Also the cutting of second growth for fuelwood was unusually heavy in this Section. Hardwoods are of course dominant, but the droughty soils of the valley lowlands are best adapted to conifers if regeneration is undertaken.

The acreage of woodland on farms runs very low in this Section (Figures 18 and 20). This is because the farms are small and, if farming is to be practiced at all, a large part of the land must be kept in crops and open pasture. Also of course the farms are generally located on the less rolling and less wooded land.

NORTHBORO

As to soils, the northern part of Northboro is predominantly rough stony land and Gloucester stony fine sandy loam. A very small part of this area is used for cropland. There is some pasture, but the largest portion of this area is forested. The central and southern portions of the town are chiefly light outwash soils with small areas of till soils on the hills or higher elevations. Most of the cropland in this part of the town is on Merrimac fine sandy loam, free from stones and easy to cultivate, but droughty and with high fertilizer requirements. The Hinckley soils usually occupy a small area between the till soils and the Merrimac soils or outwash terraces. Their best use is probably in forest.

This town has a definite drainage problem. The streams have very little "fall" and as a result sand and silt from the higher elevations are deposited along the streams as the velocity of the water decreases. This has caused much land that was formerly cropland to be abandoned. In many cases farmers state that land that was formerly cropped is now too wet to farm. Some work has been done along the Assabet River to improve the drainage conditions, but this requires the cooperation of all the landowners along the small streams if the drainage program is to be effective.

In consequence of the foregoing, only 28 percent of the land of Northboro was in crops and plowable pasture in 1938, and a fourth of this was in orchards.

There were 24 dairy herds of 10 cows or more in 1938 and 30 with 5 or more. Only 1 replacement was being raised for every 10 cows. Only a third of the hay included legumes, and only 17 acres of alfalfa was being grown. As few as 8 farms had poultry as the major enterprise. Half the poultry was in combination with other farming.

Only 6 farms specialized in vegetables. These averaged 11 acres per farm. But 28 farms were growing 162 acres of vegetables in combination with other enterprises. The 21 part-time farms were growing 16 acres of them, and the 107 residential farms 56 acres. More sweet corn was grown than any other vegetable and next in order came carrots, cabbages, beans, and tomatoes. The Merrimac soils are well suited to vegetables.

In 1935 there were 410 acres of Northboro land in fruit trees, with 380 acres in bearing trees. Five orchards had 20 to 50 acres of fruit, and 20 farms had from 5 to 20 acres. The replacement rate at that time would not maintain this acreage, but Figure 17 showed as many apple trees in 1950 as in 1925. Of the 380 orchard acres in 1935, 65 were in peaches. No doubt this acreage has declined since, but the lighter soils are favorable to peaches.

Needless to say, Northboro is well located with respect to the Worcester market and also direct roadside sale.

Case Study Farms

Special analysis was made of eight farm businesses in Northboro and of the farm woodlands in two more. In the main, attention will be given here to features of these that are related to somewhat special circumstances in this Section. Four of the eight farms were dairy farms averaging 22 cows in 1938, another was a vegetable farm with 8 cows; two were combining apples and poultry, and the other was a straight poultry farm. By 1954 two of the dairy farms had been combined, and the vegetable and one poultry farm had ceased operating. The three dairy farms remaining had 10 cows more than the four in 1938.

Farm CR — This was a small farm now relying upon 12 cows and raising no replacements, plus 2 acres of vegetables, to provide the family income, with much of the feed purchased. There was a shortage of good cropland. The soil was a combination of Merrimac sandy loam and Rumney loam, the latter especially needing better drainage than it had then. The plan worked out with the farmer called for providing better drainage of 10 acres to make it available for cropping, establishing 6 acres of ladino pasture and hay, growing 4 acres for hay and pasture, improving 8 acres of pasture by heavy fertilization and reseeding and thus greatly reducing the feed bills, while increasing the herd by 3 cows; it called also for building additional poultry housing and raising 1,000 chicks. Further investment in land improvement and dairy housing could increase the income still more.

Farm MH — This was a thirty-cow dairy farm with 9 acres of orchard and 4 acres of vegetables supporting two families. Only 4 heifer calves were being raised each year. It was already growing 15 acres of alfalfa and had improved 14 acres of pasture. The soil was Merrimac sandy loam with small adjacent tracts of low-lying Scarboro and Sudbury. The major problem was simply to increase the income so as to carry the debt load more securely. A minor one was conflict between labor on the hay harvesting and the truck crops. Improving more pasture and fertilizing more heavily, plus increasing the acreage of alfalfa, would make possible keeping five more cows and raising three more heifers a year, plus reducing concentrate purchases 500 pounds per cow. More carrots and asparagus and no sweet corn would solve the labor problem.

Farm BW — The particular problem for attention on this dairy farm was that part of the cropland was Hinckley, with slopes varying from 7 to 20 percent. From 25 to 75 percent of the topsoil had already been lost by erosion. The plan worked out called for keeping this in permanent hay and using oat hay as a nurse crop in reseeding. Also the Merrimac sandy loam was too dry for ladino pasture with the result that the supply of late summer green feed was short. This was to be solved by shifting the ladino to some Gloucester fine sandy loam now in permanent pasture. This farm also had 6 acres of orchard which had been partly neglected in recent years. The program worked out for this called for trimming and pruning, a fuller spray schedule, fertilization, and mulching with the hay grown in the orchard.

Northboro also serves to illustrate another development affecting agricultural land use — two of the eight farms analyzed are losing a total of 30 acres of their best land to the new Massachusetts Turnpike that more or less parallels Route 20 across Worcester County. Along its whole course in Worcester County, it split a score or more of farms in such a way as to separate pasture from dairy barns and the like.

The Woodland

The 168 acres of woodland on the nine farms were about 35 percent Better Hardwoods and Softwoods and 30 percent Inferior Hardwoods, mostly gray birch. No immediate treatment was planned for 97 acres, and improvement cutting and salvaging was planned for 60 acres of it.

For the town as a whole, only 2,180 acres of the 6,220 total woodland was in stands over 20 years old, and all but 140 of this in less than 40-year stands. Raymond and Chute mapped the 6,220 acres into 89 stands, worked out a "recommended treatment" for each stand, and then estimated the value per acre at 1938 timber prices of the mean annual growth for both the then "present" treatment and the recommended treatment. Table 40 summarizes these results according to classes of timberland.

These plans called for a shift to softwoods. This was because the droughty soils of the lower levels and hummocky Hinckley soils are best adapted to conifers. Pine also seeds in along with hardwoods on the stony fine sandy soils of the Gloucester series. The treatment outlined in the Northboro report on woodlands includes the following:

> The stocking with good species such as pine, ash, and hickory should be increased. The most important silvicultural treatment is improvement cutting

TABLE 40

Estimated Annual Value, at 1938 Price Levels, of Future Growth of Timberland in Northboro Town, if Managed as Then, and if Managed as Recommended by Raymond and Chute of the Harvard Forest

Timberland classes	As managed in 1938				Managed as recommended		
	Acres	Value per acre, full stocking (dollars)	Per cent of full stocking	Total value (dollars)	Acres	Value per acre (dollars)	Total Value (dollars)
Better Hardwood	1,406	2.44	65	2,230	1,638	4.84	7,928
Softwood-Better Hardwood	1,408	3.51	57	2,817	2,725	6.16	16,786
Softwood	74	6.24	52	240	1,656	9.01	14,920
Inferior Hardwood	713	2.05	42	614	—	—	—
Softwood-Inferior Hardwood	2,298	2.84	48	3,133	—	—	—
Red Maple	126	1.50	—	189	6	1.50	9
Indeterminate	196	—	—	—	196	—	—
GRAND TOTALS	6,221			9,223	6,221		39,643

to favor the better formed trees of good species, and at the same time to reduce the quantity of favored gypsy moth food — oaks and gray birch. In some of the younger stands, timely weedings should be made to improve the composition and quality of the growing stock by controlling inferior individuals that tend to dominate the stands. Because of the understocking and exposure that has resulted from repeated clear-cutting, many of the stands are in need of one or more decades of rest from cutting of any sort to recover from the past injurious practices.

Planting may be required where the present stands are wholly inferior, or on some open areas, such as abandoned pastures, where conversion to a valuable crop can be made only by planting. However, planting of conifers in pure stands should be avoided wherever possible because of the danger of insect pests and diseases which are associated with artificial conditions. Under-planting of conifers beneath light-seeded inferior hardwoods would be more feasible for protection against insect attack such as the white pine weevil than if planting were done on areas void of this protective covering.

The land-use recommendations of the Country Life Committee stress better home gardens for the families of nonfarm workers, pasture improvement, and above all, drainage. The following statements are noteworthy:

An inadequate amount of roughage is raised on many dairy farms. The shortage is made more acute by inadequate pastures. Existing pastures provide good feed in June and July, but very little in August. There is approximately 50 percent or less as much feed available in most pastures as is required. While much of the soil is inclined to droughtiness, there is land with sufficient moisture to make pasture improvement practical.

The Assabet River and many of its tributaries in Northboro are bordered by low flat lands subject to frequent floods. Stream courses are winding and sluggish. Repeated overflows have built up the stream banks higher than the adjoining land in many cases so that this land remains wet and swampy much of the time and flood waters drain off very slowly. There are many acres of land along streams in towns that were once good farm land but due to flooding are now practically useless. This is true along Cold Harbor Brook, Howard Brook, Hop Brook, the Assabet River and areas in southeastern Northboro. Reclamation of some of this land would greatly benefit many farms. Accomplishment of a drainage project, however, would necessitate the cooperation of many individuals as well as public agencies and must be preceded by careful consideration of relative costs and of the effect it would have on people and communities down the Assabet River from Northboro.

GRAFTON

Figures 41 and 42 together show both the land use and the soil classification. Grafton has an unusually large proportion of No. 3 soils of the Gloucester series, largely fine sandy loams, varying considerably in stoniness. A little of this is cropland near the roads; much more of it is wooded pasture. Most of the cropland and plowable pasture is on No. 1 land but by no means all of it. As elsewhere, the No. 1 land not being cropped is mostly well back from the roads or surrounded by No. 4 land. It is notable that the top of Kieth Hill is classed as No. 1 and the slopes as No. 4. On the county soil map, the No. 1 soil is mostly Paxton and the slopes near the north end are Gloucester and Rough Stony to the south. The orchard area reaches over on to the sloping land to the north. Most of the considerable amount of wet land is not being farmed.

The Country Life Committee of Grafton did a good job of assembling the facts with respect to its land use and agriculture and related factors, but was unable, largely because of differences in attitude and judgments among the Committee members, to formulate a set of conclusions as to future lines of development. The Town has been highly industrial so far as the employment of its people is concerned, but its industrial history has been checkered and at the time of the Committee's work the textile plants were about all that was left of its industry. Its factory workers were therefore mostly em-

Figure 41. *Land use in Grafton Town, 1935, from the Land Use Survey of the Massachusetts Planning Board.*

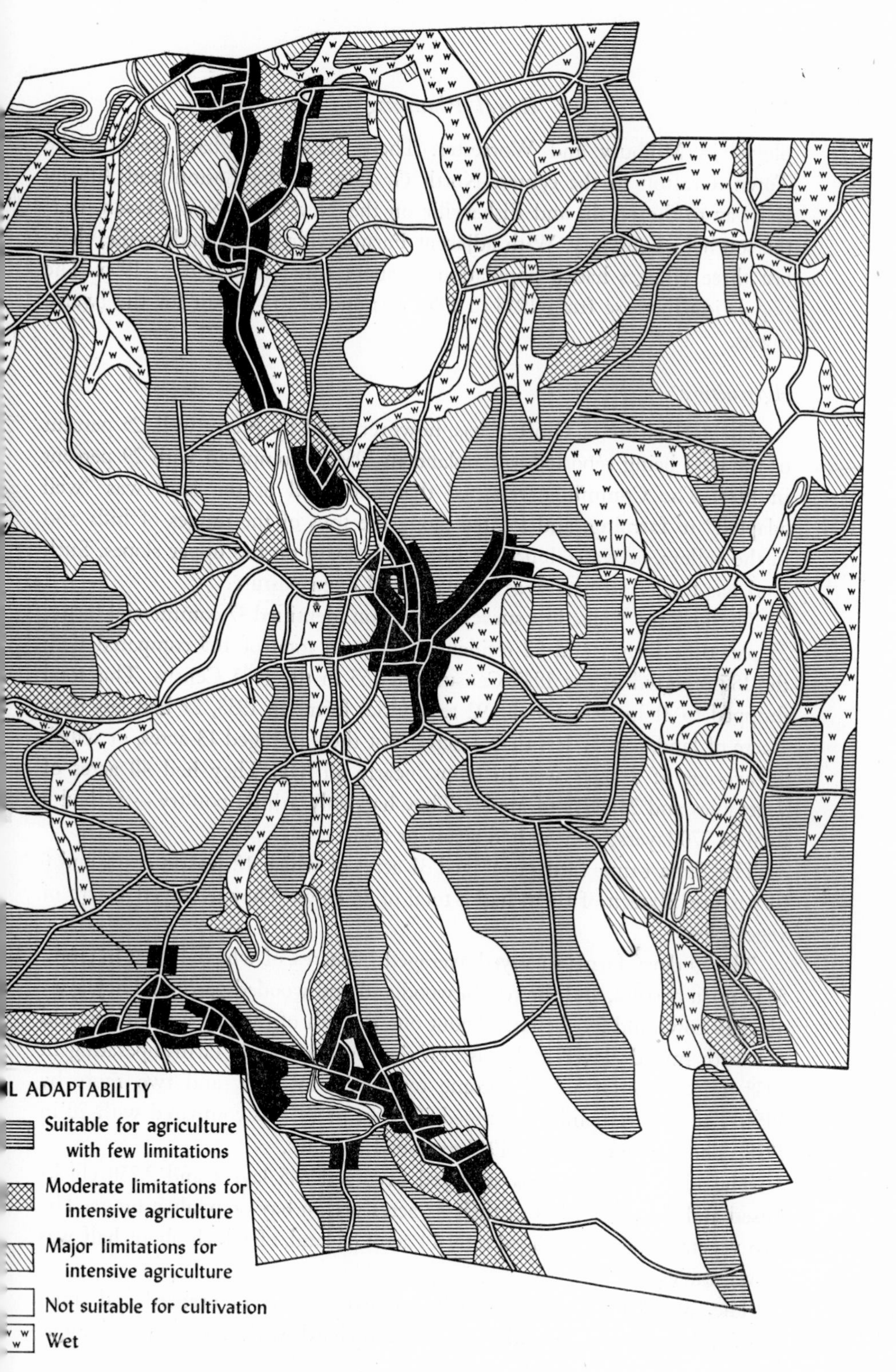

Figure 42. *Classification of the land of Grafton Town into four classes according to adaptability to agriculture.*

ployed in Millbury and Worcester. There are three urban areas in the Town, Grafton in the center, North Grafton, on the Boston and Albany Railway to the north, and Fisherville on the New York-New Haven, near the southern boundary. With adjacent Farnumville and Saundersville, these last three villages had a population of about three thousand in 1955. The population increase from 1945 to 1955 was one of the lowest for the twelve towns.

Agriculture

The agriculture of Grafton has, however, held up pretty well, 25 percent of the land being reported as cropland in 1954 as compared with 29 percent in 1925. The Committee reported that one third of the land was "well adapted" to farming, and located along the tops of the ranges of hills and in the valleys, or was Gloucester fine sandy loam on the upper slopes. Such land has tended to persist as cropland and open pasture.

The 1938 short-schedule survey of Grafton identified 47 commercial farms, 25 part-time farms, and 92 residential farms, a total of 165 compared with the 185 reported in the 1945 Census and 165 in the 1925 Census. This total dropped to 81 in 1950. Of the 92 residential farms in 1938, 27 had less than 1 acre of land, and 47 less than 3 acres. But they averaged 13 acres, of which an average of 3 acres was in crops, nearly all hay. They had 40 acres of vegetables and 23 acres of apples. They had only a little poultry — 32 had a total of 970 layers; only 15 had a cow or two.

The 25 part-time farms averaged 31 acres of which 12 was in crops and 6 in pasture. Sixteen of them had a total of 36 cows. They averaged 1 acre of vegetables.

The 29 dairy farms surveyed averaged 145 acres, of which 45 was in crops, 54 in open pasture, and the rest in woodland and wooded pasture. They averaged 19 cows and 5½ heifers. About one seventh of the hay was alfalfa, and one fifth mixed clover and grass. Of the nine case-study farms operating in 1938, one dairy farm had become residential by 1945, and two more by 1954. The four remaining averaged 39 cows in 1954 as compared with 20 in 1938. The five operating in 1945 averaged 25 cows.

The nine poultry farms surveyed averaged 645 layers and 2,750 chicks raised and 1½ cows. Most of their 32 acres was in hay or poultry range. The two vegetable farms averaged only 14 acres of land, of which about half was in vegetables.

The three fruit farms surveyed averaged 16 acres of orchard and small fruit. These do not include one large orchard with 260 acres of apple occupying the top of Kieth Hill in southern Grafton. The four remaining commercial farms combined dairy with poultry or vegetables.

Case Study Farms

Of the nine farms analyzed in detail in Grafton in 1938, four were wholesale dairy farms, three retail dairy farms, one a poultry, and one a poultry-vegetable farm. Three of the dairy farms were confronted with the problem of very small fields separated by stone walls, on heavy Sutton or Paxton soils. They were capable of sustained high productivity under the right management. Two of the farms also needed additional investment in farm buildings. Borrowing to make these needed land and building improvements presented a problem. One of these farms in addition would not have enough cropland for the twenty-cow herd considered necessary for an adequate income by the farmer. One of the larger farms had too low an output per cow and needed to cull out a third of the poorest cows and raise more replacements instead while building up the herd. This, plus raising more and better quality forage, would increase the low net income by a half even in the first three years. Another of the dairy farms had thirty cows and the operator said he wanted to develop his farm to support the largest number possible with increasing returns. The plan worked out with him called for fifty-five cows plus replacements, with the same 90 acres of cropland but under more intensive management, and 22 acres more of improved pasture. Also rye would be grown for early spring pasture.

Another of the farms exemplified the case of a professional man trying to operate a rather large farm business with hired labor and a foreman. The wages he was paying were not getting him the quality of labor and assistant-management that was needed to yield any appreciable net returns, unless the proprietor himself was able and willing to contribute much more detailed high-quality management than he had been. Few fully realize the detailed attention that the management of a dairy herd plus forage and pasture requires on land such as that in New England.

The vegetable and orchard farm studied had 11 acres in apples and 16 in vegetables, and yet was yielding a net income of only $2,000 at 1938 price levels, plus milk from two cows and poultry products for the family. The rest of the cropland was used to produce part of the hay and forage needed by the two horses and two cows. The Sutton sandy loam soils were being well managed from the standpoint of keeping up their organic content. The adjustments in the plans settled upon promised to add only $500 to the net income.

Woodland

Grafton had very little softwood in its 1938 stands of 7,010 acres, and what there was was about all in combination with the inferior hardwoods. The suggested program for the woodlands, as in Northboro, would convert these stands to Softwood-Better Hardwood, and increase somewhat the acreage of Better Hardwoods. The distribution of stands resulting would be 34 percent of the first, 50 percent of the second, and 14 percent of Softwood, yielding, at 1938 timber values, an average of $8.00 per acre per year.

A preliminary analysis of two tracts of woodland in Grafton illustrates one aspect of the problem of woodland management in Worcester County and similar areas. One of these tracts consisted of 1,500 acres on Gloucester stony land pretty well surrounded by dairy farms, mainly on Charlton and Gloucester fine sandy loam soils. It was owned in eleven different pieces and mostly in stump-sprout oak. Analysis indicated that the most effective use of this tract would be to have it divided and added to the adjacent dairy farms, if these dairy farmers could be interested in putting it under more intensive management. The other tract was thrice this size and had only a few farms nearby. The rough plan for it put all under one management with a program like that worked out for larger tracts in Chapter 10 on "Planning One Forest." Conceivably it could become a "town forest."

CHAPTER 16

Section C, Northeast Section

This Section of nine towns in the northeastern corner of Worcester County is almost as urban-oriented as is Section D. Three of its towns, Fitchburg, Leominster, and Clinton, are designated as cities by the Federal Census, with populations in 1950 of 42,690, 24,075, and 12,290 respectively. They do not, however, occupy their former town areas as fully as does the city of Worcester, nor have they arms reaching out into the surrounding towns as does Worcester. Indeed, Figure 14 in Chapter 6 shows that the 1954 Census reported 173 farms within their boundaries. Only one of the other towns, Lancaster, has an urban center large enough to be enumerated separately by the Census, South Lancaster with 1,450.

Table 41 shows, however, fully as strong a movement out of the urban areas into the country as in Section D. The three cities had a total population of 80,000 in 1950, and gained only 410 in the ten years from 1945 to 1955; the excess of births over deaths almost exactly equaled the net out-migration of 8,000. The net in-migration of the three towns of Lunenburg, Lancaster, and Sterling was 3,460, and of Westminster in Section A, 1,100. Harvard's, Bolton's, and Berlin's net in-migration of 710 no doubt was partly from Middlesex County.

That Fitchburg, Leominster, and Clinton are primarily manufacturing cities is shown by their average ratio of one factory worker to every four in their population, slightly higher than Worcester's. Such ratios are possible only with a large fraction of the factory workers living outside the boundaries of the city-towns.

The leading manufacturing lines in Fitchburg are metal products (25 percent), machinery (23 percent), and paper products (18 percent); of Leominster, textiles and clothing, plastics, and machinery; of Clinton, fabricated metal products, printing, and textiles and clothing.

TABLE 41

Population and Other Relevant Data by Towns in Section C of Worcester County

Town	Population		Percentage increase, 1945 to 1955	Average number employed in town's industries in 1955	Number of farms	
	1850	1950			1925	1950
Fitchburg	5,000	42,696	−2	10,550	132	68
Leominster	2,200	24,075	5	5,720	186	83
Sterling	1,600	2,170	43	30	165	88
Clinton	2,300	12,290	0	3,850	23	22
Lancaster	1,600	3,600	26	135	111	67
Lunenburg	1,300	3,910	99	50	227	94
Harvard	1,600	3,980	50	—*	130	87
Bolton	1,200	960	29	—*	112	78
Berlin	900	1,350	35	—*	118	90

—* = No data available.

The maps in Chapter 6 show that agriculture has held up in Section C just about as it has in adjoining Sections B and D, in terms both of percentage of cropland and of number of farms. Sterling is an outstanding agricultural town, having expanded its orcharding and broiler output in recent decades. Its farms have been getting larger. It produces more milk than any towns in the County except four in Sections A and F. Sterling and Harvard each had more than 20,000 apple trees in 1950, leading in the County by a wide margin. Harvard's orchards are smaller and spread over the whole town. The orchards in these northeast counties are part of what is referred to as the Nashoba apple district of Middlesex and Worcester Counties.

Because the interest in this study is in rural land use, Sterling was chosen for the more intensive analysis.

LAND USE AND SOILS

Figure 43 shows the distribution of land use in this Section between urban and farm and nonfarm woodland. It also marks off the tract in Lancaster and Harvard that is now in the Fort Devens military reservation. Only 24 percent of land in this Section was in farms in 1954. Of this 24 percent, about half was cropland and open pasture, around a fourth was woodland, and a tenth was wooded pasture.

It will be noted at once in Figure 44 that the No. 1 soils are most prevalent in the northern towns and in or close to the urban areas. This is as one

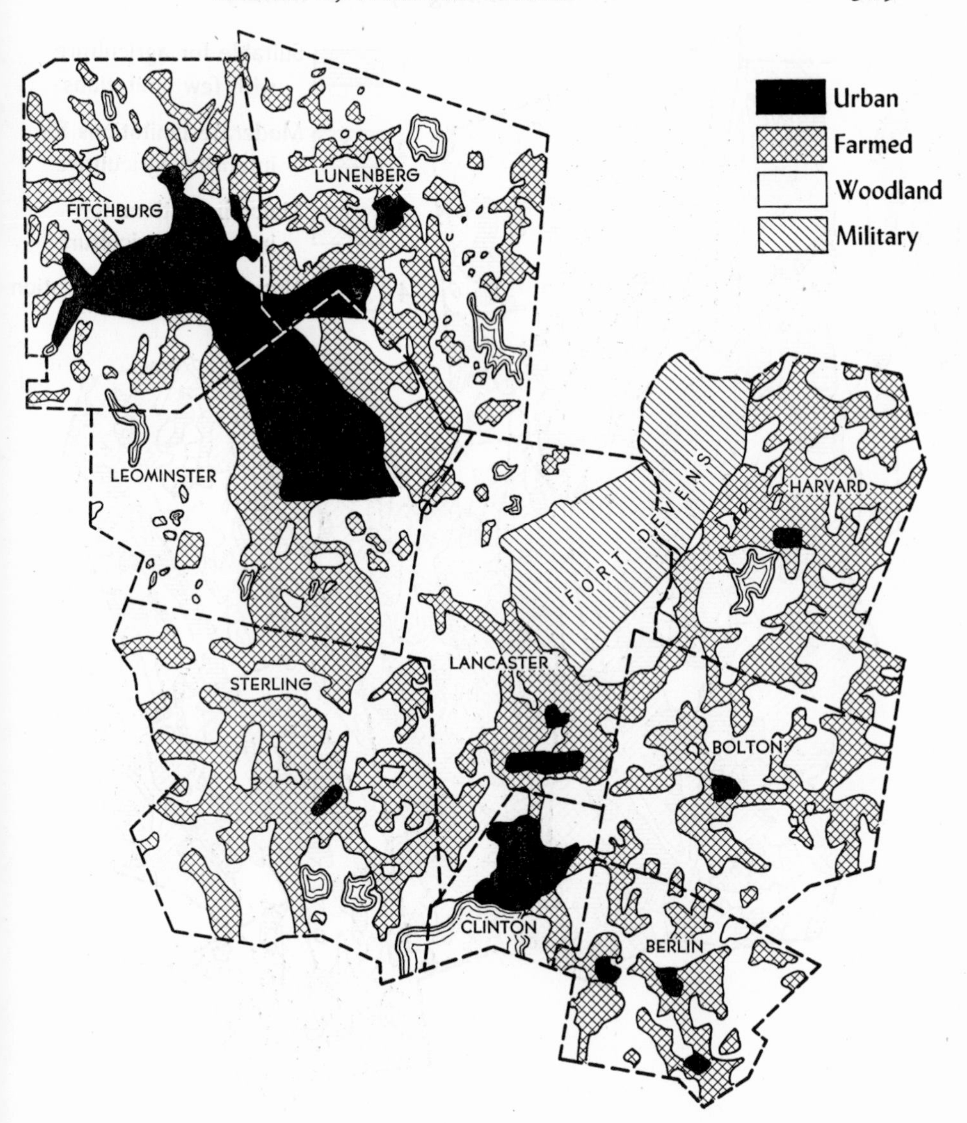

Figure 43. *Major land use in Section C of Worcester County.*

would expect — villages did not start, or if they did, did not develop into cities, within tracts of poor land. The railroads, when they were laid out, for the most part ran through the better land areas. Lunenburg has the largest proportion of No. 1 and 2 land of any of the towns, and Leominster comes next. Sterling's better lands are in its southeast sector and in the center.

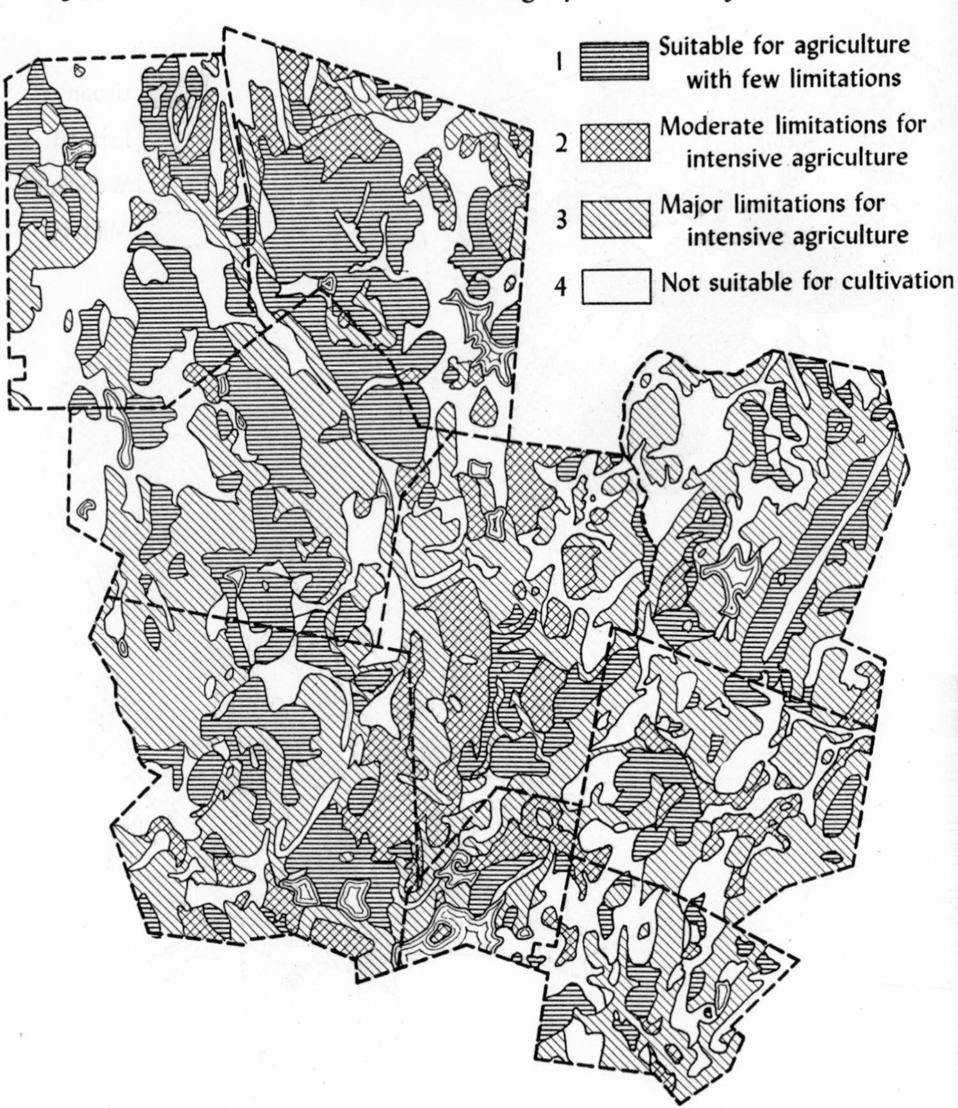

Figure 44. ***Land classified into four soil groups, Section C of Worcester County.***

Apparently a good deal of No. 3 soil is included within the boundaries of farms in Harvard, Bolton, and Berlin as well as in Sterling.

The No. 1 soils in this Section include Charlton loam, Paxton loam, Gloucester fine sandy loam and some Bernardston, Merrimac and Sutton, and scattered areas of Suffield, Hadley and Agawam. The Bernardston silt

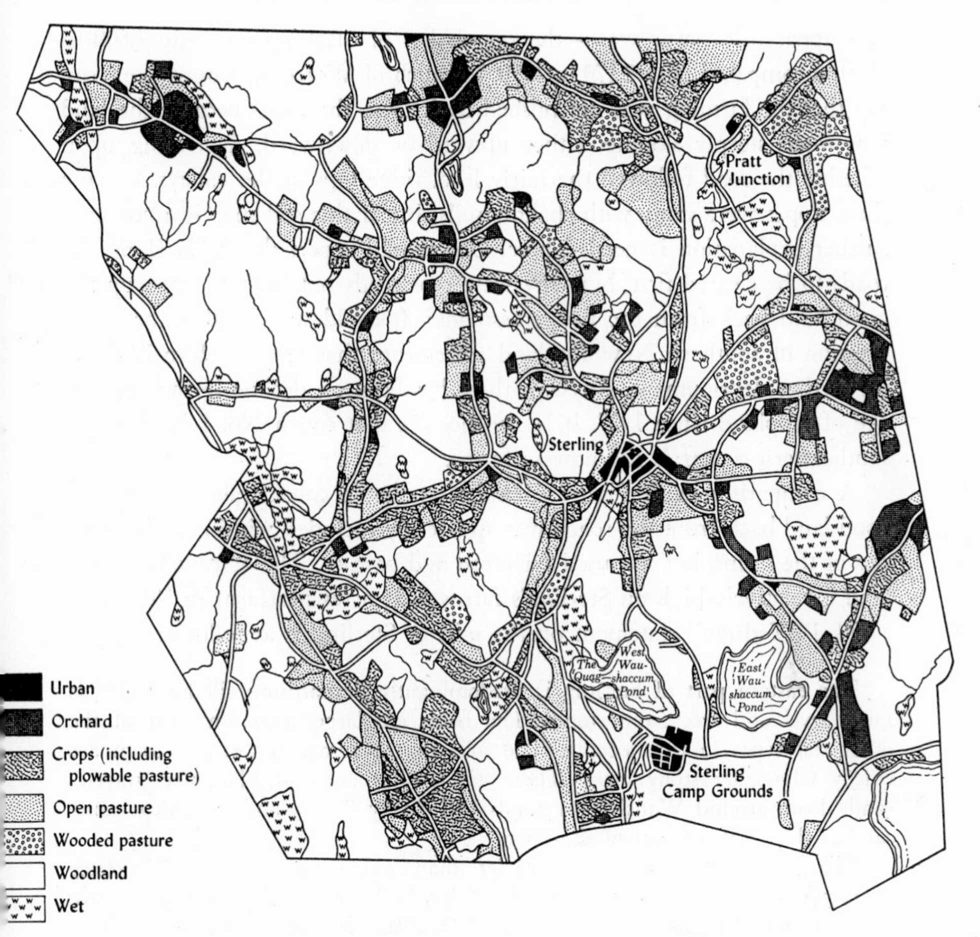

Figure 45. ***Land use in Sterling Town, 1935, from the Land Use Survey of the Massachusetts State Planning Board.***

loam is in a belt in eastern Sterling and western Lancaster. The No. 2 soils are sandy rather than sandy loams of mostly the same series, or stony Sutton or Charlton loams with a little Hollis and Buxton.

STERLING

Figure 45 makes it evident that it is no accident of history that Sterling has more agriculture than the surrounding towns. Half of its area at least is classified as having No. 1 soil, and most of the remainder is No. 3 rather than No. 4. When land use and soils are thus shown on one map, the question that arises is why so much of the No. 1 land is not now being farmed, and apparently never was — the population of Sterling was only 1,600 in 1850 as compared with 2,170 in 1950. In much of Worcester County, one can say that the farming was not pushed back from the roads because the land was more steeply sloping, either upward or downward, depending upon whether the road followed the fairly level ridge tops or the valleys. Usually these slopes were stony with shallow soils. But if this soil map is accurate, a further explanation is needed here. One would expect the fields along the roads to be cleared first, but why were crossroads not built to open up the good land back from the first crossroads? It could well be that the retrogression of southern New England agriculture that set in before 1840 cut off further development. Anyway, there has been no decline in the percentage of cropland since 1925. It is also notable that much No. 1 land in the southeastern corner is not now in farms.

A comparison with Figure 46 indicates that a considerable part of the good land back from the roads was apparently included within the boundaries of the farms, but not used for crops and pasture. The acreage of woodland is relatively high on Sterling's farms — 34 acres per farm in 1950.

N. P. Tedrow's statement on the soils of Sterling is as follows:

The eastern part of Sterling is predominantly Bernardston silt loam and is fairly level and free from stones. The fields are larger than on most of the other soil types in this locality. The soils in the remainder of the town are chiefly Gloucester stony loam. There are smaller areas of Merrimac gravelly sandy loam around Waushacum ponds and Rocky Brook, and Hinckley loamy sand in the northern part of the town.

The Bernardston soils are heavier than most soil types in Worcester County and where the topography is level may be imperfectly drained. They give large yields of hay, and several large apple orchards are located on the less level areas.

In considerable contrast is Tedrow's statement for Berlin:

The southeastern part of Berlin and a narrow belt extending from the northwestern to the southeastern corner are predominantly light-textured outwash soils of the Hinckley and Merrimac series. Most of the ridge tops are rough stony land of Gloucester fine sandy loam. There are also small areas of Gloucester loam and fine sandy loam scattered throughout the town.

The fertility and productivity of these soils is low in comparison with that of some of the neighboring towns. The till soils are shallow and droughty with bedrock outcropping in numerous places. The outwash soils are droughty and lack natural fertility. High applications of commercial fertilizer are necessary to produce satisfactory yields. The till soils are very stony. Where such land is in farms a number of fields have been cleared of stones, but tillage operations are still difficult. Pasture fields have been partly cleared of stone. The fields are separated by stone walls.

The dairy farms are small with a very limited amount of cropland. The pastures are very rough and brushy. Very little effort has been made to improve

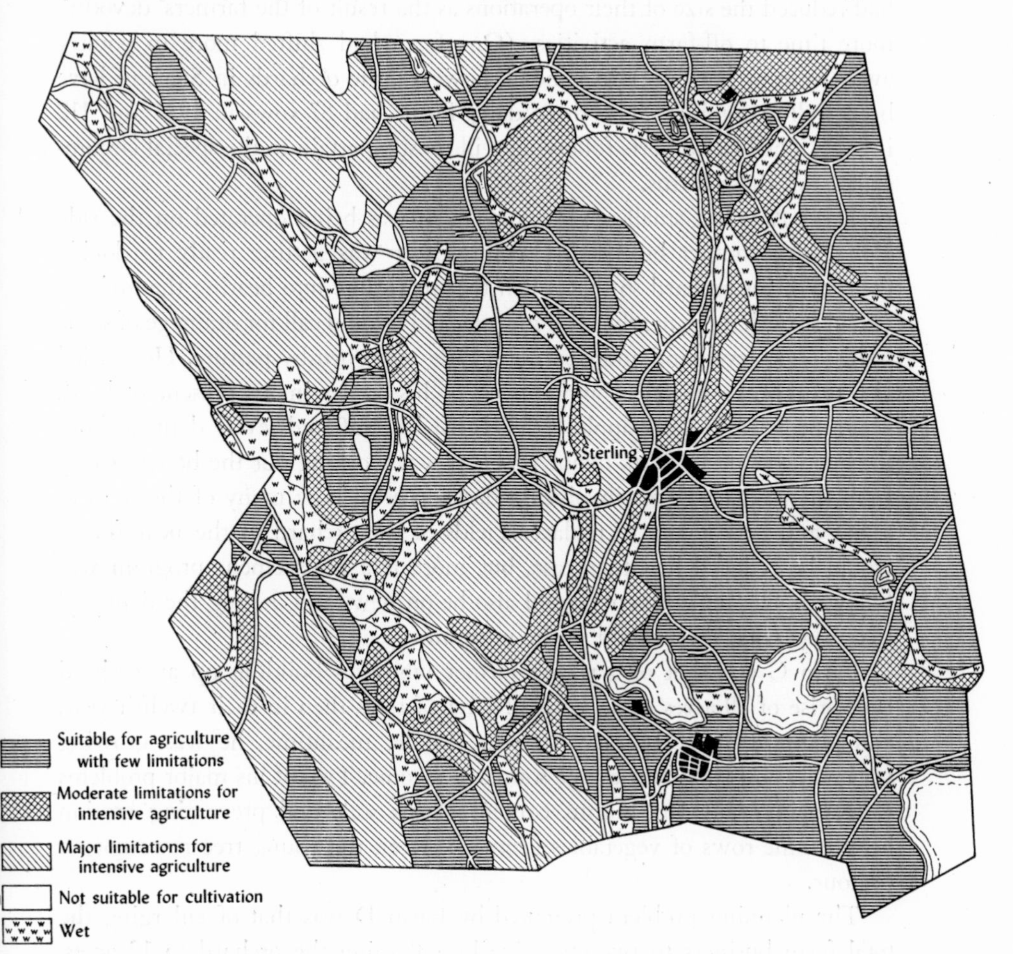

Figure 46. *Soils of Sterling Town classified into four groups, plus wet land, as in other towns.*

old pastures. There are only three or four orchards that are well cared for. The soils in this town are not well adapted to fruit production.

Case Study Farms in Sterling

Of the eight farms in Sterling analyzed in some detail in 1938 and 1946, all but two combined two or more lines of production and two were part-time farms. Farms A and B were fruit farms. Six of the eight farms had apple orchards which were very largely on Bernardston silt loam soil. Only one of the eight farms had become residential by 1954, but two of the farms had reduced the size of their operations as the result of the farmers' devoting more time to off-farm activities. (One farm had shifted more to poultry away from orcharding.) In general, however, the orchards in Sterling have been well-maintained. The three dairy farms had 87 cows in 1938 and 112 in 1954. The brief reports following will mostly pertain to the special circumstances on these farms.

Farm A was a small apple farm which was being operated on the side along with another business. The proprietor was getting ready to double the size of his orchard so that when the trees came into bearing the orchard would furnish more nearly a full income. This would call for drainage of some of his lower level land and clearing a little more brushy pasture. He needed also to improve the yield and quality of his apples in his present orchard.

Farm B was a large apple orchard that had suffered severe damage from the hurricane of 1938. Its major problem was working out the best recovery from this damage. This involved a decision as to how many of the trees to repair and how many to replace. Yields of the orchard in the near future would be reduced in either case, but more if a replacement program was followed. The replacements could also be on new land, letting the damaged trees bear what they would in the meantime.

Farm C was that of a young farmer who was building up an orchard enterprise of 30 acres or so with 12 acres of trees then in their twelfth year, and planning to add 4 acres a year. In the meantime, he was growing vegetables and strawberries as a source of income. Two of his major problems were maintaining the humus content of his soils and preventing erosion between the rows of vegetables grown between the young tree rows not on contour.

The planning problem presented by Farm D was that of enlarging the total farm business to two-man size by enlarging the orchard to 12 acres, or by improving some more fairly sloping Gloucester sandy loam brushy pasture and adding to the dairy herd. The decision was to do both.

Farm E was combining 14 cows, 13 acres of orchard, and 450 hens plus 1,200 chickens on a farm with 55 acres of Bernardston silt loam cropland plus 50 acres brushy pasture and 8 acres of improved pasture. It was not yielding enough income to support the son's family along with the father's. The plan chosen to develop, after analyzing alternatives, was not to enlarge the orchard enterprise but to manage it more intensively, and to raise the dairy herd to 24 cows plus replacements with higher yields per cow, as a result of including 23 acres of light alfalfa in rotations and improving 13 acres more pasture.

FLOODING AND DRAINAGE

As already indicated, this area is largely drained by the Nashua River flowing into the Merrimack. It also serves as the disposal channel for the mill wastes of the industrial plants. With a high concentration of paper mill wastes from the factories of Fitchburg, the wastes accumulate in the north fork of the Nashua during periods of low flow. When the Nashua reaches flood stage, the water overflows the banks and inundates the adjacent land. Carried with the flood waters are the wastes that accumulated in the channel. As the water recedes, the land is left covered with wood pulp scum.

The conclusions of the Seminar group working on this Section were as follows: The channel grade should be investigated. Where the flat sluggish reaches occur, the channel should be dredged. The channel should have levees constructed where necessary to confine the flood waters in the channel. By confining even the largest discharges in the river channel, scouring velocities will prevail that will flush the accumulated industrial wastes to the sea. Implementing the plan will call for a special appropriation from Congress.

There are many marshy areas scattered throughout the nine towns considered here that result from inadequate surface drainage. In many cases these wet areas can be reclaimed by the construction of drainage ditches. Considerable progress is being made in draining individual farms through the Soil Conservation District's program of technical assistance. Before drainage is undertaken, however, the soils should be classified in detail. Some marshy soils upon close investigation might still be classified as Class 3 or 4 after drainage. In such cases drainage may not be economically justified. If the plan for a farm shows that additional cropland is desirable, the alternative of clearing land of trees or stones must also be considered. The position of the land in the farm organization may bear heavily on whether or not to drain.

A serious drainage problem exists along the Still River in the Town of Harvard. The problem involves a number of farms and will have to be solved by cooperative action of the group. The Still River flows parallel to the Nashua River and constitutes the trough of the Nashua flood plain. The Nashua has a mature channel with a sluggish grade as it flows through Harvard. Repeated overflowing of the Nashua during flood stages has deposited sediment along the banks creating natural levees. Under these circumstances, the slope of the flood plain is away from the river to the trough.

A major difficulty with a problem such as this is that the technical agencies charged with planning the solution are loath to spend much man-power on investigations unless they are assured that the landowners will follow through with construction. They do not wish to put sizable investments in plans that are not likely to be executed. On the other hand, the landowners are reluctant to commit themselves to a construction program until they have details on the relative merits and costs. The net result is that each waits on the other and nothing gets done. This is a difficult box from which to work one's way out.

SUBURBAN RESIDENCES

Of much interest for this and other parts of Worcester County should be the Seminar group's statement on the subject of suburban land use. Not all, of course, will be willing to accept it.

> The increasing tendency towards building residences in the rural areas competes with agriculture for the land. There really isn't much competition because residential users are willing to pay much higher prices than farmers can afford per acre and can secure the best land. No. 1 land around Fitchburg, Leominster, Lunenburg and Sterling is in danger of being developed for suburban homes.
>
> Every effort should be made by the town planning groups to get No. 3 and No. 4 land used for subdivisions, particularly the droughty soils. These soils make good building sites, make excellent roadways, provide good drainage and afford good cesspool disposal. For home gardening purposes, the limitations of droughtiness and low nutrient level can be overcome by irrigation and by adding fertilizers, organic matter and topsoil.

RECREATIONAL USE OF LAND

In the Northeast Section there are over ninety-two thousand people who could benefit from the development of recreational areas and facilities. In addition, many persons from the Worcester area would share in the use of such developments. The lag in recreational development in this area is typical for the County, and for that matter for most of Massachusetts. There are numerous ponds, lakes, wooded areas, and picnic spots that could well serve the public if the people would be willing to place recreation development higher in the budget of town, county, and state government finances. In an industrial area complicated by shifting economic conditions it is particularly likely that expenditures for recreation will be considered secondary to roads, transportation, schools, and services. In such a situation the attitude toward recreation is likely to be that it cannot be afforded. This attitude by those who determine the town, county, and state policies is a major problem in the consideration of recreational development.

The State Conservation Department has, however, stocked most of the lakes or ponds and brooks with fish. One of the problems is access to these waters. Woodlands adjacent or surrounding them may be owned for the pleasure of owning them, with no particular plan in mind for using or developing the holding. These wooded areas surround many of the ponds and streams within the area, thus cutting off access by the public. The more populated an area becomes, the less likely that private lands remain accessible to the public because of the misuse of the privileges by a few persons.

THE COUNTRY LIFE COMMITTEE REPORTS

Berlin

In line with Tedrow's description of Berlin's soils, the State Planning Board classified only 20 percent of Berlin's soil as of "good adaptability." The Country Life Committee, however, laid out five areas, making up 35 percent of the Town, as suitable for agriculture with "only minor adjustments," and another 12 percent in four areas as suitable for agriculture but "needing major adjustments." But included within these areas are many tracts of steeply sloping land, or hummocky or swampy land, too small to show separately on a town-wide map. The rest of the land is nearly all hilly stony land covered with trees and brush. All but 30 percent of the forest is Inferior Hardwood or Softwood-Inferior Hardwood.

The Census of 1935 had identified 72 farms, 32 of whose proprietors had worked off their farms an average of 143 days. Only 15 of the farms had 10 cows or more, and 11 farms had 300 hens or more, or turkeys. Also 7 farms had 20 acres or more of vegetables. The number of apple trees had risen from 8,500 to 10,500 in the preceding ten years, but the number of peach trees had declined from 10,400 to 2,700.

The more notable recommendations of the Country Life Committee were a return to a larger acreage of peaches, improvement of carefully selected pasture land, the raising of more dairy replacements, and larger farms.

Lancaster

The Country Life Committee made its report on Lancaster just after the government had bought 4,000 acres, including some farms, in the northeastern part of the Town for the Fort Devens reservation. Most of the 45 percent of land classified by the State Planning Board as of "good adaptability" is in the southern half of the Town. The Country Life Committee gave a No. 1 rating to 37 percent of the Town in three areas located outside of this reservation, and a No. 3 rating to only 24 percent of the Town in four areas located outside the reservation. The No. 1 soils were Bernardston largely, either heavy silt loams on the uplands or well-watered fine sandy loams on the flats adjoining the Nashua River and its branches. Much of the No. 1 land, however, has been allowed to revert to brush and trees, so that in 1938 only 14 percent of the Town was in cropland and plowable pastures and 72 percent was in woodland and brush.

There were 23 dairy herds in the Town with 10 cows or more in 1935, 7 commercial poultry farms, and 9 farms with orchards of 5 acres or more, 5 of these rather large. There has since been a considerable growth of residential farming in Lancaster, the families finding employment in Clinton or Leominster.

The most pertinent of the recommendations of the Country Life Committee were as follows:

> There is a minimum of good hayland on dairy farms and the quality and rate of hay production are low. There are many idle hayfields on properties the owners of which are not engaged in farming. Improvement of such fields would maintain the owner's equity. If a long-term lease could be worked out, farmers might be able to afford to improve these fields and cut hay from them. This would be of value both to owners and farmers and would improve the appearance of roadsides in the town as well.
>
> In the southwestern part of the town all the farms but one are for sale. Most of these farms are not abandoned, although much of the land is not being worked. The majority of the farms are too small for successful dairies, as they would hardly support more than 10 cows. They are more suited to use as country homes or as commercial poultry farms.

WOODLAND

Of the 76 percent of the 132,000 acres of land in Section C that was not in farms in 1954, about all was woodland or brush except that occupied by the cities and rural residences, roads, streams, lakes, or swamp. In addition, around 17,000 acres of the land in farms was in woodland or wooded pasture. The total of woodland must have been around 98,000 acres or 75 percent of the total area of the town. No special cruising was done of any of the towns in this section, as was done for Northboro in Section D. The State Planning Board's 1939 Land Use Planning Survey, however, showed that in general, as in Berlin and in Sterling, the major portion of the stands were Softwood-Inferior Hardwood and Inferior Hardwood. One reason for this is probably that in this part of the County the white pine had come freely into the old fields and pastures as they had been abandoned, and when this pine was removed the hardwoods following had been cut for fuelwood when only partly grown, leaving stump-sprout clusters and inferior hardwoods in their wake.

The nine farms case-studied in Sterling had an average of 36 acres of woodland out of an average of 140 acres per farm. This was around 40 percent Better Hardwood, 20 percent Softwood-Better Hardwood, 25 percent Inferior Hardwood and 10 percent Softwood-Inferior Hardwood. But much of the woodland on these farms was on Bernardston soils or other soils in the same soil association. The management proposed would have converted all of this woodland to Better Hardwoods except that on the droughty soils.

CHAPTER 17

Section B, Northwest Section

This Section of eight towns in the northwest corner of Worcester County had only 46 percent of its land in farms in 1925, Section D being next lowest with 50 percent. Its land in farms has fallen off a half since then just as has that of Sections C and D. It is less urbanized than these other two Sections, although it has three cities, Gardner, Athol, and Winchendon, with populations in 1950 of 19,580, 9,710, and 4,020 respectively. The census classifies Gardner Town as a city and reports no rural population for it. It reported 40 farms for it in 1954. Athol had a population of 1,840 outside its urban area, and Winchendon 2,520. Of the 470 farms in Section B in 1950, all but 220 of them were in the three towns of Westminster, Templeton, and Athol. It is not competition with cities, however, that has kept down agriculture in this Section. It is instead the high proportion of rough stony or Class 3 land that has been in forest continuously.

Only one town in this Section, Winchendon, was studied intensively. Country Life Committees, however, functioned also in Westminster and Templeton.

POPULATION AND INDUSTRY

Table 42 presents a very interesting picture of population growth in this area. For the recent period 1945 to 1955, there is almost a perfect inverse correlation between the size of the population in 1945 and the percentage growth in the following ten years. There is the definite suggestion in this that the families moving out into the open country for a place to live are able to live as well in an area with little agriculture — like Phillipston, Templeton, and Royalston — as in a more thriving farming area. Westminster, of course, is furnishing homes for the factory workers of Gardner, Fitchburg, and Leominster. Gardner employs 1 factory worker for every 3.8 of its own residents; Athol, for every 3.3; and Winchendon, for every 5.2.

Athol's factory workers live in Petersham, Royalston, and Phillipston as well as in Athol and across the line in Franklin County.

TABLE 42

Population and Other Relevant Data by Towns in Section B of Worcester County

Town	Population 1850	Population 1950	Percentage increase, 1945–1955	Average number employed in town's industries, 1955	Number of farms 1925	Number of farms 1950
Royalston	1,400	830	13	——*	112	34
Winchendon	2,300	6,585	4	1,270	182	48
Ashburnham	1,600	2,600	11	260	113	66
Athol	2,000	11,550	4	3,460	172	80
Phillipston	500	640	57	——*	86	30
Templeton	2,100	4,780	21	360	164	72
Gardner	2,200	19,580	0	5,270	55	40
Westminster	1,700	2,770	63	45	131	110

——* = No data available.

The differing populations of these towns in 1850, and particularly their growth in the century following, is explained in part by the fact that Gardner and Athol are located on the Boston and Albany railroad. This gave them a better chance to develop industrially. Gardner got an early start in the manufacture of chairs and other furniture. Today 60 percent of its labor force in manufacturing is engaged in the making of furniture and fixtures. Other lines are toys, sporting and athletic goods, and stoves and other heating apparatus. The leading manufacturing lines in Athol are machinery, shoes, toys and sporting goods, and textile products. Although Winchendon has long been known as the "toy town," its manufacturing is now well diversified, including also furniture, tubs and pails, paper cartons, women's clothing, and so on. Ashburnham's ten firms all manufacture furniture and wood products. This concentration on wooden products in this area was based on local supplies of wood in its period of great growth. Today much of the wood is shipped from other parts of the United States and even from abroad.

LAND USE AND SOILS

Figures 47 and 48 show land use and soil classification for this Section in the same manner as do similar charts for the West Central and Southwest Sections. Westminster and Templeton have the highest percentage of their land in crops, but that is only around one tenth of it. The soil map shows an overwhelming proportion of No. 4 soils in all the towns, but especially in Royalston and Ashburnham, and in the northern parts of Athol and Templeton. These are Gloucester series soils, mostly stony sandy loam, stony fine sandy loam, with associated Rough Stony area. Finally,

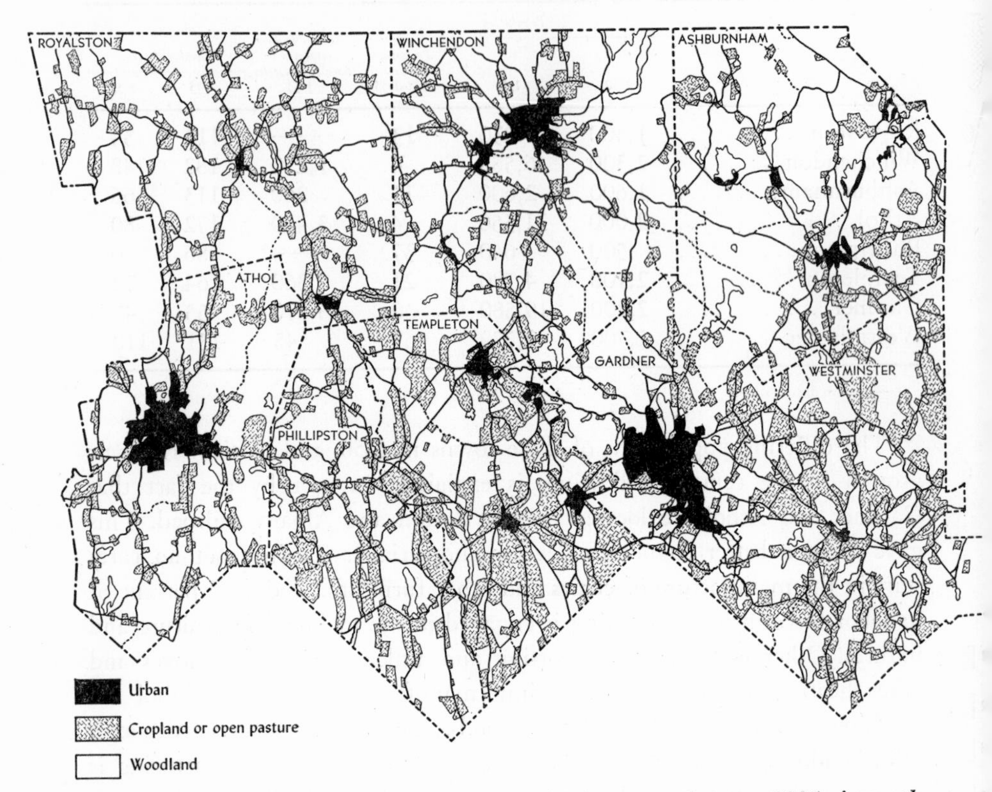

Figure 47. *Major land use in Section B of Worcester County, 1935, from the Land Use Survey of the Massachusetts State Planning Board.*

areas of Gloucester sandy loam are classified as No. 3 in Winchendon and elsewhere. The No. 1 soils in the north-south belt in the center of Winchendon are mostly Charlton fine sandy loam. The sizable stretches of No. 1 soils in eastern Templeton are Charlton or Brookfield loams. Athol has some No. 2 Merrimac sandy loam along its southwestern border and No. 1 Gloucester loam south of its center, and of Gloucester stony fine sandy loam farther to the south. Gardner's and Westminster's sizable areas of

No. 1 soils are mostly Charlton. In general the soils of Section B are of lighter texture than of those of other parts of the County.

AGRICULTURE

Leaving out the city-town of Gardner, there were 463 farms in Section B in 1950. Certain interesting facts concerning these can be obtained from

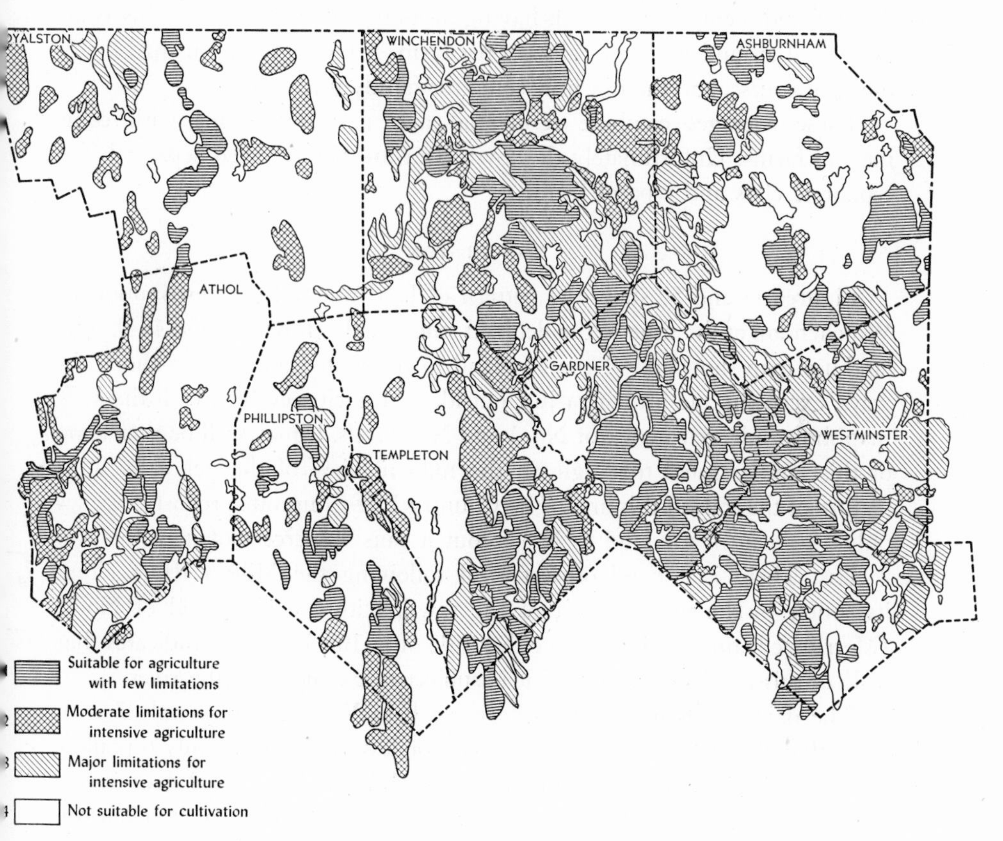

Figure 48. ***Land classified into four soil groups, Section B of Worcester County.***

tabulating township data furnished by the census especially for this project. Only 373 reported any cropland harvested at all in 1949, and half of these harvested less than 10 acres, and only 43 harvested 30 acres or more. The average farm had 13 acres of harvested crops (mostly hay, of course), 6 acres of cropland used for pasture, 4 acres of other open pasture, 15 acres of woodland pasture, 40 acres of other woodland, and 9 acres of other land, making a total of 89 acres. It can thus be seen that not much farming was carried on on these farms — only 23 acres were really farmed. Although 284 of these farms reported an average of 6.4 cows per farm, only 131 of them sold any dairy products; and these sold an average of $2,500 worth per farm; also 163 of them sold an average of 5,000 dozen eggs in 1949. Only in Westminster was the ratio of chicks sold to eggs sold very high. Finally, 23 of the farms grew 36 acres of vegetables for sale. Figure 67 reports Westminster and Templeton as each having around 5,000 apple trees. This is an average of around 40 trees of all ages per farm. A few of the farms had many more, of course, and the rest only some for family use.

These averages combine residential and part-time farms with commercial farms. Unfortunately the town data are not reported separately by economic class and type of farm.

WINCHENDON

Figures 49 and 50 show the pattern of land use and soil distribution in Winchendon at the time of the detailed study of this town around 1940. The land-use map shows all of the cropland to be located adjacent to the highways, except in one little area just outside of the city, even though the soils map shows a large expanse of No. 1 and No. 2 soils. It may well be that some of this land is rated too high on the map in view of the generally light texture of the soils in this area. The Country Life Committee report classifies only 6 percent of the land as No. 1; but it puts 40 percent of it in the No. 2 class. There is a band of wet land following the Millers River along its course in the western part of the town, with a wider band of No. 2 (Merrimac loamy sand) soil on either side of it. But Figure 49 indicates that little of this is farmed. Much of it is subject to overflows of the river.

The dairy herds have always been small in Winchendon — only 7 with more than 4 cows in 1935, and 62 with 4 or less. There were only 6 poultry farms in 1941. The readjustments that seemed desirable on the 2 dairy farms analyzed as cases were of the same pattern as those chosen on the Charlton loam soils in the West Central Section — reducing feed bills and enlarging herds by including more alfalfa in the hay and more ladino in the pasture. There was no wholesale market for milk in Winchendon at the time, and these dairy farmers were retailing their milk. They were still doing this in 1956. The poultry farms studied could be enlarged without over-taxing the families' labor resources, but some outlay on poultry housing would usually be involved. This is of course in line with developments in the past fifteen years. One poultry farm had some good potential cropland that was being rented out as pasture. The alternative of keeping a herd of 9 cows to supple-

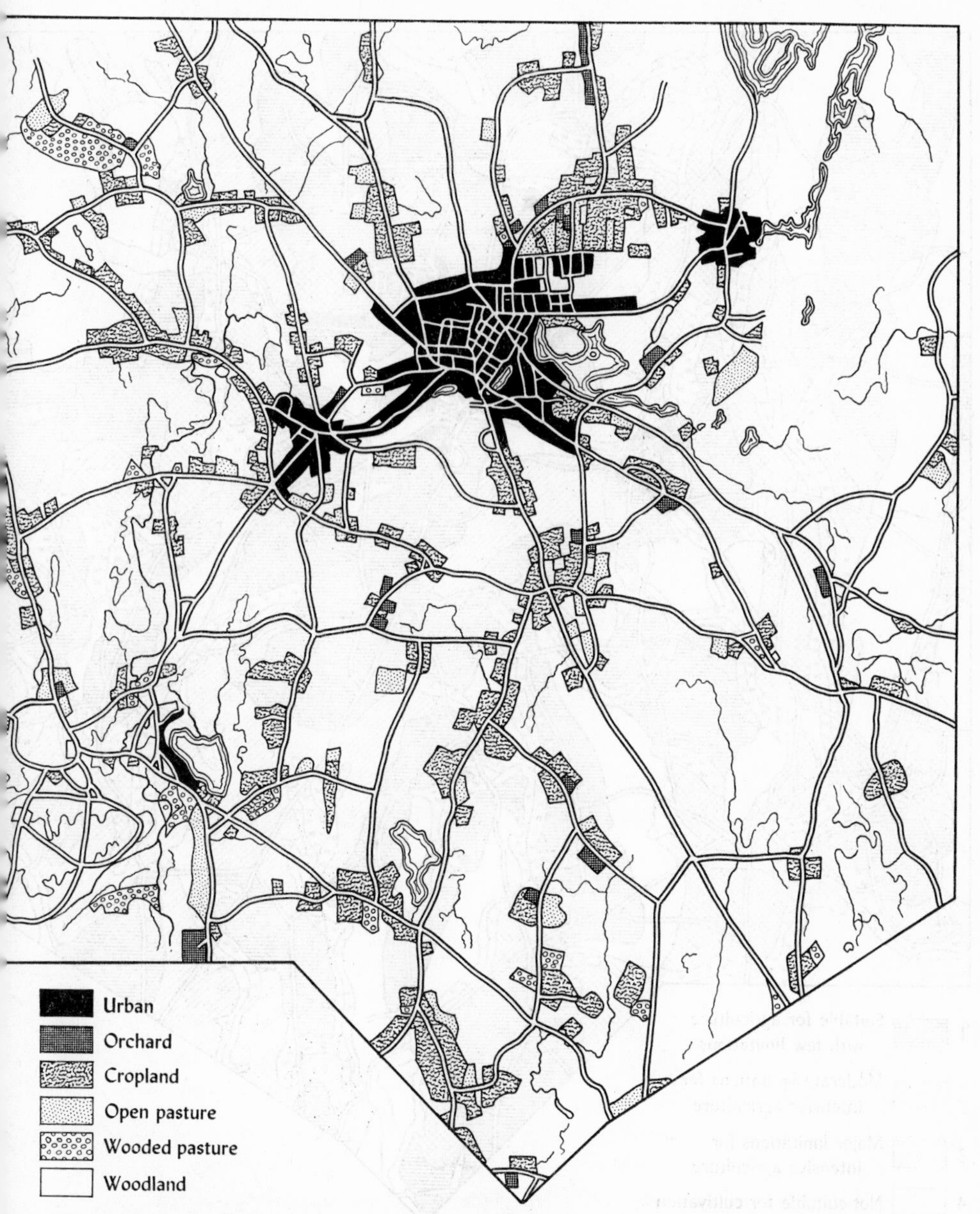

Figure 49. ***Major land use in Winchendon Town, 1937, from the Land Use Survey of the Massachusetts State Planning Board.***

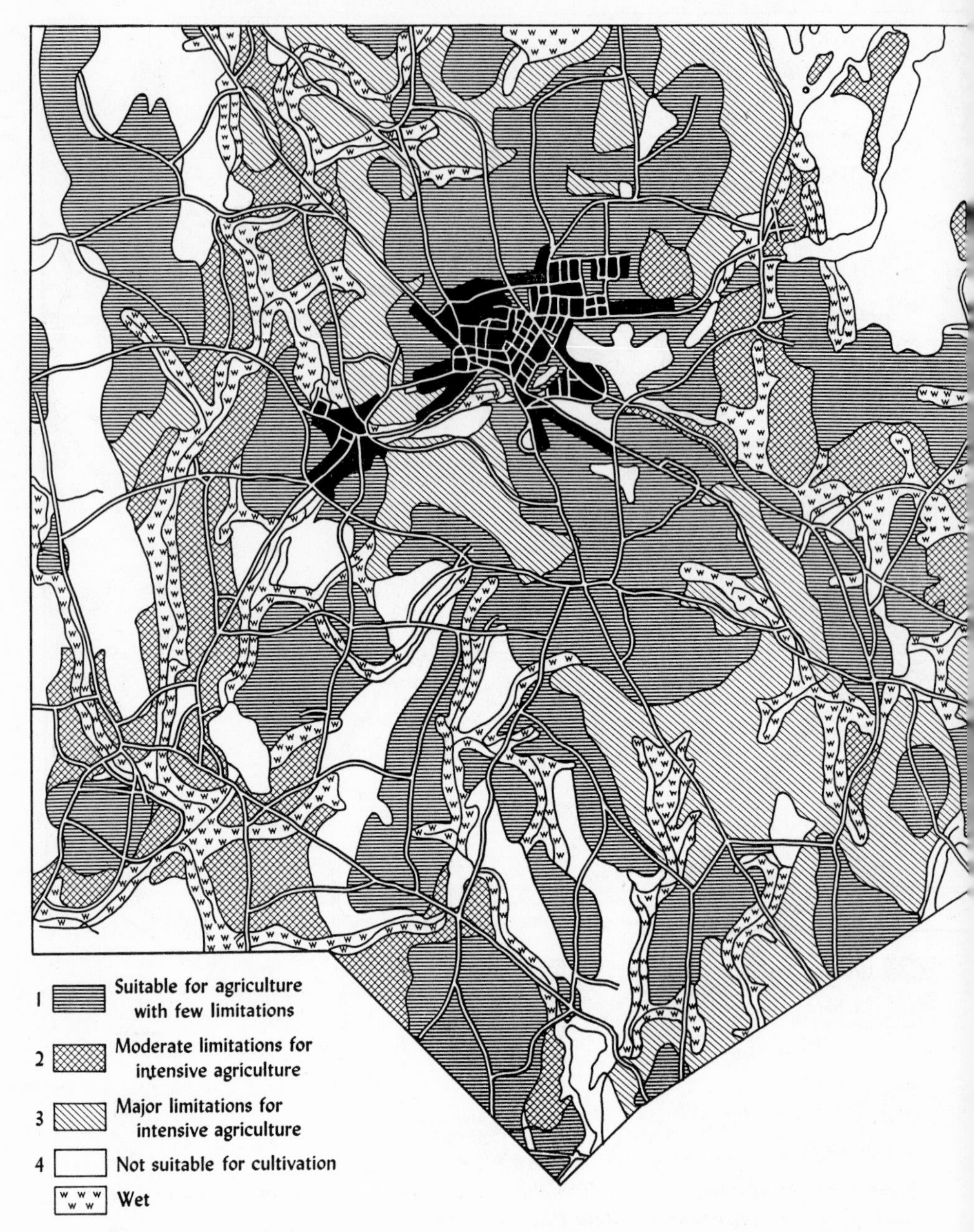

Figure 50. *Land of Winchendon Town classified into four soil groups, plus wet land.*

ment the poultry enterprise seemed to promise a surer addition to income than enlarging the poultry enterprise. The part-time farms were mostly either dairy, vegetable, or dairy-vegetable. The three studied had 12, 22 and 24 acres of cropland and were keeping 2, 0, and 2 cows, and 20, 50, and 35 hens, respectively. The vegetable farm had 2½ acres of vegetables. The analysis indicated that these farms had potential for a considerably larger output, and that the head of the household or family members had time for this if they chose to use it in this way. But this is not an unusual situation on part-time farms in southern New England, nor for that matter in the nation generally. One of the processes by which cropland acreage is reduced is by the transition of farms too small to fit the modern economy to part-time farms, and then an increase in the off-farm work and neglect of more and more of the land.

Over 70 percent of the land of Winchendon is in forest. These woodlands have long been cut to supply raw material for the local woodworking plants. Only on a small part of the woodland area have careful cutting and forest management been practiced. Over most of the land, especially on smaller holdings, indiscriminate cutting and clear-cutting have been the rule. But a small proportion of the wood used in the local industries now comes from local woods. Much timber is imported from northern New England and from the Middle West.

The Otter River State Forest is located in southwestern Winchendon. The Town has a forest on Mellen Road. In the eastern part of the Town, all the forest land is privately owned, much of it in large holdings between 2,000 and 3,000 acres in size. Many of these large holdings are held by residents, although some of them are in nonresident ownership. According to the 1935 agricultural census figures, less than 20 percent of the woodland was owned in connection with farms.

Hurricane damage in Winchendon was severe. About 13 percent of the woodland acreage suffered total destruction. In addition to this, there was a good deal of partial destruction over most of the rest of the woodlands. Practically none of the trees over 40 years of age were left standing. Salvage operations following the hurricane were very complete in Winchendon, better than for any other towns in the state except Amherst and Petersham. Everything worthwhile was salvaged.

The forests in eastern Winchendon — 7,700 acres in total — really join with 7,000 acres in western Ashburnham. The light sandy soil of this area favors the growth of softwoods, especially of white pine. Mixtures of softwoods and inferior hardwoods are also common. The hardwoods consist largely of gray birch, aspen, and red maple. Stands in general are even-aged.

In this tract as a whole, over 60 percent of the woodland is a combination of Softwoods and Inferior Hardwoods, very largely Inferior Hardwoods. This leaves, however, 35 percent of Better Hardwoods. About two thirds of the trees were in the 21-to-40-year age class.

A trial analysis was made of a possible 1,100-acre forest farm on a typical tract of this land with all the land in forest except 50 acres that was in crops and pasture and with a small dairy herd. In Table 43 are estimated the average yearly inputs and outputs and value of the timber products at the prewar level of prices which were at least a third lower than present prices, for six periods.

TABLE 43

Estimated Yearly Inputs and Outputs and Value of Product by Ten-year Periods on a 1,100 Forest Tract in Winchendon Town under Good Forest Management

Ten-year period	*Man labor (man-days)*	*Horse labor (team-days)*	*Output sawtimber (m.b.f.)*	*Cords*	*Value of product (dollars)*
0–20 years........	620	40	304	390	1,320
20–45 years........	720	55	80	365	2,230
40–50 years........	925	75	125	435	2,900
50–65 years........	1,610	135	355	470	8,650
65–75 years........	940	60	100	335	3,430
75–80 years........	1,360	105	145	690	4,330

The first of these periods, 0–20 years, would be devoted to improvement cutting and weeding. Toward the end of the 20-to-45-year period, some of the older of the 20-to-40-year age stands would be harvested, but cordwood from thinnings would still be the largest output. It would not be until the 50-to-65-year period that most of the sawlogs from the present stands would be harvested. In the 75-to-80-year period, some of the trees left from the selection cutting in the 50-to-65-year period would be ready for harvest. The stand by this time would begin to approach a sustained-yield basis. At this stage, this forest farm would be a three-man enterprise, plus extra harvesting labor, without the dairy enterprise. But in the first 45 years, two men could perform most of the forestry operations. The income from the dairy herd would be important in these years.

If this analysis were made today, a more diversified market for what is classified as cordwood would be available, and this would add to the income as well as the higher levels of timber-product prices generally.

If one will remember that they were made back in 1941 following a long depression period, the following suggestions made by the Winchendon Country Life Committee are interesting and significant:

Successful dairy farming in Winchendon requires 20 to 25 cows and sufficient land to raise at least most of the annual replacements and all required roughage. The history of the small 5- to 10-cow farms during the past 15 years or more has been that of failure. The larger farms seem to be prospering. Any prospective purchasers of farms should seek sufficient acreage for 20 to 25 cows and replacements.

Hay crops in town are very short both on the active and inactive farms. The average yield is less than one ton per acre and the quality is low. If the land were well farmed these yields should be two to two and one-half tons per acre. These low yields are an important factor contributing to lack of success on dairy farms.

Pastures in town have a very low carrying capacity. Very little improved pasture is available. Growing good pastures is as important as obtaining good hay yields.

Local industry uses about 14,000,000 feet of timber products annually. About 60 percent of the requirements are produced locally. Much of the imported lumber could be produced locally under good forestry management practices. Good quality logs as small as six to eight inches in diameter could be used by the wood-working establishments. Good logs can be trucked economically a distance of 60 miles. Farm woodlots could be managed at a profit if revisions in the forest tax system permitted an adjustment in tax payments on farm woodlots.

There are many families with available land that do not have home gardens. Many of these families are in low-income groups or are welfare recipients. There are unused resources of land and time available for growing home gardens in some of these homes. Increased use of vegetables that can be grown in a home garden would improve diets and decrease cash outlay for these families.

WESTMINSTER

It has already been noted that Westminster is the most agricultural of the towns of Section B. Not only this, but its agriculture seems to persist, with 110 farms reported in 1954 as compared with 131 in 1925. The 1945 Census, in fact, reported 205 farms. A good part of the explanation of this history is in the following paragraphs from the Country Life Committee Report:

Farming in Westminster Town is primarily part-time farming, and about 90 percent of the farmers are Finns. All of the farming has held its own or improved during the last 15 or 20 years. The larger farms and those returning the largest gross income are in the extreme northern part of the town and across the southern section. A good many of these farms are combination dairy and poultry enterprises, and there is a good deal of marketing of small quantities of vegetables and berries through the marketing cooperatives. There has been an increase in both dairy and poultry products produced in Westminster during the last 10 or 15 years, as well as an increase in farmed land and valuation of farm land and buildings.

With the passing of subsistence agriculture after 1850, there came a decline in farming and the abandonment of land. Since that time, stone fences in woodlands and brush-grown pastures have become common. Since the early 1900's when the Finnish people began to enter the Town, many of the farms were brought back into production. Now Westminster is numbered among the agriculturally important towns in northern Worcester County. The change has been toward part-time and commercial agriculture, of which small poultry and dairy farms or combination farms are the most numerous. There are no large orchards and no commercial vegetable growers except for one or two cases.

A good many of these small farms in the center of the Town have acreages of brushy pasture from which they gain an important part of their income from the sale of blueberries. Blueberries occupy the steep stony hill pastures, and represent an important source of income, in many cases sufficient to pay the taxes. The size of this income from blueberries is sufficient to make up what might have been gained by improving these fields for pasture for dairy cows.

It is evident in Figure 48 that a much larger fraction of the land in Westminster was classed as No. 1 by the State Planning Board Survey than was true in Winchendon; also 16 percent of Westminster area was in cropland and plowable pasture as against 6 percent for Winchendon; also only 58 percent of Westminster's was in woodland as compared with 70 percent in Winchendon. Westminster had much more brushy pasture.

With very little industry in the Town, 40 percent of its population was reported as agricultural around 1940. But very many of the workers in the farm families were employed in Fitchburg, Leominster, and Gardner. Combining farming with other occupations is a well-established pattern among the Finnish people elsewhere in the United States. But this pattern of living is changing rapidly. The Country Life Committee's report has the following statement on this point:

> Most of the farms in town, particularly the part-time farms, are so small in size that the young people growing up on them must go elsewhere to earn a living. These farms are not large enough to support the parents and the family of a married son or daughter. Most of the young people are leaving the farms.

Many of these leave because they see no opportunity to make a satisfactory living by remaining.

Other statements from this report are the following:

Cooperative effort in Westminster has been effective in marketing small berry, poultry, and egg production from small farms. This method of marketing has saved the farmers enough to make it possible for them to pay for farms when they otherwise probably could not have done so.

The total amount of hay produced in the town is not quite adequate to feed all of the livestock. This is particularly true on the larger farms. Many of the poultry farms and smaller dairies sell hay to the larger dairy farms. Low quality and yield both are factors in the inadequacy of hay.

There is a shortage of pasture in town. The character of much of the soil is such that the grass is very short and brown during much of July and August. There is less than 700 acres of open pasture in the Town, very little of which is improved.

There are at least 14,000 acres of woodland and about 5,500 acres more of brushland and blueberry pastures. Most of the woodlands, except for a few state-owned areas, are in farm ownership. Lots are mostly small in size, less than 100–150 acres. Most of this is in low-quality stands. Much of the timber is conifer growth or mixed stands of conifers and inferior hardwoods. Nearly all of the merchantable timber in town was destroyed by the hurricane. There was a total destruction on about 700 acres and partial destruction on about 7,500 acres. There is little interest in farm forestry particularly because of the hurricane and lack of demand for native woodland products.

TEMPLETON

Templeton differs from Westminster mainly in having some industry of its own, so that its 680 of farm population around 1940 made up only 13 percent of its total population. Templeton factories have been employing around 360 in recent years. Part-time and residential farming is prevalent, with 46 percent of those classified as farm operators working off the farm an average of 163 days in 1935, and since then the number of farms has been reduced by a half. The percentage of land classified as crop and plowable pasture was reported as 17 percent in the State Planning Board's survey in 1938, with 49 percent of woodland, and 9 percent in swamps and water bodies.

The parts of Templeton shown in Figure 48 as having No. 3 and No. 4 soils — mostly to the west and north — are mostly Gloucester stony sandy loam, Merrimac loamy coarse sand, and Hinckley loamy sand. These soils all have a very coarse texture and are droughty. The Hinckley and Merrimac soils are free from surface stones, but their low natural fertility and droughtiness makes them unsuitable for agricultural purposes. The Gloucester stony sandy loam is also droughty and contains a large number of surface stones and boulders, which limits the agricultural possibilities of this soil. The southeastern part of the town consists of Brookfield loam, Brookfield stony loam, Charlton loam, and Hinckley loamy sand. Of this group, the Brookfield loam and Charlton loam have agricultural possibilities, but the remainder are unsuitable for cropland. The Brookfield soils are shallow but can be used for cropland. Only in extremely dry years will crops on them suffer from lack of moisture. There are several areas of Muck and poorly drained soils along the streams and in the low level areas.

There were 140 families with one or more cows in Templeton in 1935, but 74 of these had one cow and only 14 had 10 or more. Most of the poultry was in combination with small dairy herds.

The Land-Use Planning Survey classified 57 percent of the woodland in Templeton as Inferior Hardwood or Softwood-Inferior Hardwood, and most of the rest of it as "Hurricane Destroyed." Three small tracts, totaling about 600 acres, are State-owned.

The Country Life Committee's suggestions as to land use were centered on woodland management, pasture improvement, and home gardens.

CHAPTER 18

Summary and Projection

Now that we have reviewed and analyzed section by section, the agriculture and land-use situation in Worcester County, two of the towns, Petersham and Hardwick, in much detail, and eight others in lesser detail, it will be useful to take an over-all look at the County situation. This over-all review will be in terms of developments in the recent past, the more general of these reaching back to 1925, and of the outlook and major re-adjustments ahead.

The reader undoubtedly became aware as he moved from Chapter 12 forward that the authors were carrying out their announced intention of giving different aspects of our problem particular attention in the different chapters. For example, the effect of the urbanization process received special attention in Sections D and C, the public finance aspects in Section D, woodland management in Section A, and recreational use of land in Section B. All of these could have been considered in this same detail in all the sections, since all are pertinent in all the sections. But from the point of view of the planning process, it seemed best to deal with each of them most fully in the particular section where it is of largest importance.

The most important conclusion to be reached is that in terms of both land in farms and number of farms, the declines underway from 1925 to 1945 continued after 1950, after allowing for the more restricted definition of a farm by the census. A sharp distinction, however, needs to be made between commercial and other farms. The number of residential and part-time farms has increased while the number of commercial farms has decreased. The increase of the first has been enough in numbers to offset in good part the loss of commercial farms in Sections D, C, and B. The residential farms have figured most largely in this, there being a tendency for part-time farms to become residential.

AGRICULTURE

Dairy Farming

Although since 1925 the number of commercial farms has declined, agricultural output has not in the better farming areas. This is clearly evident since 1938 in the case-study farms. The 98 of them in Hardwick and the eight other towns (excluding Petersham) in 1938 had become 84 by 1945 and 68 by 1954. The number of dairy herds had declined from 71 to 59 to 48. But the herds averaged 22 cows in 1938, 26 in 1945, and 35 in 1954. They totaled 1,680 cows in 1954 as against 1,560 in 1938. More important, these herds were averaging over 800 pounds more milk per cow, and were raising a third more of replacement heifers. Thus the changes from 1938 to 1954 that were closely observed on the Hardwick case-study dairy farms were duplicated, although not without variations, in the case-study farms in the eight other towns.

The expansion of dairying on these particular farms came about in several ways. First and foremost was an absorption of other farms by purchase or more often merely by renting additional crop and pasture land. But further pasture improvement by some combination of liming, fertilization, and reseeding was partly responsible on about half the farms, improvement of the hay crop on about an equal number, and clearing of additional land on about a fifth of them. The acreages per farm thus benefited, however, were relatively small in most cases and usually less than half of that outlined in the farm plans worked out with the farmers. The dairy farmers had found it easier and simpler to take over the use of land in nearby farms that the owners no longer wished to use themselves. The increase in output per cow in these farms was in most cases more largely due, as reported for Hardwick, to feeding more purchased concentrates than to feeding more and better farm-produced forage and improved pasture; but a considerable part of it was due to the latter.

Can the history of these seventy-one dairy farms, however, be taken as faithfully portraying that of the dairy farms generally in the County? Did not the planning assistance which they received in 1938 and 1945, and follow-up help from the County Extension staff, lead to their expanding their operations more than otherwise would have happened? Matching the particular changes made against the plans indicates that the answer to the second question is surely "yes." But it also indicates that special circumstances in the family, or in the immediate vicinity of the farm, played a clearly larger role. And these circumstances were of kinds that were common all over the County. The planning analysis did, however, make the families more conscious of the possibilities of increasing the family incomes, and therefore helped them be more ready to take advantage of situations that arose.

If the census counts were not erratic, and the case-study farms were a good sample of all dairy farms, all that one would need to do, of course, is to compare the changes in the two to see what additional changes on the case-study farms could have been due to the planning and extension aid. The nearest to such a comparison that is possible is given in Table 44. Separate 1954 census data are not available for North Brookfield and Mendon. The increases on the seven case-study dairy farms in these two towns were very large, 55 and 90 percent respectively. They included four farms that had greatly expanded their operations by buying or renting other farms. The three case-study farms in Winchendon were still more abnormal. And it is now even clearer than before that the expansion in Hardwick was unusual for the County as a whole.

TABLE 44

Comparison of Changes in Numbers of Cows on Farms Reported by the Censuses of 1950 to 1954 and on the Case-Study Farms in 1945 to 1954 in Five Towns in Worcester County

Towns	*1950*	*1954*	*Percentage change*	*Percentage change in case-study farms, 1945 to 1954*
Sterling	1,180	948	−20	−10
Grafton	760	783	+3	+45
Northboro	390	410	+5	−10
Sutton	1,030	897	−13	−10
Charlton	960	838	−13	−7
	4,320	3,880	−10	+2

The Census of 1950 reported 28,205 milk cows for the County on 2,469 farms, and the 1954 Census, 26,845 cows on 1,742 farms. This was an increase from 11.3 to 15.4 cows on the average farm. But these averages are mainly determined by the large number of farms formerly with one or two cows, the number of which has been declining.

One can safely conclude from the foregoing data in spite of their limitations that county-wide shifts in dairy farming were under way, and that the planning and extension aid on the case-study farms accentuated these on the seventy-one case-study farms, but did not change their direction greatly.

One other comparison in the census data is significant. The 1950 count of milk cows included 627 heifers that had calved during the year; the 1954 count, 1,031. This indicates the raising of more replacements.

The emphasis in the foregoing has been upon the shifts in the more recent years. Everything indicates that these began as early as 1925. But they have been much faster since 1938–1940, and especially since 1945. The most important conclusion of all is that these same shifts are likely to continue, and likewise the accelerating rate, at least for the next few decades. The dairy farms will continue to decrease in number and become larger in terms of number of cows per farm and still more in terms of milk output, but not in terms of labor force. Not only will the remaining dairy farms mechanize more of the field operations, but also more of their barn operations. If nothing else, the growing scarcity of men willing to be hired hands on farms, in view of their other alternatives, will bring this about.

As in the recent past particularly, the increase in average size of dairy farms will come about in good part as a result of the disappearance of small farms as dairy farms. A few of them will become part-time farms and remain so for a while. In general, however, the dis-economies of small-scale operation of dairy farms will eliminate these part-time farms in the near future. For the most part, the improved land in the smaller farms will continue to be rented to neighboring farmers, or sold to them, and this will in turn raise the average farm size. The sooner this land is bought the better, because then its productivity is more likely to be maintained. The barn is likely to be rented or bought with the land and is often used for the young stock and dry cows.

Another way in which the dairy farms will enlarge is that with increasing mechanization more and more land can be farmed, and more and more cows fed and cared for, with a given labor force. The family-sized dairy farms will in time mostly keep twenty-five cows or more plus replacements. A well-managed dairy farm big enough to use economically a field hay baler or forage chopper, or both, can also in most cases use one or more full-time hired hands and pay wages enough to attract such labor. This largely accounts for the nine herds of 40 cows or more, averaging 67, in the forty-eight case-study dairy farms still operating in 1954. The protection from having a 15-acre crop of good alfalfa or other clover hay caught in a rain, or having the haying season stretched out over several weeks because of rainy weather, may repay twice over the interest and depreciation on an investment in a baler or chopper.

Size measured in number of cows will also continue to increase because of the increasing productivity of the crop and pasture land in present farms. On a majority of the dairy farms in Worcester County, output per acre can be doubled and more on half the cropland, plowable pasture, and other open and not too stony pasture. Of course, there is always the question as to whether this will increase the *net* income of a particular farm. The largest determining factor in this decision will in most cases be the fitting of the scale of operation to the labor force, equipment, and barn size. If these will be more fully employed by increasing the output by increasing the productivity of the land, the gains will be large. If, however, more labor must be hired, or equipment bought, or barn space built to use the additional field and pasture, there needs to be enough increase in output to employ these somewhere near fully if the income gains are to be sizable.

A question of this kind, however, cannot be safely answered without regard to the effect of a general increase in supply on the blended prices of milk in any federally administered market. A few farmers can increase their output with no appreciable effect on price, but not dairy farmers generally, even in the Worcester milkshed. As the population of southern New England grows, there will of course be demand for more fresh milk, and probably a slight increase in demand per person with increasing per capita income. But the potential increase in supply far exceeds the prospective increase in demand. Almost exactly half of the milk produced in the Boston milkshed in 1955 was in excess of Class I sales. This surplus is available for southern New England markets. Therefore any dairy farm adjustments in the next ten to twenty years at least must be carefully considered from the standpoint of their effect on total supply and prices. Enlargement of herds by absorbing too small dairy farms is clearly in the right direction. But pasture improvement and the like could easily be pushed too fast. In general, this type of adjustment should be limited largely to farms with too few cows to use the existing labor force and equipment adequately.

Three other types of adjustment can also be made without upsetting the balance of supply and demand for milk: one, substituting more farm-produced, high-protein roughage and pasture feed for purchased concentrates; two, increasing the average production per cow by culling out the low-producing cows; and three, raising more replacements and buying fewer cows.

Finally, something needs to be said about one other general possibility, namely, the lowering of costs more than prices with increasing output, so that *net* incomes are actually increased. This is easily possible on groups of farms in one milk market, but much more difficult if the increase in output is widespread. Nevertheless, it should be a goal toward which to work; otherwise public support of research and extension is not warranted in the short run.

Poultry Farming

The ninety-eight case-study farms in Worcester County in 1938 included eleven that were primarily poultry farms. Two of these combined a small orchard with poultry and another a small dairy herd. Only eight of these were still operating in 1954, but two dairy farms in Hardwick had become poultry farms. This does not imply that the number of poultry farms in the County had decreased. But no new case-study farms were added at the time of the 1945 re-study to make up for those that had ceased operating. As in Hardwick, in the County as a whole a significant number of farms too small to support an adequate dairy herd had been shifting first to dairy-poultry, and then to poultry alone, since as far back as 1920, but especially since 1940. Also some fruit farms had made a similar transition. The three poultry farms that had ceased operating had become residential farms.

The large increases in poultry production in Worcester County from 1940 on did not result, however, so much from an increase in number of poultry farms as from increasing the scale of operations of the farms already operating. This is more evident, however, in the census and other public data for the County than in the case-study samples. Only three of these, in fact, made large increases. Most of the large poultry farms have developed since this project was started in 1938, and therefore they were not included in the 1938 sample.

Some of the important shifts in the poultry farms that appeared in the case-study farms were the following:

1. A general shift from a laying flock plus raising enough chicks to provide enough pullets for replacements and selling the male birds as roasters, to more diversity in types of poultry farms, as indicated by the following:

2. buying sexed chicks on three of the farms and thus raising fewer chicks;

3. selling more broilers and raising fewer birds to the roaster stage;

4. more hatches per year;

5. specializing more in broilers, in hatching eggs, or in baby chicks.

This list of changes does not include increasing egg output per hen by earlier culling, better feeding and breeding, and the like, nor reducing the feed input per pound of broiler meat, nor reducing losses from disease. Also as pointed out in the section on Poultry Farming in Chapter 9 on "Planning a Farm," there has been a large increase in the output of poultry products per day of man labor. Without all these, New England poultry producers would not have been able to compete effectively with other areas and expand this industry as they have.

Nor does the list include specifically the trend in the poultry industry toward factory-type commercial operation. The farm on such units continues to furnish the land for range and the buildings for laying hens plus some broilers or roasters; but more and more of everything else is produced off the poultry farm or by other types of poultry enterprises such as hatcheries. Along with this, more and more of poultry production is being financed on a contract basis. (This is more prevalent, of course, in competing poultry areas, especially the newer ones, than it is in southern New England.) Also along with this, the expansion of the industry in this and especially the newer competing areas is being promoted by those producing the feed and the baby chicks.

In such a situation, no type of poultry production is likely to over-expand very long. Usually the over-expansion in a single year is enough to bring prices down to a level that causes losses to part of the poultry farmers and suppliers, and even in the year following there may be under-production.

In such a highly commercial situation, competition between areas is very keen. An area that does not advance in technology as fast as the rest will find itself year-by-year with fewer poultry farms and more abandoned brooder houses and the like. In the years after 1940 when New England poultry production was doubling in volume, an expanding demand for better fresh eggs and broiler meat was a larger factor in this. Another factor was sharing in the big New York market, due in good part to a more rapid advance in technology in New England than in some other areas competing for this same outlet. The future of poultry production in Worcester County therefore depends much on its ability to keep pace in the technology race. With the growing scarcity and higher wages of farm labor, output per man-hour will be an increasingly important part of this race. The areas most likely to furnish the strongest competition are in the piedmont sections of the South where labor is cheaper than in New England. In fact, poultry production, nearly all on a contract-farming basis, is expanding rapidly clear across the South from the Carolinas to Missouri, Arkansas, and Texas.

Orchard Farming

Counting in the three farms with orchards in Hardwick in 1938, a total of eighteen of the original ninety-eight case-study farms had commercial orchards. Only eight of these were primarily fruit farms. Three of these were large orchards, averaging 88 acres per farm. The other five averaged 20 acres. At that time six of the eighteen were combining orcharding with dairying, three with vegetables, and one with both vegetables and small fruit. One of the five was a large operation with 50 cows and 54 acres in fruit trees. There was a total of 459 acres of fruit trees on the eighteen farms, but about 15 percent of this acreage was in nonbearing or young trees.

By 1954, the eighteen farms with orchards had shrunk to eleven; but 3 of the orchards had been absorbed in the eleven. Other than case-study farms had absorbed 2 small orchards. Also five had changed ownership. The total acreage in the eleven orchards had shrunk to only 430. This, however, was because two of the large orchards had increased their acreage by 60. The remaining orchards had shrunk from 272 to 184 acres. Part of this was due to the conversion of 40 acres of orchard on one farm into a gravel pit. The other 48 acres of orchard that had disappeared altogether were partly on poor orchard sites and neglected because its yields were so low. Hurricane damage was a factor in other cases.

As pointed out earlier, and noted in the analysis by Sections, the census figures indicate a decline in orchard farming between 1925 and 1950 in all the towns but Grafton, Northboro, Berlin, Harvard, Sterling, North Brookfield, Phillipston, and Southbridge. Four of these towns were in the eight in which case studies were made. Accordingly, the decline was greater in the County as a whole between 1938 and 1954 than indicated by the eighteen case-study farms.

As to timing, most of the decline in orchard acreage came after the 1945–46 re-study, but two of the farms with orchards had become residential by 1946. Only 4 of the 18 orchards were combining other orchard fruit with apples, peaches on all 4 and pears on 2. These were all but one in Sterling. The peaches were being grown as fillers in young plantings in at least one of these farms.

Successful orchard farming calls for an effective command and application of a large amount of special knowledge and skill. Those who have it and use it can prosper in this line of production in Worcester County. The future of such farming in the County depends largely upon the number of young men who are reared with enough interest in it to acquire these skills and knowledge and are financed in getting started in this field of production. There will continue to be a good New England demand for apples and even peaches produced in New England. It is true that the hazards of growing any fruit are somewhat greater toward the northern limits of production, but in compensation for this there are usually certain properties of northern fruit that make it preferred in the markets of the region.

Small Fruits and Vegetables

These are considered in one group because they are combined on some of the farms and because they have been affected in the same way by the increasing consumption of fresh supplies shipped in from the South and the far Southwest. By the time the local supplies of these come on the market, consumers have already been using the shipped-in supplies for several months, and the quick-frozen supplies of some of them the year round.

The general effect of this has of course been a large reduction in the acreage of both small fruits and vegetables in New England. Nevertheless, there is still good demand for a good quality of the local products in their seasons. No shipped-in supplies will satisfy the demand for locally produced sun-ripened tomatoes, or freshly picked sweet corn. On the other hand, unless the local growers can produce and deliver a uniform quality vegetable that can be wrapped in standardized packages, they will find themselves losing their market for most vegetables to large-scale growers farther away.

Only one of the case-study farmers was specializing completely in vegetables, and he was owning or renting land in several towns and growing the types of vegetables that are grown extensively in sizable fields — squash, cabbage, rhubarb, and the like. At the start of the project in 1938, only eight of the ninety-eight farms studied were growing vegetables for the market. They had a total of 45 acres in vegetables, excluding the one large specialist. Still, the vegetables were secondary to dairying or orchard fruit or poultry on all but two of these farms. Three of these eight were growing a total of 8.5 acres of strawberries and two acres of raspberries in addition to vegetables or apples. By 1954, only three farms, besides that of the large specialist, were still growing vegetables, on a total of 26 acres. One of the farms had become residential, another had shifted entirely to poultry, and the other three were orchard farms that had quit growing vegetables as a supplementary crop. Only one was still growing strawberries. The shifts out of vegetables came after 1946, and were mostly associated with transfers of ownership.

It will occur to the reader after the foregoing review that the most distinctive feature of the changes reported in this chapter is away from crops that require hand labor toward those whose operations can be increasingly mechanized. No doubt this trend will continue. Some poultry farming must fit into this pattern.

WOODLANDS

The potentials of woodland development in Worcester County are analyzed most fully for Hardwick and the West Central Section, and for the four towns of Charlton, North Brookfield, Sutton, and Mendon in Chapters 13 and 14. The possibilities of gains on individual farms are also exemplified on the nine case-study farms in Northboro. How these timberlands came to be chosen for fuller analysis needs explanation. At the outset of this project, a sample cruising of the woodlands in the whole County was made, using as a base the road, farmstead, and land-use maps of the Worcester County Land Use Planning Project. The County woodlands were classified roughly into six forest land-use classes according to the type and condition of their timber stands. For example, in the areas numbered 1, Better Hardwoods and Softwoods were about equal. Those numbered 2 were dominantly Softwoods, and those numbered 6 were dominantly Better Hardwoods. Following the hurricane, the cruise was checked and the extent of the damage was recorded. Also at this time some careful analyses were made of the management possibilities of different forest land-use classes of land, and actual management plans were developed for representative sample tracts. The Town of Hardwick was covered most thoroughly, and next in order the twelve other towns named.

The Softwood stands were scarce in the County after the hurricane of 1938. Such as there were were estimated in the plans worked out in the eight West Central towns to yield, at roadside prices for logs and bolts prevailing in 1946, average gross annual incomes per acre, over the lifetime of the stands, ranging from $13.50 to $15.70 per acre according to the adaptability of the land to softwoods. The comparable yield for the Better Hardwoods, making up two thirds of the woodland in five of the West Central towns, was $9.27 per acre; and for the Softwood-Better Hardwood stands making up a third of the woodland in the nine towns, from $9.40 to $11.10 per acre. Inferior Hardwoods, yielding only $2.30 per acre, made up only a very small percentage of this area.[1] However, in most of the towns in the other

[1] These values now seem to be somewhat on the high side. Timber prices are no longer rising as they were just after the war.

Sections, Inferior Hardwoods made up a fifth of the woodland, and in many of them, especially to the North, the Softwood-Inferior Hardwood combination occupied around half of the woodland.

In general, the management plans worked out for the farm woodlands promised at least to double the prospective income as presently managed.

On the large MWDC tracts in the West Central Section, with only one fifth of Inferior Hardwoods and a third of Softwood-Inferior Hardwoods, the average gross return per acre was estimated at $6.30 per acre at B intensity of management, the present level, but at three times this under high-level management.

The type of woodland management proposed in the case-study farms in Hardwick and elsewhere put major emphasis by far on natural restocking following improvement cutting and weeding, even though this might not give more than two thirds of full stocking on much of the woodland. Planting was in general proposed only for poor pasture areas to be added to other woodland. Fencing cattle out of pastured woodland was proposed on most of the farms.

The intensity of forest management that will prove most advantageous depends of course on the demand and supply relationships for timber products in coming decades. *The Timber Resources Review* of the U.S. Forest Service in its most nearly realistic projection assumes that prices will rise 25 to 30 percent by 1975, at which level supply and sawtimber stock will be much more nearly in balance; that they will be in close balance in 2000, but with prices 40 to 50 percent higher than now. At these higher prices, of course, other materials will be substituted increasingly for wood. Improved forestry technology, both in growth and utilization, however, would check these price rises and the substitution, and hence price rises less than 40 to 50 percent after 2000 can more reasonably be expected.

The foregoing is in terms of national averages in which remaining old-growth timber in the West plays an important part. For Eastern softwoods considered separately, the market will be much tighter; but for Eastern hardwoods, much less tight. The question facing woodland owners in Worcester County is what combination of better and more intensive forest management and higher prices will reward them best. The case analyses for individual farms indicates that most of them, with the prices in prospect, can add significantly to their incomes if they will fit woodland operations of the sort described in with their other farm operations. But this will call for a revision of their ways of thinking about their woodlands, and of their work plans from month to month and week to week, that the older among them at least will be slow to make. Accordingly we cannot expect rapid progress in this direction in the next decade or two.

The nonfarm owners of small tracts will in most cases be even slower to make changes. The tradition among most of them is to own these pieces of timberland, pay the relatively low property taxes on them, and wait for a chance to sell some stumpage occasionally. Very little of this land is tax delinquent. Only some drastic reorganization of the present handling of these lands can change this situation. This could take the form of some form of public assistance, such as marking of trees to be cut and more intensive extension education, or cooperative management, or timber industry participation, or consolidation of holdings, or some combination of these.

URBAN ASPECTS

This aspect of the development of rural land use in Worcester County can be summarized very briefly. The cities have been encroaching on farming ever since Worcester County began to be industrialized in the modern sense with the building of the railroads. But this encroachment has acquired new strength and in part taken new forms in recent decades. The principal new form is the spreading out of the cities much more thinly in their outer circles, not only residentially, but with a good deal of trade and even industry to go with the residences. The new strength is in the greater disposition of members of farm families to find employment in the cities. A little of this is because the jobs are nearer to them. More of it is because of the general high level of urban employment that has prevailed. The data for the different towns show that more and more of the nominal operators of farms now have off-farm jobs part or full time. But while the effect of this trend is toward increasing the number of part-time farms, a counter effect results from the tendency for already part-time farmers to farm less, in most cases renting their pasture and hay land to other farmers, but sometimes in effect neglecting and abandoning it, so that the acreage of crop and pasture land in the County is definitely declining.

The drift just described should increase the number of so-called residential farms. It does, but so far as the census count of farms is concerned, a goodly number of the residential farms of 1950 were classified only as rural residences in 1954 because they were making so little use of their land; and likewise from 1940 to 1950. As a result, the total number of farms has been declining markedly since 1940, and by no means is all of this due to changes in census definitions and practices.

There is little reason to doubt that the drifts that have just been outlined will not continue. They will be checked, but only for a time, if we have a period of considerable unemployment.

In terms of area, this urbanization process will be most active near the larger cities. But it may also have pronounced effects in smaller cities with flourishing industries. It may not be equal in all directions out from a larger city.

The public finance problems associated with these urbanization trends are analyzed in detail for Section D and need not be summarized here except to say that each of the towns must face them squarely, and that they are becoming more acute each year.

CHAPTER 19

Sub-Area Planning Units

In the statement of objectives in the opening chapter of this book, strong emphasis was placed on the need for dividing political area units like towns or counties into smaller area units having certain common properties that make it possible to analyze the land and other resources within them more or less as one and thus economize on planning effort. It was said that whenever any agency like a county agricultural extension service or a soil conservation district, and especially when these two agencies and the others in a county together, set forth on an undertaking to improve land use and living in a county, it needs, or they need, if their efforts are to be fruitful, to organize them on an area basis. This means dividing the county or town into sub-area units each consisting of the territory that needs about the same pattern of change or readjustment. The agency, or agencies, involved can then work more or less in a group with the farm and other operating units in each of these sub-area units.

It should be obvious by now that this particular objective has not been altogether achieved in this project as here reported. What is reported in this book are rather the results of a number of ventures in such sub-unit area planning, mostly with the town as the unit to be subdivided. Following is a brief outline of these ventures:

1. That of Dr. Beaumont in Figure 3 in which the County is divided into six areas according to the group of soil series dominant. It is clear that these areas would not serve well for any administrative undertaking other than soil surveying and analysis.

2. That of the group at the Harvard Forest which after cruising the woodlands of the County mapped them in six forest-type classes. This map would be useful in laying out a forestry program for the County. It is not reproduced in this book.

3. The detailed mapping of major land uses by the Massachusetts State

Planning Board. These land uses are here grouped into three or four classes in the Figures according to Sections. They are also shown on a larger scale in more detail in the maps for some of the Towns.

4. Similar detailed mapping by the Massachusetts State Planning Board, in seven classes, of the soils of the County. These soil classes are here usually combined into four and shown in the Figures by Sections. They too are here shown on a larger scale and in more detail for some of the Towns.

5. For a few of the Towns, the land-use and soil classes are matched on the same map.

6. The State Planning Board also classified the land in each town on three different bases, as follows:

Cover — cropland and plowable pasture, stony and woodland pasture, woodland and brush, and residential, commercial, etc.;
Adaptability to agriculture — good, limited, and unsuited;
Forest types — better hardwoods, softwoods, etc.

7. The Country Life Committees, in the towns for which they prepared reports, drew upon the Planning Board's classifications and mapped their towns into numbered areas, as for Mendon in Figure 51. Areas 1 and 10 were put in the class of good adaptability to agriculture and needing only "minor adjustments"; Areas 5 and 9 were classed as of limited adaptability and needing "major adjustments"; Areas 2, 6, 8, and 11 were then in forest and designated as possibly usable in agriculture, in poultry or residential farming. Areas 3, 4, 7, and 12 were called residential and recreational. Following are the descriptions of several of these areas and their potentials, chosen as illustrative:

Area 1 is the best agricultural part of town and is located on the broad top and gentle upper slopes of the ridge extending northwest, south and southeast from Mendon Center. The soil is mostly loam and fine sandy loam and about 90 percent of it is well adapted to agriculture. The remainder of the soil is a stony fine sandy loam or wet land with limited adaptability or unsuited to agriculture. Approximately 90 percent of the land is open, over half of which is cropland and the rest pasture. The cropland is in large continuous areas.

This area has most of the large dairies and orchards in town. It is crossed in two directions by main-travelled hard-surfaced highways. It is well served by both gravel and hard-surfaced roads. On the main roads, within one and one-half miles of Mendon Center, are many very attractive homes with no farming enterprises of any kind.

Area 5 is located on the flat terraces, hummocky land, and lower hill slopes west of Mill River. Not more than 10 to 15 percent of the soil is well adapted to agriculture. About half of the well adapted soil is a fine sandy loam (Gloucester Series) and the rest is a sandy soil that has a gravel subsoil. The rest of the soil is partly dry and gravelly and of limited adaptability to agriculture or is wet swampy land unsuited to farming. Approximately 65 percent of the area is open

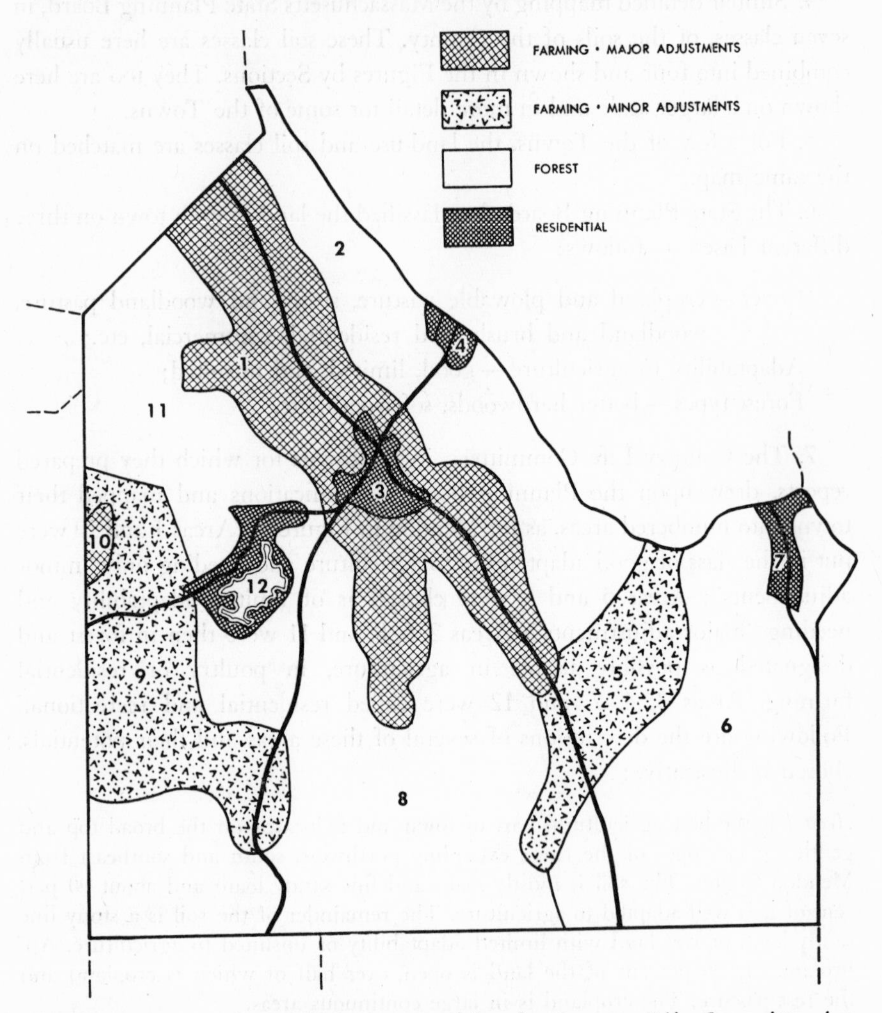

Figure 51. *Town of Mendon as mapped by the Country Life Committee into twelve sub-area units, and four suitability classes.*

land, mostly cropland in poor condition and in small segregated pieces. There are only a few farms or part-time farms in the area and several residences. There are two hard-surfaced roads connecting with Mendon Center and with Blackstone to the south. There is one short dirt road and three short gravel roads serving the rest of the area.

Area 8 is a forest area in central and southwestern Mendon. The topography is steeply rolling and hilly. The soils are about 75 percent rough stony land unsuited to agriculture and the rest stony fine sandy loam of limited adaptability to agriculture. The area is entirely forested except for a few acres of cropland and pasture land in the southwest corner. The trees are mostly young hardwoods or brush. The only farm is a dairy. Three gravel roads cross the area and there are two abandoned roads. A few residences in the southwestern part are occupied by people who work in Uxbridge.

Area 12 — The Nipmuck Pond section is an area of summer camps and amusement parks. Some of the camps have, during the past few years, been used as permanent residences and there are a number of homes along the roads north of the pond. Many of these dwellings are too small, unattractive and lacking in facilities to be very desirable as permanent residences, a fact which is more characteristic of this area than of any other part of town.

This procedure was first developed in connection with the pilot work in Hardwick, which was mapped in thirteen areas. Not only were these areas described as illustrative for Hardwick, but the Country Life Committee spelled out the adjustments that were needed in each; in the three dairy-farming areas, Nos. 1, 2, and 3, for example, in terms of pasture improvements, rotations, reseeding, liming and fertilizing of hayfields, and the like.

8. Finally came the kind of detailed area classification that was developed for the Town of Petersham and shown in the zoning map in Figure 33 in Chapter 12.

It should be apparent by now that an undertaking of this sort is by no means obvious and simple, that the breakdown of a larger area unit into smaller and more homogeneous ones depends upon the particular attributes that are selected as a basis of classification. Present land use can be the basis, or soil type, or some combination of these. The basis used by the State Planning Board in its land-use planning project was "suitability for agriculture," but even then a wide choice was left as to how much homogeneity would be required, and how large the area of a certain kind of land had to be before it was singled out as a separate area unit.

It should be obvious that the six Sections into which the County is divided for the purpose of mapping and analysis in this book would not serve well as sub-areas for county administration purposes. The exigencies of fitting the section maps to the page in this book forced some grouping of the towns contrary to the principle of putting like towns in the same sub-area. But with some adaptation the fit would not be too bad. For example, Petersham should be grouped with Athol and the towns in Section B, and Hardwick with a group of agricultural towns to the south.

One other approach to the mapping of a county or larger unit into subarea units is that developed back in the 1930's by I. G. Davis for Connecticut. Professor Davis worked out a classification of land-use areas and mapped the whole state in accordance with it in detail down to areas sometimes no larger than two or three farms. His basis of classification was largely what farm management specialists call "type of farming," but other bases could be used. He did differentiate between dominantly farming and forest tracts, between part-time and commercial farming areas, and mixed and specialized farming; also between purely residential rural areas, residential farming areas, and part-time farming areas.[1] Given such a map, any service or agency, or collaborating group of these, would be able to segregate its territory within boundary lines to fit its particular undertaking.

At one stage in the Worcester County project, Harry Norcross,[2] then on the staff of the project, mapped the towns of Worcester County largely by type-of-farming areas. Thus, he mapped Grafton into a dairy-farming area, a dairy-poultry-vegetable area, a part-time farming area, and a recreational area.

Mapping by type-of-farming areas and the like tends to suggest a static approach to land-use planning — improving but continuing present use instead of possible shifts in use.

[1] Connecticut Bulletin 213, "Types of Farming and Type-of-Farming Areas in Connecticut," 1936.

[2] Now on the staff of the Agricultural Marketing Service in Washington, D.C.

CHAPTER 20

Community Planning

It was explained at the beginning of this book that its objective is in the main to report a series of undertakings in planning in Worcester County ranging over the period from 1937 to 1953. One of these undertakings is reserved for separate treatment in this chapter, as announced at the end of Chapter 1. It is here described as an undertaking in "community planning." Of course the planning done by the Country Life Committees and reported in Chapters 11 to 17 was community planning, but although the results of it in terms of recommended programs have been briefly reported, little has been said about the process by which these recommendations were chosen. This latter has been reserved for reporting and analysis in the case of the Harvard Seminar in Land Use and Conservation working community by community with the public officials of a group of towns, most intensively in six of them, in 1953.[1] This was in addition to, but related to, the Seminar's assistances in the planning for Sections A to F already reported.

Two things need clearly to be recognized about planning on a community basis. The first is that even though the area may be the political unit of the town, there is likely to be an urban center in this town, and its resources and people and their welfare are taken into account along with those of the surrounding rural area. The planning experience reported in this chapter therefore embraces more than the rural planning of the title of this book, although these urban centers in many cases are so small that they would be classified as rural population in the census. The second is that benefits greatest to communities as a whole, which are the objectives of community planning, may transcend those of individual families and firms as such. They are also likely to have a longer time-span. This does not mean that planning for indi-

[1] This undertaking was under the leadership of Dr. Ayers Brinser, director of the Seminar; and this is his report of the undertaking.

vidual farms or other operating-units has no place in community planning. Quite the contrary; only when the alternative lines of action of the individual units are clearly discerned is it possible to weave them together into a pattern of the greatest good for all.

The purpose of community planning is to create a comprehensive design to guide the use of the community resources. In the last analysis the measure of the value of any plan is the productivity of the action it stimulates. The physical plan itself is but one incident, and that by no means the most important, in the community planning process. Before the planning document can be drafted, accurate and complete basic data must be collected covering a wide array of fact and experience — the nature and extent of the land resources, the history of their development, and the institutional patterns controlling their present and future use. These data revealing resource capability then have to be related to the objectives agreed upon by the community. Next the means to meet these objectives must be weighed to select those which will work at the highest level of efficiency consistent with the political and social values of the community. Once this critical decision is made, the responsibility for executing the planned activities can be assigned to an agent. All of these steps are directed toward ultimate action. Once the action is taken there remains the task of evaluating the effectiveness of it in meeting the planned objectives. Finally there must be a provision to modify the plan to meet new objectives as they arise either because of unanticipated external influences or the changing situation created by the plan itself.

THE COMMUNITY PLANNING PROCESS

Community planning covers the whole spectrum of community activity, and consequently it engages the attention of many different agencies, both public and private. For some it may be an informal program scheduling of day-to-day activities; for others it is a long-range design for community investment. The objectives of the various agencies vary with the different duties assigned to them by the community. Where there are active town planning boards, differences among the objectives may be reconciled in an over-all community plan. More frequently the process of reconciliation takes place informally in the desires of the Board of Selectmen, the town finance committee, or in town meetings. Usually in all of these instances the span of time covered by the plan covers little more than a year and the range of issues considered is narrowed down to those things requiring immediate attention. This is planning of a kind but not planning in the sense of designing a program of community investment of its human and material resources to create a more desirable future for the community and the people living there.

In actual life, the initial impetus for this longer-range more comprehensive planning usually comes from a threat to the accepted community pattern—such as from an industry moving into a rural town, or the encroachment of the urban sprawl of a nearby city. To become aware of the threat produces no consensus about what should be done beyond the conviction of the traditionally minded members of the community that change should be prevented at all costs. Planning for them is a loaded blunderbuss kept in the corner to repel marauders. This kind of planning *in extremus* creates no agreement about how the planning process should operate. The all too frequent result is a restrictive ordinance to preserve some measure of the *status quo*. One would scarcely call such activity planning! In several of the Worcester County towns investigated in this analysis, however, this was the situation when the study was undertaken.

The first requirement in setting in motion a real planning process in these towns was to provide for the coordination of the work of those to be engaged in making the plan. Coordination and integration are frequently credited with having certain magic powers of synthesis. In recent literature dealing with the management of public agencies, these terms run through the argument like incantations to thwart the powers of selfishness and discord. In the case at hand, at least, the acceptance of the need to coordinate the work of the planners had to be preceded by an agreement as to the policy around which the coordination was to occur. In its most simple terms, the policy agreed upon was that the planning process as applied here should be essentially a program of community education. This decision dictated that the key agency in the initial phases of planning should be the County Extension Service. Extension had, in each of the towns to be planned, a local community organization. The focal point of these organizations was the agricultural activity of the community. But the members themselves, as leaders in the community, represented practically all of the active groups in the town, such as the Parent-Teachers Association, the town officials, the church, and the veterans group.

When the Land Use Seminar at Harvard decided to undertake a planning analysis of these towns, the Director of the County Extension Service arranged for a meeting in the town with these community leaders to discuss the problems of the town with the members of the Seminar. When an outside group such as this comes into a community there are at once major barriers to be overcome, barriers erected both by the people in the community and by those coming into the town. It was essential that at the very outset it be generally understood that the Seminar was coming into the community not to tell people what to do, but rather to learn from them what might be done and how they would prefer to do it. This was essentially a joint consultation with the people in the town so that the Seminar and the townspeople could learn about the resources of the town together. The intention was that out of this investigation would emerge the fundamental issues concerned in the use of resources in terms that would be understood by the whole community.

This last is a point that is frequently slighted. All too often in the past the critical problems unearthed by planning studies have been presented to the town in terms that the townspeople did not fully understand. In part, that misunderstanding came from the imperfect knowledge of the planners who saw the resources of the community as physical elements without relation to the uses which from the point of view of the townspeople made them resources.

THE PLANNING OPERATION

The first towns selected were those like the town of Charlton which had pressing and immediate problems of development. These problems served as a point of departure for stimulating a discussion of the total issues. But since the purpose of the meeting was to open the general problem of developing the resources of the community it was essential that the members of the Seminar attending the meeting should come prepared with a general knowledge of the area.

The collection of this preliminary information about the community required the cooperation and understanding of a large number of individuals and agencies. From the point of view of their function in relation to the planning process, these agencies could be divided into two groups. In the first were those who were informed about the physical resources of the area. Foremost among these was the local Soil Conservation District staff which had prepared farm plans for many of the farms in the community and had collected data on problems related to water supply, drainage, and flooding by local streams. The Massachusetts Department of Commerce had collected data concerning highway development, traffic flows, and employment opportunities in and around the town. The Country Life Committees then functioning had prepared a report in the late 1930's showing the resource-use pattern in the community, particularly as it related to agriculture and forestry resources. Further information about forest resources was made available by the Office of the State Forester.

A second group of agencies was concerned with the management of town affairs. Foremost among these were the three key town committees, the Board of Selectmen, the Board of Assessors, and the school committee. These agencies are particularly valuable as sources of information about the present situation. A few towns had town planning boards but in no case had these boards developed a comprehensive survey of the community's resources, nor had they made any projection of the possible development of these resources. In several other towns, one important source of information was the town finance committee. When consulting these groups a major purpose was to enlist their interest in the planning process to the point where they would at least be willing to cooperate with the development of the plan, and, to the degree that it was possible, participate as working members of the planning group.

The information gathered from these sources, buttressed with town data supplied by the United States Census, and the data used in the planning analysis in Chapters 11 to 17, provided the necessary information for two maps of the towns prepared by the Seminar. The first of these maps indicated the present use of the land resources, and the location of structures and highways. In general it was a picture of the situation at that time. A second map indicated possible areas for different types of development. In the meetings with the town officials these maps were of critical importance and at once evoked the interest of the townspeople. In addition they diverted attention from the immediate issue which had served to bring the people to the meeting and focused it on the larger problem of total development, thereby placing the present issue in a broader perspective.

The discussion concerning the first map, that of the present situation, was very useful in bringing out important corrections in that map. These corrections very frequently indicated the direction and kind of change that was going on in the community. This in turn was then related to the second map showing potential development, and again further corrections could be made. In almost all instances the important final result from this meeting was the awareness of the people of the town of a new range of possibilities. Seeing the community as a whole created new perspective not only as to the use of present resources, but also as to their potential. The emphasis in the planning process was thus shifted from the negative use of prevention of change to the more positive conception of new development.

In addition to the maps, a second type of data was presented at these preliminary meetings. This was statistical information showing the trend of economic development in the community: types of employment, shifts in trading areas, size of farms, soil classifications, relation of the village to the surrounding area, and value of products produced in the town. Other data indicated costs and returns from the expenditure of public money. In these communities, located as they are in an area of expanding urban development around the cities of Worcester, Fitchburg, and Gardner, this information brought forth two critical issues in the town meetings. The first was the cost to the community of developing services and installations such as water supply and roads to meet the demands of a population moving into the town as a residential area from which to commute to work in the nearby cities. The second and frequently most hotly disputed question was that of school costs. In practically every instance, the townspeople were divided into two camps concerning the development of the community and the expansion of the schools. One camp resisted every attempt for further growth on the grounds that the community could not afford the costs, and the other insisted that a modern community must provide better services and invite growth. The assumption was frequently made that the Seminar group presenting the information represented the latter group since it was concerned with community planning. It was a matter of primary importance to make clear that the information was being presented for two purposes only: first, to indicate what was known about these costs, and second, to find out from the people themselves what it was they wanted to secure from their tax expenditures. It was only when it became patently clear that the Seminar group was neutral on these issues that it was possible to elicit from the meeting a fully cooperative attitude.

Whenever possible, representatives of the various agencies supplying information to the Seminar planning group were present at the meeting of the townspeople. It was important for them to explain to the other townspeople the part they could play in supplying further information for a planning group in the town. Because of this, it was especially important for the representatives of these agencies to understand the nature of the planning process employed by the Seminar group and to have previously arranged to coordinate their information to fit into the planning procedure.

A major purpose of the town meeting was to bring the development of the community into a clear perspective and provide the basis for analyzing alternative ways of meeting the objectives of the community. Perhaps more important, the discussions at these meetings established a preliminary order of the relative importance of these town objectives. In general the meetings left the Seminar planning group with a clear indication of how to proceed in laying out alternative means of moving forward from the present situation to a more productive use of the resources of the community. These alternatives fell into two general categories which were not independent of one another but which provided two workable positions from which to start an analysis of community development. The first of these categories was the economic development of the resources of the community. In most of these towns the traditional economic activity had been agriculture. In practically all of the towns, the number of farm operating units had been declining, although with the increased mechanization of farming and the consequent adjustment of farm size, the income earned in the towns by farming was relatively stable and in some cases had been increasing. Small farms were being consolidated into larger farm units, but in the process of consolidation, areas of potentially good agricultural land were being abandoned while capital was being spent on improving less productive soil by drainage, clearing it of stones and obstructions and stump sprouts. The map of the soil resources of the town indicated that there could be a better allocation of these resources.

The second problem related to this adjustment of land resources was a growing conflict between the use of land for agriculture and the expansion of the community residential area. Particularly in those towns near cities, it was inevitable that agriculture near the village center would have to retreat and the problem became one of locating other areas within the community which would be suitable sites for farm operating units. A major issue in this case was to arrange for an orderly adjustment of the tax valuation on land in the process of shifting from agriculture to dwelling areas which would make the process of expansion an orderly one. Too often the assessors had raised valuations on agricultural land before there was any demand for it as building lots, with the consequence that the farmer was paying a heavy tax penalty which made it difficult for him to compete with other agricultural producers for his market.

In most of these communities there was a growing demand for rural residence and part-time farms by people whose major employment was in one of the nearby industrial towns. Frequently these sites were chosen primarily on the basis of the cost of the land and buildings rather than of their suitability for such uses or of the effect of the location upon town costs for providing school transportation and other community services. Maps indicating areas where such type of development could contribute most to the community and at the same time be most productive as farmsteads were useful in indicating the kind of solutions that could be applied to problems of this sort.

A major consideration from the point of view of the future development of the town was a projection of employment opportunities. Not only was it essential to discover the size of the labor market, but also the probable wage rates and job stability. In communities whose future development seemed to lie primarily in the direction of becoming bedroom towns for nearby industrial centers, these data were necessary for drawing up a budget for future expenditures for developing community services, highways, schools, and similar investments.

All of the communities studied in this way had substantial land resources that were capable of much more productive development under present and immediate predictable price structures. This is especially the case in the forested areas in most of the towns. Usually woodland had been so recently cut or carelessly managed that the possibility of developing such land for the production of timber required a long-term investment in management that few people could undertake. Except where forest land was attached to a farm operating unit and could be developed along with the agriculture, the major uses of this forest land were for watershed protection, recreation — either as a public development or as a site for summer residences — and in some instances as a town forest to be brought up to a level of productivity that would yield a net return to the town. In most cases these uses of forest lands were not mutually exclusive, but the development of these resource values depended upon a coordinated management of forest land.

Within quite recent times, water has become a scarce resource in these communities. In the larger towns, or those with some industry, particularly those lying along the Nashua River, stream pollution and inadequate flow for municipal and industrial purposes has become a major issue. In other towns, the development of water resources is becoming important to supply water for irrigation, and occasionally for domestic uses. With the growth of population, a very important demand has grown up for the use of streams and ponds for recreation, either as sites for vacation homes or as public areas for swimming, fishing, and boating. Very rarely in the town meetings was there any general awareness of the growing scarcity of water, or of the potential value of the water resources in the town. One town was shocked by the refusal of an industry, which would have had a major effect on the economy of the community, to locate there because of the lack of a suitable source of water to be used in a cooling process and to supply their projected housing development.

The political issues in town development stemmed primarily from the fact that the political agencies in the towns were operating on a day-to-day basis and without consulting one another before taking action. Theoretically the Board of Selectmen in the New England town are responsible for coordinating the functions of the Highway Department, the Finance Committee, the Board of Public Health, and so on. Actually, however, the selectmen operate as overseers of the various political agencies within the community rather than as a coordinating committee. The town budgeting process, which is the key to community development, is conceived as a matter of accepting present costs as given and then fixing the tax rate at a level high enough to meet these costs. The selectmen are concerned with holding costs to a minimum but there is little incentive to consider the problem of investing in the development of the town.

As a consequence of this, a major interest at most of the meetings was the level of taxes rather than the value of services that could be bought with tax funds. Some towns had finance committees which again were concerned with holding costs down rather than exploring possible future investments. Some towns had planning boards but in practically all cases the planning board conceived of itself as an agency established for the purpose of setting up some type of zoning, and then acting as the executive agent for the zoning ordinance. Once again they were approaching the problem of community development in negative rather than positive terms. Health, police, highway, and housing standards, in so far as the community was concerned, were controlled largely by standards set up under the general legislation of the state and county. Most towns, for example, were unaware that under Massachusetts law they could control the building of undesirable jerry-built housing developments under the powers of the state health codes. The school committee, which under New England town government is a semi-autonomous body with the power to vote its own budget, also regarded its problem wholly as one of meeting present costs and attempting to find ways of avoiding the price that the expansion of the community would inevitably exact. It was only reluctantly that they would consider the possibility of reducing school costs by consolidation with schools in neighboring towns. This was an issue that was thought of largely in terms of losing local authority rather than one of presenting the possibility of improved public education in the community.

All of these issues came out in the meetings held with the townspeople.

The discussions were designed to present these questions not as separate problems but rather as related aspects of the total problem of community development. The give and take of public debate brought out that while each problem would have to be solved individually, the selection of the best among the alternative solutions depended upon relating them to a comprehensive plan for the development of the community as a whole. This in turn led in the direction of the conclusion that some agency in the community such as a town planning board should be responsible for developing such an integrated program, and that such a town planning board should direct its efforts not toward developing zoning ordinances, but rather to working with the town by consultation with all of the groups in the community to create a program for community development. This required accepting the definition of the functions of the planning board as education and research, and therefore assuring that it would elicit both the assistance and support of the community as the plan was developed. In this way the board would forestall becoming an isolated executive agency coming into conflict with the other economic interests of the town and the political powers of the Board of Selectmen. The concluding meeting in all the towns was devoted to the way in which such a planning agency could be created in the community either as a separate planning board or as a part of the function of the Board of Selectmen or some similar group.

The Seminar planning group took the information that had been gathered at the town meeting and incorporated it into its projections for development of the community. Members of the group then returned to the town and consulted with the selectmen, assessors, school committee, and other town officials as well as individuals within the town to determine what alternative developments would be most satisfactory. This material was analyzed and budgets set up indicating the costs and returns from such developments. These budgets were of two kinds. First were budgets for the community as a whole indicating possible investment in community development. Equally important were budgets for individual operating units such as farms, part-time farms, and similar land resource enterprises. These budgets also indicated costs and the returns from possible alternative development of the resources available to those operating units and thus served as a measure of possible growth of the community and opportunities for further private investment. A report was then prepared indicating the general areas of possible growth, the available opportunities, possible costs, and returns to both public and private development projects. These reports were made available to the town.

ACCOMPLISHMENT

It should be made clear that the work of the Land Use Seminar in this project was wholly inadequate for the development of a comprehensive community study. Its major purpose was to illustrate how the planning process could be applied and to stimulate local interest in carrying out such projects. Given the time at hand and the experience of the people involved, the most that could be done was to indicate the possibilities.

This limited approach to the problem, however, did bear fruit. A considerable amount of interest in the planning process was generated in the County. Before the seminar concluded its work, it had had requests from many more towns to set up meetings and prepare reports than could be accommodated. In an attempt to meet this demand it was decided to establish a school for town governing and planning officials in the County. The manager of the Worcester County Extension Service arranged with the Harvard Forest in Petersham to hold a series of three consecutive meetings to last from 6:30 in the evening until 11 o'clock. Town selectmen, assessors, members of school committees, finance committees, planning boards, and Soil Conservation District supervisors were invited to meet with representatives from the State University at Amherst, the state Department of Commerce, and members of the faculty of the Graduate School of Public Administration to discuss the planning process. The first meeting was devoted to working out an acceptable definition of the planning process, agreeing upon its primary educational orientation, the use of the budget technique in developing and assessing alternatives, and establishing the necessity of developing an over-all map of the resources of the community and their potential use.

With this as a background, a second meeting was held in which sources of information for creating such a plan were outlined. All those attending the meeting were given mimeographed information indicating who could be called on for assistance in providing data that would be useful in setting up the general plan. The third meeting was devoted to the function of the planning agency in the town. The discussion hinged upon ways of achieving a coordination of the agencies involved in the process of planning and of eliciting the active support of all members of the community both to provide information and to help in defining the objectives that the plan should attempt to reach. It was emphasized in this meeting that the planning board's function was primarily that of providing the town with information in such a form that it could better understand its present situation and the possibilities that lay before it. This information would have to be developed by consultation not only with governmental agencies, both in the town and out, but with representative groups such as the Parent-Teachers Association, the Farm Bureau, the Grange, the church groups, and representative individuals. Continuing consultation of this sort was designated as a fundamental function of the planning board, both in developing a plan to be presented for the town to consider and act upon, and also, once a plan had been adopted, as a means of modifying and developing the plan as conditions changed.

The planning board's function as it was defined in this meeting was one that excluded it from taking on executive functions, such as that of administering a zoning ordinance. The planning here was conceived of as a process of working out desirable alternatives and presenting them to executive agencies, or providing for creating such agencies and then evaluating the work of these agencies in continuing the planning process. A final point of emphasis was that planning did not aim at a total and final program for development, but rather it established practical solutions to problems and schedules of investment to provide orderly change.

It would be hard to measure in concrete terms the results of this enterprise. In most cases the work of the Seminar stimulated discussion of the critical issues in the town and served as a device for creating effective town planning boards. In a few instances these planning boards have already become effective in achieving a more orderly development of the residential areas in the town. After several years of discussion, one town which had been unalterably opposed to a consolidated school finally voted unanimously within the past year to join such a system. Another town has made a series of investments in developing the water resources of the community for recreational purposes.

The planning process as it has been employed here is a relatively slow one, and if it is successful, such success will have to be measured over a long period of time. It will not be a matter of meeting present emergencies so much as one of avoiding such emergencies in the future, and of providing for a faster rate of development than will otherwise come. Certainly the plans presented by the Seminar group were inadequate as the basis for a specific program of town development, but the continuing interest in the planning process as it applies to communities in the county would seem to indicate that the real purpose in undertaking this project has been in some measure achieved.

CHAPTER 21

The Public Agencies and the Organizations Concerned in Rural Planning

The foregoing twenty chapters, except Chapter 8, concern themselves with a particular undertaking in rural planning. In the final two chapters, the authors have tried to put together what they have learned from participation in and observation of planning both in and outside of the Harvard Seminar. In this chapter will be described the public agencies and organizations that are concerned in such planning and their general functioning. The final chapter will be devoted to the planning operation itself and its adaptation to rural planning. Only those agencies that operate in Worcester County are considered.

The Cooperative Extension Service

The functions of the Cooperative Extension Service, with its integration of federal and state activities, are broadly defined in its enabling act, the Smith-Lever Act of 1914, as follows:

That in order to aid in diffusing among the people of the United States useful and practical information on subjects relating to agriculture and home economics, and to encourage the application of the same, there may be inaugurated in connection with the college or colleges in each State now receiving, or which may hereafter receive, the benefits of the Land-Grant Act of 1862 and the Morrill College Endowment Act of 1890, agricultural extension work which shall be carried on in cooperation with the United States Department of Agriculture.

That Cooperative Extension work shall consist of the giving of instruction and practical demonstrations in Agriculture and Home Economics to persons not attending or resident in said colleges in the several communities, and imparting to such persons information on said subjects through field demonstrations, publications, and otherwise: and this work shall be carried on in such a manner as may be mutually agreed upon by the Secretary of Agriculture and the State agricultural college or colleges receiving benefits of this Act.

The primary function of the Cooperative Extension Service in agriculture and home economics is therefore education, which emphasizes learning by doing. It is performing this function for an ever widening range of subject matter and with the aid of an increasing number of techniques. Some of the areas and ways in which it is functioning are counseling on farm problems; securing application of the findings of research on the whole range of farm operations from land use, soil treatment, crop and livestock production to better farm management and business methods, better homes, and better farm and community living; working with rural youth; helping farmers solve problems through group action; mobilizing rural people to meet emergencies; and developing an understanding of the economic and social factors affecting family living and agriculture in general.

Early extension work gave major emphasis to improved farm practices. The emphasis is now shifting more to the farm and family as a unit and to the community as a whole. It is realized increasingly that Extension has an obligation to help rural people understand the complex social and economic problems, local, national, and international, which confront them. Furthermore, the Smith-Lever Act clearly states that Extension's field of educational responsibilities extends to all of the people of the United States.

Some of the basic trends that will affect Extension's future job are the substantial growth of financial assets of farm people and the need for educational assistance in wise spending; the expanding interest of rural people in the broader problems of their community, their nation, and the world; and the continuation of technological progress.

Among the effects of technological progress are (1) a need for more knowledge of the use and maintenance of machinery, (2) an increase in the capital required for efficient farming and rural living, (3) a widening of the gap between efficient and inefficient farmers and a resulting displacement of farm labor, (4) increased production, and hence the need for greater emphasis on marketing and distribution, and (5) continuous changes in the home, with new opportunities and new problems for the homemaker.

Another trend which affects Extension's future is the growing field of 4-H club work and older youth work. It should be stressed that people are agriculture's most valuable resource. Work with people as such, rather than with individual problems, must be emphasized.

Other trends which will be important to Extension in the future are the need for rapid expansion in the field of conservation of natural resources; the need for expanding emphasis on individual farm and home planning; the decreasing number of farm families and the increasing number of rural nonfarm families; and the continued need for, and emphasis on, better rural health and rural educational services.

Several aspects of the Cooperative Extension Service are particularly important from the standpoint of rural planning at the county level. One of these is the focal position of the county in the conduct of extension work. The county is the point of actual contact of the Extension Service with rural people and their problems. At the county headquarters are stationed the county agent, in most counties a home demonstration agent, and in a good many counties a 4-H club agent or assistant county agent, or both. Many counties have extension staffs of five or more. The Worcester County Extension Service office is located in Worcester and maintains a staff of from twelve to fifteen specialists.

The Extension Service at the county level usually has the counsel of an advisory committee drawn from the people of the county. This committee assists in drawing up the annual extension work-plan for the county. An increasing number of counties now have some sort of a longer-range plan outlining the goals and objectives to be realized. In Worcester County the Extension Service is supervised by a board of Trustees for County Aid to Agriculture consisting of nine members appointed by the County Commissioners.

Next in order are over two thousand extension subject matter specialists who work out from the Land-Grant Colleges into the counties and help the county staffs. Over half of these are specialists in agricultural production and conservation. In Massachusetts approximately fifty specialists are stationed at the University of Massachusetts and are available for assistance in Worcester County.

The Extension Service is called upon to perform many functions which may come under the heading of service, but it is not possible to draw a fine line of distinction between education and service. If the Extension Service tests soils for a farmer or an extension forester marks trees to be cut, this looks like pure service; but both can be done in such a way that the operator gets a very potent dose of education from them. The process of learning by doing, which agricultural education favors, by its very nature combines service and education.

Much of the educational work carried on by the Extension Service in the past has been the teaching of practices and skills. The teachers have tended to be very dogmatic in giving specific instructions regarding such things as amounts of seed or fertilizer to apply. The learning process has been aided and accomplished by actually carrying out the practice or skill.

In the fields of economics and other social sciences the teaching process cannot be dogmatic. The teacher must help the learner by giving him background information and training him in the arts of logic in order that he might arrive at his own conclusions and answers. Here again, the process of learning is by doing, that is, by the learner actually working out his own answers, his own farm and home plans, and so forth.

In the fields of public policy and program determination, group decisions must be made, and here again the learning process is most effectively achieved by doing, but in this instance "doing" means discussing situations and alternatives with one's fellows and arriving at group conclusions through the use of enlightened group dynamics in an environment which observes the principles of democratic procedure.

The Agricultural Research Service — The State Experiment Stations

The Agricultural Research Service conducts fundamental, applied, and developmental research relating to the production and utilization of agricultural products, and administers control and regulatory programs closely related to this research. These regulatory programs involve enforcement of plant and animal quarantines, meat inspection, and the control of diseases and insect pests of animals and plants and related activities.

Work is carried on at the Agricultural Research Center located at Beltsville, Maryland, and at more than six hundred stations throughout the United States and in more than a dozen foreign countries. Most of this research is cooperative with other Federal, State, and other public and private agencies having similar objectives.

The Agricultural Research Service administers the Federal Acts granting funds for the support of research in agriculture, the rural home, and rural life by the Experiment Stations of the various states.

Although the Agricultural Research Service and the State Experiment Stations do not usually maintain personnel at the county level unless experimental activities happen to be located within the county, their research work does have a bearing on the various technologies which affect land-use patterns within each county. Ordinarily it is not their function to take a hand directly in assisting farms and other operating units with their planning activities. But they do make a major contribution to the objectives and end results of such planning by furnishing a scientific basis for the technologies that are incorporated in improved operating unit plans and by supplying input-output and other data indicating the effects on yields and conservation of different soil-management practices, pasture-management practices, cropping systems, livestock-management practices, woodland-management systems, disease and pest controls, and the like.

As will be explained later, the first major step in planning procedure is to assemble all available research information for use as a background for developing alternative policies, plans, and programs. This calls for close cooperation between county planning groups and the research workers at the State Experiment Stations, and will reveal important gaps of urgently needed research. As a result research programs may be expanded and redirected. Much of the new research required for planning will call for collaboration of economists, soil scientists, and plant and animal scientists. Usually the need for expanded research work in farm management and marketing will become evident.

The Soil Conservation Service (*S.C.S.*)

The Soil Conservation Service was established in 1935 under authority of the Soil Conservation Act (Public Law No. 46, 74th Congress) and was charged with the responsibility of developing and carrying out a permanent national soil and water conservation program. The principal duty of this agency is to assist farmers and ranchers in locally organized, farmer-directed soil conservation districts, through its planning technicians and other soil and water conservation specialists who live and work in the districts. There are now about 2,900 such districts covering 1.4 billion acres and including over 4.5 million farms and ranches in the United States and its possessions. Worcester County is divided into three districts and the S.C.S. maintains three work units and offices within the County. Each is supervised by a board of three supervisors elected by the farmers.

The Service has the federal responsibility for the National Cooperative Soil Survey; this includes responsibility for soil surveys by all agencies, not just those of the Service. The Service also is responsible for administering the flood control and river investigation activities of the Department of Agriculture.

Technical personnel of the Service are specialists in determining land needs and methods of solving soil and water problems. Staffs are composed of agronomists, agricultural hydraulic and cartographic engineers, biologists, foresters, soil scientists, range-management specialists, and land-management and conservation-planning technicians. Although they are specialists in one or more of the agricultural sciences, the soil conservationists are trained to coordinate all knowledge pertaining to land and water for the special purpose of planning and applying land-use adjustment and conservation practices needed to repair erosion damage, increase yields, preserve and improve the productivity of soils, and conserve water resources.

In assisting farmers and ranchers with their soil and water conservation problems, the Service goes through four principal steps. First, it makes a detailed acre-by-acre soil survey of the farm or ranch. The survey information on soil type, slope, amount of erosion, and other environmental factors is presented on a map which shows the soil-type areas grouped according to their capabilities for use — whether they are best suited for cultivated crops, grass, timber, or wildlife — and their management needs. Soil surveys adequate for conservation planning had been completed on nearly 425 million acres of farm and ranch land by the end of 1953.

Second, the operator and technician together draw up a conservation farm plan. This provides for various alternatives in the treatment and use of the land according to its needs and capabilities as indicated on the soil map. The plan is so designed that it enables farmers to go ahead with their most needed conservation measures immediately, and then gradually to complete their basic conservation plans as they proceed with regular farming or ranching operations. At the end of the fiscal year 1953, technicians of the Service had helped farmers and ranchers to prepare 1,300,000 conservation farm plans.

The third step involves the application of practices called for in the plan. The soil conservationist gives the necessary technical guidance. The landowner may do most or all of the work himself. He may hire special equipment or obtain it through his soil conservation district.

Fourth, there is the continuing job of maintaining the farm conservation system after the practices have been applied to the land. The Service provides the guidance needed for such maintenance. Also, as research develops refinements and improvements, the technicians explain them to the farmer in order that he may put them into practice to his own advantage.

The Service's over-all program is administered by the Administrator and his staff from the central office in the U.S. Department of Agriculture in Washington, D.C. The Service maintains fifty-one state and territorial offices which perform technical and administrative functions to provide service to field personnel.

Each state or territorial office serves as headquarters for a state conservationist, a conservation engineer, a soil scientist, and a soil conservationist who together serve the area offices and work units of the respective states. Each of the approximately 300 area offices supervises several of the 2,900 work units. Each work unit is staffed by a professional conservationist and one or more aids who work directly with farmers and ranchers.

Subject-matter specialists (engineering and watershed planning specialists, plant technologists, soil scientists, and cartographic field units), each serving a group of states, are located strategically throughout the United States to provide scientific and technical guidance and training, and for production of soil maps, farm plans, and other essential working materials.

Under authority of the Flood Control Act of 1944, the Service plans and applies flood-damage prevention measures and practices in eleven major watersheds comprising approximately 30 million acres. Detailed flood prevention plans are prepared and applied to tributary watersheds and are used for scheduling quantities and types of measures to be applied or installed throughout the major watersheds, and for determining the relationships between flood prevention benefits and costs.

In addition, the Service started watershed protection planning and operations in 1953 on small watersheds, as authorized by the 83rd Congress. The purpose of the program is to demonstrate the practicability of complete watershed protection as a means of conserving soil and water resources, alleviating damage from floods, silting of reservoirs, impairment of stream channels, and other upstream land and water problems. The work in the watersheds is carried out in close cooperation with soil conservation districts and other local sponsoring groups and individuals.

The Service also has the responsibility for assisting in the national, state, and county Agricultural Conservation Program of the Department of Agriculture. It contributes to this program by providing needed technical assistance to farmers and ranchers who participate in the cost-sharing provisions of the Agricultural Conservation Program, next to be outlined.

The Agricultural Conservation Program Service (ACPS)

This is the name given in November 1953 to the former ACP (Agricultural Conservation Program) of the PMA (Production and Marketing Administration). In the field, this program is administered by what are now called Agricultural Stabilization and Conservation Committees. The Agricultural Conservation Program had its origin in the Soil Conservation and Domestic Allotment Act of 1936. This in turn grew out of the Agricultural Adjustment Administration (AAA) created by the original Agricultural Adjustment Act of 1933. When this original Act was declared unconstitutional, Congress shifted to soil conservation as a basis for shifting acreage from soil-depleting crops in surplus production — cotton, corn, tobacco, wheat, etc. — to soil-conserving crops not in surplus production. There was presently combined with the ACP payments to producers a program of commodity loans without recourse, and another one of compensatory payments for crops with prices below parity. The community and county staffs and advisory boards set up to administer the conservation program also administered these two other programs. They also became War Boards during World War II with special wartime duties. In 1945, these programs were all consolidated into the one federal and state organization called the PMA. To administer this program in Worcester County, an office is maintained in Worcester under the supervision of a three-man farmer-elected committee.

Prior to 1951 the ACP operated quite independently of other soil conservation agencies. On February 15, 1951, Secretary of Agriculture Brannan undertook, in Memorandum 1278, to coordinate the activities of the ACP with those of other conservation agencies, mainly with the S.C.S. and the Forest Service. The memorandum provided that, under the direction of the Assistant Secretary of Agriculture, the S.C.S., the Forest Service, and the PMA were jointly to determine the soil conservation practices to be included in the ACP and the rates of payments for these practices. This joint undertaking was called the Agricultural Resource Conservation Program (A.R.C.P.). The Land-Grant Colleges, Farmers' Home Administration, Agricultural Extension Service, and the Boards of Supervisors of Soil Conservation Districts were also invited to participate. Under this memorandum the S.C.S. was given the responsibility for all technical phases of "permanent-type" soil-conservation work. Permanent-type practices were defined as those practices mainly of an engineering nature — terraces, sod waterways, revetments, strip cropping, dams, and the like. Departmental Reorganization No. 2 of November 1953 gave this joint program "Service" status with primarily the same functions.

Beginning in 1954 an attempt was made to adapt conservation to local needs through the teamwork of representatives of the Soil Conservation Service, Extension Service, Forest Service, Farmers' Home Administration, officials of Soil Conservation Districts, county and community farmer committees, and others. Under broad national and state authority, county programs were developed and operated in line with the following general policies:

(1) The county programs encourage maximum conservation with emphasis on practices on which federal cost-sharing is most needed.

(2) They encourage those conservation practices which will result in the most enduring conservation benefits practicable.

(3) The conservation costs are shared with a farmer or rancher only where he requests it before the conservation work is begun, and then only after he has satisfactorily performed the conservation practices.

(4) The conservation costs are shared only on practices which it is believed that farmers would not carry out to the needed extent otherwise. In general, practices which have become a part of regular farming operations on a particular farm or ranch are not eligible for cost-sharing.

(5) The rates of cost-sharing in a county or state are the minimum required for substantial increases of needed conservation.

(6) Farmers and ranchers are expected to assume responsibility for the upkeep and maintenance of conservation practices for which costs are shared under the 1954 program. Cost-sharing is for the initial establishment of such practices.

The United States Forest Service

The Forest Service owns and operates approximately one fifth of the forest area in the United States. The functions of the Forest Service with respect to other forested land are:

(1) cooperation with the states in fire protection, the federal government contributing half of the costs;

(2) technical assistance to private timber owners, both large and small, in managing their forest properties;

(3) research — scientific investigations in the utilization of forest products, in forest and range management, etc.;

(4) cooperation with the states in extension in forest management.

The primary function of the Forest Service is to carry out the responsibility of the federal government in working out solutions to the nation's forestry problems. Stated more explicitly, this means, in the national forest, technical management for the production of timber, forage for livestock, water, wildlife, and recreation. It means the protection of public lands from fire and tree diseases, as well as the integration of management of all forest resources in order that they will contribute as fully as possible to economic betterment. On the privately owned forest lands, which in major part are badly handled from a national point of view, it means cooperation with the states and private agencies in protection against fire, insects and disease, in forest planting, and in obtaining improved management practices.

The attainment of these objectives requires the conduct of a large amount of research in all phases of forest and forest-range management, both independently and in cooperation with other technical and industrial agencies.

In its management of national forests as operating units, the Forest Service of course includes all the resources of the land, not only timber but grazing, waterpower, recreation, wildlife, and even agriculture. It particularly emphasizes the multiple use of the forest lands.

In the matter of farm forestry, the Forest Service's contribution has been indirect rather than direct. It has made basic information and trained personnel available for other agencies to use in direct contact with farmers, and furnished funds to the states for cooperative undertakings.

State Forestry Agencies

Like the U.S. Forest Service, the State forestry agencies both manage publicly owned forests and serve woodland owners, especially the smaller ones, in various ways. The development of fire protection systems has been one of their responsibilities, as well as the development of nurseries for growing the planting stock. Most state forestry agencies also provide some form of management and marketing assistance.

The State forests generally are supervised by the State Forester. The agency with which the State Forester is connected varies among states, however. In twenty-one of the thirty-six states that have state forests, forestry is a division of a state conservation department or a department of natural resources, with the State Forester in charge of the division. This setup prevails in Massachusetts. The Division of Forestry maintains a district forester in Worcester County.

Extension Service Forestry

Forestry Extension is a part of the Agricultural Extension Service program of the land-grant institutions. Extension foresters are employed by the state extension director and are normally stationed at the agricultural college. The extension foresters work in cooperation with the county agricultural agents and give assistance in response to requests from particular counties.

Provisions of the Clarke-McNary Law of 1924 inaugurated the farm forestry extension activities. Originally a fund of $100,000 was set up to carry out the extension provisions of the Act. Public Law 392 of the 81st Congress amended the original Clarke-McNary Act by increasing the authorization for extension forestry work to $500,000 annually.

Generally, extension forestry work is classed as the promotional phase of farm forestry. Its purpose is to stimulate the owner's interest and convince him that good forestry practices are worth while. The programs are carried out with a group approach.

The extension forester's work includes many activities in teaching (forestry short courses), public information (such as talks, radio, and newspaper), collecting and publishing market data, woodlot marking, logging, and planting demonstrations.

The extension forestry service is so organized that it can influence great numbers of the rural population. In a few states extension foresters do some service work, but most of them are conducting educational work only. This service has taken the initiative in promoting farm forestry demonstrations in cooperation with other agencies who are equipped to furnish follow-up services arising from the demonstrations.

Cooperative Forest Management

The Cooperative Forest Management Act of 1950 authorized the Secretary of Agriculture, acting cooperatively with the "state foresters" or equivalent officials, to advise farmers and nonfarm woodland owners in the management, harvesting, and marketing of their trees, and to provide technical services to all private forest landowners and operators in cooperating states. The appropriation made to a state is determined by the Secretary of Agriculture after consultation with a national advisory board of not less than five state foresters of states participating in the program. The amount paid to any state must not exceed a similar sum expended by the participating state agency. Congress has authorized $2.5 million per year to carry out the provisions of the Act. Some of the activities covered by this Act were included in the Cooperative Farm Forestry Act (Norris-Doxey) of 1937, which was replaced by the enactment of this new legislation. These activities are of course in addition to cooperative fire prevention control and tree planting under the Clarke-McNary Act.

Although the Act does not so state, it is designed to furnish aid especially to small forest owners and small processors of forest products. Only 4 percent of the cutting on these small holdings is rated as good, while 71 percent is rated as poor or destructive.

It is the intent of the legislation that the professional men working under its authority shall not compete with the private consulting foresters; in fact, it has led to a greater demand for the services of private foresters.

The administration of the provisions of the Act in the different states is subject to a cooperative federal-state plan provided for in the Act, but this does not prevent variations from state to state to fit the state needs and conditions.

In general, the states handle most of the work with state employees. Forest Service personnel are charged with the responsibility of advising and verifying the standards of the state administration.

In many states there has arisen a situation where more than one agency offers "on-the-ground forestry service." A great number of the states have drawn up a memorandum of understanding which specifies the responsibilities of each agency as well as joint responsibilities. Generally the agreements recognize that one agency depends on another for certain features essential to its work, and to supplement and complement its efforts.

An increasing number of organizations are now active in farm forestry work; among them are the State Departments of Conservation, the Extension Forestry Service, the Soil Conservation Service, and the Forest Service.

Of all the agencies engaged in farm forestry work, the closest tie is between the State Conservation Departments and the Extension Service. Both agencies recognize the need for close working relationships. A joint policy statement on the subject was endorsed by both groups, the Association of State Foresters, and the Land-Grant College Association, in 1948. Agreements of a similar nature exist in many states between the State Conservation Departments and the Soil Conservation Service.

The agreement between the Secretary of Agriculture and the State Foresters under which the Act of 1950 is administered specifies that "full advantage will be taken of services and assistance available from other agencies of the State and Federal Government. The State will endeavor to coordinate its conduct of the Cooperative program with related programs of other agencies."

The Farm Credit Administration

The capital resources available to an individual farm or forest operator affect strongly the use he is able to make of his land. Probably no other one factor, unless it is the ignorance or indifference of the operator himself, stands as strongly in the way of land improvements and developments that would raise the productivity of half of the land in the United States to a level at least a third higher than at present. If the operator does not have the capital himself, why does he not borrow it? Part of the answer is that there is no place where he can borrow it.

This fact was recognized before 1910 and Congress sent a commission to Europe to study the public and cooperative agencies providing credit to agriculture there. Out of this interest evolved the Federal Farm Loan Act of 1916, the Agricultural Credits Act of 1923, and eventually the Farm Credit Administration (FCA) in 1933.

The FCA, created by Executive Order in March, 1933, brought together under one administrative agency most of the existing federally sponsored agricultural credit agencies. These included the Federal Land Banks and Federal Intermediate Credit Banks then under the Federal Farm Loan Board, which was under the Treasury Department, the regional agricultural credit corporations that had been set up under the Reconstruction Finance Corporation in 1931, and the emergency seed and feed loan agency of the U.S. Department of Agriculture. The FCA was transferred to the USDA by Presidential Executive Order in 1939. By act of Congress it was taken out of the USDA in 1953.

The FCA coordinates and supervises the activities of four farm credit systems: the Federal Land Bank system, the Production Credit system, the Intermediate Credit Banks, and the Banks for Cooperatives. The Federal Farm Loan Act of 1916 greatly increased the availability of long-term farm-mortgage credit but it did not meet the needs for intermediate and short-term credit. The short-term credit needs were more adequately provided for in establishing the banks for cooperatives, the production credit corporations, and the production credit associations in 1933.

General policies of the Farm Credit Administration in Washington are determined by the Federal Farm Credit Board. These policies are administered by the Governor and his staff. Policies of the Farm Credit district banks and corporations are determined by district boards of directors. At the local level, each Production Credit Association and National Farm Loan Association likewise has its own board of directors.

Federal land bank loans are made on the security of first mortgages on farm land and buildings. The loan may be made in amounts from $100 to $100,000 but not in excess of 65 percent of the appraised "normal value" of the farm.

The interest rate for Federal land bank loans on April 1, 1954, was 4 percent in 9 districts, 4½ percent in 2 districts, and 5 percent in one. The loans are made on an amortized basis for terms of not less than 5 nor more than 49 years. Payments may be made on an amortized basis for terms of not less than 5 nor more than 40 years. Payments may be made in advance if desired. Money loaned to farmers is obtained through the sale of consolidated Federal farm loan bonds to the investing public.

The Federal land bank system is completely owned by farmers through the National Farm Loan Associations (NFLA's), of which there are now 1,125 in the United States and Puerto Rico. These Associations receive applications, recommend or disapprove them for loans, and service the loans that are made. Each borrowing member of a NFLA is required to purchase stock in his Association equal to 5 percent of the amount borrowed. The Association in turn purchases a like amount of stock in the Federal Land Bank. When the loan is paid in full the stock in the Bank is retired at par and the association retires the members' stock in the same manner. In line with cooperative principles, the Federal Land Banks may distribute dividends to the associations and these may distribute dividends to the borrowers. In 1953 this system was providing about 15 percent of the outstanding farm mortgage credit of the United States.

The Federal Intermediate Credit Banks (FICB's) are banks of discount and do not lend directly to farmers. The major part of Intermediate Credit Bank business is with the Production Credit Associations (PCA's). In 1933, Congress created twelve production credit corporations and provided for organizing a nationwide system of Production Credit Associations. The membership of these consists of the borrowers who must own stock in the association as in the case of the National Farm Loan Associations (NFLA's). The PCA's obtain their loanable funds largely by rediscounting farmers' notes with or borrowing from the Federal Intermediate Credit Banks. The loans are for one year usually, but may be renewed in the case of expenditures that will not pay out in one year, like many purchases of farm machinery. The interest rates vary, but in March 1954 the prevailing rates were 5¾ and 6 percent. In addition, many PCA's have a loan service fee. The losses have been very low — a total of about one sixth of 1 percent of the cash advanced to date. In 1953, the PCA loans outstanding were about one fifth of the amount of similar loans held by commercial banks.

The banks for cooperatives, set up in 1933, include twelve district banks and a central bank in Washington, D.C. These district banks make direct loans to cooperatives on commodities and for cooperative facilities and operating capital. Borrowing associations are required to own stock equal to 5 percent of the amount borrowed for operating capital and facility loans, and 1 percent of the amount borrowed on commodity loans. The interest rates charged by the banks for cooperatives vary by districts and type of loan. The range on April 1, 1954, was as follows: on commodity loans, 2¾ to 3¼ percent; on operating loans, 3 to 3½ percent; on facility loans, 4 to 4½ percent.

The FCA appears to be an elaborate setup of publicly sponsored agricultural credit to supplement that provided from private sources. Still there are some inadequacies in it. Major gaps are credit for forestry development and for grazing land development. In general, the FCA still makes relatively few loans for periods of two to five years for land development and other intermediate-term purposes except on real-estate mortgages, and many of the farms needing such loans are already mortgaged and it is difficult to enlarge the mortgage.[1] The kind of a loan needed for such development is often what is called an open-end mortgage — one that advances the capital only as it is needed in carrying out, say, a five-year program of development, and calls for payment only as the improvements yield returns.

A distinctive characteristic of the Farm Credit system is the fact that, while the federal government provided substantial amounts of capital for the various banks and corporations of the system, the law made provision for the retirement of the government's investment as capital is built up through sales of stock to farmer borrowers and through the accumulation of earnings. All government capital previously invested in the Federal Land Banks has been retired. The production credit association and the banks for cooperatives are in the process of retiring their government capital.

One question needs to be raised with respect to the carrying out of this policy, namely, whether the local associations will be left with enough capital to meet the credit needs of their areas in depression years, or even in years of crop failure. The Farm Loan system probably has adequate capital to meet such local situations, but it is to be doubted if the Production Credit system now has.

The Farmers' Home Administration (FHA)

In addition to the establishment of the cooperative farm credit system, designed to provide a comprehensive credit service to farmers and their cooperatives on a sound business basis, the Congress has from time to time made special provisions for direct loans in order to meet credit needs which could not be financed through private or cooperative credit institutions. Such

[1] Since this was written, the PCA's have begun to make loans for longer terms.

direct loans have been designed to fill the gap during periods when private credit facilities were strained because of the government's financial needs, to finance expanded food production under circumstances involving extraordinary risks, to supply supplemental credit during periods of extreme economic stress, to assist farmers and stockmen in areas of local disaster, and to supply credit to low-income farmers on a supervised basis with the objective of eventually placing such farmers on a sound financial basis, thus enabling them to obtain their credit requirements through normal channels.

Congress began making special provision for disaster credit in agriculture soon after World War I through the Agricultural Credit Act of 1921 administered as a function of the War Finance Corporation. Later in the 1920's, drought and flood emergency seed and feed loans were provided. The biggest agricultural disaster of all came with the Big Depression of the 1930's. To assist in meeting the short-term credit needs of farmers and stockmen during the early 1930's, the Reconstruction Finance Corporation was authorized to establish a regional agricultural credit corporation in any of the twelve land bank districts (now Farm Credit districts). Under that authority twelve corporations were chartered in 1932. These corporations handled a substantial volume of loans, particularly in the range livestock areas. Their operations later were transferred, by executive order, to the Farm Credit Administration, and eventually to the FHA.

The Land Bank Commissioner loans were provided to handle the real-estate mortgage end of this situation. The Land Bank Commissioner of the Federal Farm Loan system was provided with a fund of $200 million to make real-estate mortgage loans on a more liberal basis than could be made by the Federal land banks, including second real-estate mortgage loans. Later the Federal Farm Mortgage Corporation, the assets of which are expected to be largely liquidated in the near future, was created to finance such Commissioner loans. In the meantime, what is now the FHA was in the process of evolving. It began in the form of outright relief grants or work relief under the Federal Emergency Relief Administration (FERA). Out of these evolved in 1935 the Resettlement Administration, dedicated to the idea that the best way to relieve down-and-out farm families was to relocate them in new communities and provide them with better community facilities. About this time, the idea of also furnishing relief in the form of "rehabilitation loans," to farm families where they were, led to the "standard rehabilitation loan," a combination of a short-term and intermediate-term loan. The "annual advance" part of it was repayable each year, and the other on an open-end basis, usually with a five-year limit. Presently the Farm Security

Administration (FSA) was set up to administer these loans. By 1940, well on toward a million of such loans, part of them with supplementary grants, had been made. Many were made which were not really repayable, and should have been grants instead, and about 1940 these were reclassified as "collection only" loans, which meant that no more annual advances would be made. The supplementary-grant feature was dropped in 1942.

In 1937, the Bankhead-Jones Act, providing for assistance to tenants mainly for the purchase of farms, was passed. This was set up as a unit in the FSA.

With wartime prosperity, the funds voted the FSA were considerably reduced. In 1946, Bankhead-Jones aid was made available for farm enlargement, the name of the agency was changed to the Farmers' Home Administration, and other loan services were added. Following the War, the Bankhead-Jones funds were enlarged to help GI's purchase farms.

From the beginning, loans made by the FSA and FHA were restricted to those who were unable to obtain credit from commercial banks and other public credit agencies. Considering the circumstances under which the loans have been made, it is remarkable that the collections on the rehabilitation-type loans, including collection-only cases, have been 88 percent of the scheduled repayments. Of course, wartime prosperity and inflation played a considerable part in this.

A major explanation of the success of this program has been that some kind of a farm plan has been required as a basis for the credit, and the credit has been used to put the farms and farm businesses in condition to repay the loans.

The FHA program as now operating provides credit as follows to farm families unable to obtain credit from other sources:

1. Operating loans — the former rehabilitation loans. Advances are made up to 100 percent of livestock and machinery purchased, plus funds needed for operating expenses. Funds are advanced for necessary capital needs, for grass seed, fencing, portable buildings, feed, fuel, seed, livestock, and machinery. To meet the individual need, it can be a short-term operating loan or a loan of intermediate terms. The repayment period is up to 7 years, maximum loan, $10,000.

2. Farm-ownership loans — including tenant-purchase, development, and farm-enlargement loans as well. These enable an applicant to borrow up to 90 percent of needs to purchase the farm and make needed minimum repairs and development to buildings and land. Development loans are made to

farm owners to improve the unit's resources. Enlargement loans are made to enlarge units that are uneconomically small. Repayment is on a 40-year basis at 4 percent interest.

3. Farm housing loans are available to all farm owners, landlords, etc., to provide credit, many times on second mortgage, for new houses, barns, etc., repairs or additions to existing necessary farm buildings. Title II of the Housing Act authorized long-term loans at 4 percent interest.

4. Loans for soil and water conservation — These loans help farmers to use their farm land wisely through providing adequate financing for soil conservation, water conservation, and drainage improvements. The ceiling on such loans is $25,000, the maximum repayment period, 20 years.

After receipt of an application and approval of the county committee, the basic needs of the family are determined and agreed upon by the family and the FHA. Through a procedure of farm planning, the objectives are set forth and the steps to reach them. The merits of the loan are determined from the farm plan and committee recommendations. The family is given farm management assistance throughout the life of the loan.

A county committee is appointed in every county including Worcester County to assist the county supervisor as well as borrowers. Its main function is to approve or disapprove applications for loans. Loans cannot be made if the county committee disapproves the application; however, an application they approve may be disapproved by the FHA staff. County committeemen are paid on a per diem basis for travel and subsistence; they cannot be borrowers or act on applicants related to them.

The Agricultural Marketing Service

The Agricultural Marketing Service was created within the United States Department of Agriculture in November 1953. The Agricultural Marketing Service administers programs relating to: (1) marketing research, outlook, and related statistical and economic research; (2) crop and livestock estimates; (3) marketing services, including market news, standardization, grading inspection, and classing of farm products; (4) freight rate services; (5) marketing regulatory programs; (6) marketing agreements and orders; (7) surplus removal, export, and diversion programs; and (8) the National School Lunch Program.

Obviously many of these services are of vital interest to and have an effect on the well-being of Worcester County agriculture. The Worcester market area is regulated by a Federal Milk Marketing order, hence the Agricultural

Marketing Service maintains an office in Worcester. Many of the other activities of the Agricultural Marketing Service are administered from regional offices in the Boston area. These include the crop reporting service, the market news service, the grading and inspection services, and the surplus removal, and the school lunch programs.

Other Federal Agencies

Several Federal agencies have a bearing on rural planning in Worcester County inasmuch as they provide basic background data. These include the National Cooperative Soil Survey (now administered by the Soil Conservation Service) which provides maps of soil types and associated land characteristics in a wide range of detail; the United States Geological Survey which provides typographic maps and assembles data on water resources and surface geology; and the Bureau of the Census which provides data on population, agriculture, housing, manufacturing, and distribution down to the county level and in some cases information at the town level.

Numerous other Federal agencies could be listed which affect rural activities in Worcester County through their Cooperative administrative tieups with State agencies. For example, the Department of Labor provides facilities for farm labor placement through the State Division of Employment Security; the Bureau of Public Roads provides funds and some degree of supervision through the State Department of Public Works; the Department of Education and Public Welfare provides funds for vocational education on a cooperative basis through the State Department of Education; and the Fish and Wildlife Service cooperates with the State Department of Natural Resources.

Other Federal agencies whose programs vitally affect land use, but not in Worcester County, include the Bureau of Land Management, the Bureau of Reclamation, and the Bureau of Indian Affairs in the Department of Interior, the National Park Service, and river valley authorities such as the Tennessee Valley Authority.

State Government

By virtue of their inherent powers and the Tenth Amendment to the Constitution, the states exercise a residuum of powers with respect to land. They exercise a wide range of police powers, but only with respect to matters not under federal control. The federal government exercises police power over the lands which it owns. The states share with the federal government the exercise of eminent domain and the power of taxation.

In general, the states exercise their powers with respect to land use through two types of instruments, state boards or commissions, and state-created public corporations. State commissions are for the most part concerned with promoting health, safety, and welfare. In addition to direct regulation under the police power, some of these agencies have powers of appropriation which allow them to acquire property for public use. Notable among these are the park commissions and the commissions on public lands which regularly acquire land for public use and development, using the power of eminent domain where satisfactory purchases cannot be made.

Creation of public corporations is made possible through detailed enabling legislation which specifies the extent of the powers of such corporations. A public corporation is organized for a limited purpose and must confine its operations within that limitation. Such corporations generally enjoy powers of appropriation and of taxation.

Following is a partial list of State agencies whose activities directly affect the well-being of the rural areas of Worcester County.

The Massachusetts Department of Agriculture administers the state laws pertaining to agriculture and functions along the broad lines of regulating and promoting agriculture. A State Soil Conservation Committee appointed by the Governor advises the supervisors of the various Soil Conservation Districts which are instruments of the State organized under a special state enabling Act.

The Massachusetts Department of Natural Resources through its wild life activities and its Division of Forests and Parks administers regulatory and promotional programs for the State's nonagricultural natural resources. Some of these programs are partially supported by Federal funds under cooperative arrangements.

The Massachusetts Water Resources Commission is the agent of the Commonwealth for coordinating all activities of federal, state, and other agencies in the conservation, development, utilization, and disposal of water with emphasis on the minimization of damage by erosion, floodwater, and sedimentation in the watersheds.

The State's Land Grant College, the University of Massachusetts, with its Extension Service and State Agricultural Experiment Station, has been treated earlier. The Massachusetts Department of Education provides leadership to all local school committees and administrators; hence its programs and policies exert influence on educational activities throughout Worcester County. The rural areas are especially interested in vocational training not only in agriculture but in nonagricultural trades and skills as well, for not all rural youth can expect employment in agriculture, especially now when agricultural efficiency is increasing rapidly, thus making it necessary for more rural youth to seek opportunities in the secondary and tertiary industries, services, and professions.

Through the Department of Education's Division of Vocational Education, vocational agriculture training is offered in day courses varying from short periods to four years of training for agricultural careers. Courses are offered in county agricultural schools (none in Worcester County) and in high school agricultural departments. There are five of the latter in Worcester County. Out-of-school youths and adults are served in special evening school programs.

County and Local Government

County and local governments exert influence on resource development in many ways. This was well illustrated in the last chapter's discussion of community planning activities as conducted under this project. In some states, rural planning became institutionalized by the enactment of rural zoning ordinances during the period of the 1930's. In the main, land-use planning has been a coordinated effort to determine the best uses of the physical resources of a county. State, federal, county, and town agencies have worked together in a multi-level context in planning the future potential development of a region. The actual implementation of these plans is a function of other agencies than local government. As for zoning ordinances, local government generally can be invested by the state with the necessary power to assert control over land use. The most effective weapon in this control is the zoning ordinance giving counties or towns the power to regulate the use of land according to determined use capabilities.

With no zoning ordinances, the actual direct control of land use by counties is limited to the following:

1. Acquisition of title to land by counties by purchase or by tax deed. In some of the states, much of the land of low utility reverts to the counties through tax delinquency. Shifting western wheat lands from production into grass through tax deed process is one example; with cut-over areas, tax delinquency is used to build up county forests and withdraw farm lands of low productivity from agriculture.

2. Resettlement of isolated families by arranging land exchanges.

3. Use of highway set-back ordinances.

4. Land acquisition for highways and school relocation. It is apparent that these direct controls have limited application.

Where zoning ordinances are in force a land-use planning committee can divide the land into areas fit for farming, recreational, and residential areas, restricted districts fit only for forestry and wildlife uses, and industrial and commercial districts; and the zoning ordinances can make land use conform with this classification. Zoning ordinances can thus play a vital part in any farm-planning program. Any farm expansion project must fit into the framework of the existing county zoning ordinances in these areas where they exist. Zoning is especially effective where patterns of land use are in a state of transition, as in the urban-rural fringe or the forest-farm fringe.

In Wisconsin the zoning act provides for zoning land for agriculture, forestry, recreation, and, in some resort regions, recreational service use. In Michigan, the enabling act has been broadened to include soil and water conservation, and all-year residents may be zoned out of certain areas. All New England states have zoning acts.

Where a zoning ordinance exists, the town type of government, as it commonly occurs in New England, has the power to administer the zoning ordinance. In the Midwest, the county, not the town, is given the sovereign authority to regulate the use of land, and towns play a rather passive role. Local action, however, may be initiated at the town level through open hearings calling for changes or repeal of the ordinance. Such public hearings at the town level may be highly instrumental in achieving change.

In Massachusetts, the state government grants zoning authority to the local town or city government. Local governments by a two-thirds vote of the people can enact zoning laws and building codes and these with sub-division control measures can be used to guide residential business and industrial development. Under the Massachusetts laws, land cannot be zoned for agricultural, forestry, or recreation uses per se, but by controlling business and industrial development and the density of residential building rural areas become residual for agriculture, forestry, and recreation uses.

CHAPTER 22

Rural Planning—General

The two principal authors of this report have been studying and experimenting with planning as applied to land use and rural living ever since the Worcester County project was started in 1937. Much of the experimental effort has been more or less joint between them. The senior author has been stimulated greatly in this and learned a great deal from his close association with Harvard colleagues in the Seminar in Land Use and Conservation and from the succession of graduate students in this Seminar. These men have mostly been on annual leave from the agencies named in the last chapter. The junior author participated in this Seminar for several years, and in 1955 put together some of the results of his study and thinking in a thesis "The Evolution of Rural Planning."

In these circumstances, the authors have felt an obligation not to stop with the reporting of the Worcester County rural planning experience, but to relate this to other rural planning experience and with planning theory and practice in general. This takes the form in the pages following of a review and analysis of rural planning procedure, that is, of the means for developing, integrating, and coordinating rural policies and programs. These means have not been dreamed up by the authors or by the members of the Seminar; they have evolved through the evolutionary process of developing rural policies, plans, and programs in the country at large during the past hundred years and especially during the last twenty-five years. They have been tested more or less in Worcester County in the period under review, but the testing began long before and has been undertaken in other places, especially in the County Land-Use Planning movement reported in Chapter 8.

WHAT IS PLANNING?

Let us first make sure that all of us conceive of planning in the same way. Planning is in essence the preparation for decision-making. In a democratic society like ours, decision-making is basically done by the people. But if the decisions of the people are to be wise, they must be founded on a good understanding of the relevant facts and factors in the situation. The planning process assembles these facts and analyzes them to bring out the relationships among them. This tells us what the situation is and how it came to be what it is. But it does not tell us how to change it, because before that can be done we need to make up our minds as to where we want to go, as to what we want the changed situation to be like. Experience has taught that the best procedure for this is to determine from our analysis of the facts and relationships how different possible courses of action will work out, that is, what results will follow from them. The name that is coming to be applied to these different possible courses of action is *alternatives.* Once these are clearly delineated — and understood, the citizens in a democratic society are in a position to make the wise decisions that are necessary.

It is clear now that there are really two major parts to this preparation for decision-making, or planning. The first is assembling the facts, analyzing them, and stating the alternatives and results. This is *research.* The other part is making the foregoing known to and understood by the decision-makers. This is *education.*

It will also be evident, from the planning outlined in Chapters 9 to 20, that the operating units being planned can cover a wide range: individual farms or business firms or forest holdings; publicly owned forests or other enterprises; households or families; social groups, like parent-teachers associations; communities; sub-area units; soil conservation districts; watersheds; milksheds; political units like towns, counties, states, and nations; and so on. An important distinction is between planning done *with* the individual or group or other unit concerned, and planning done *for* any of these. The farm planning outlined in this book has been largely *with* the farm family; the nonfarm forest-holding planning very largely *for* rather than *with* the owners of the land — it simply was not practical for those who were doing the planning in this case to get together with the numerous and scattered owners. The community planning of the Country Life Committees was both with and for, but much of it was rather superficial, for the simple reason that personnel was not available to conduct the research and education necessary for wise decisions. The more closely associated the decision-makers can be with the planning operations, the better prepared they will be to make the decisions.

The word planning fell into disrepute in the United States during the 1940's. It became associated with totalitarian procedures and was vigorously condemned as anti-democratic. Obviously the planning by totalitarian governments was not with the citizens. Neither was it for them as they saw their interests. Nor were they given any choice in the decisions. Such planning has nothing in common with the planning we are considering here.

Nevertheless, there is a chance of confusing the two when some political unit or government agency sets up a planning board or staff. Not only may this staff go about its task with very little association with those who are going to be affected by the decisions made, but it may make definite recommendations to the executive who then accepts or rejects them after little if any consultation with those concerned. It is important on all occasions to guard against such conduct of planning and thus prevent the spread of confusion as to the role of planning in our society. The condemnation of planning becomes ominous and a critical threat to democratic institutional procedures. It is especially alarming in an age when the tempo and need for decision-making is increasing along with our rapidly accumulating knowledge of the arts and sciences.

Highly pertinent in this connection was the attempt at planning, outlined in Chapter 8, in the agricultural sector of our economy under the leadership of the United States Department of Agriculture and the Land Grant College system under the Mount Weather Agreement from 1938 to 1942. The Agreement evolved in response to the many problems arising from the rapidly mushrooming development of institutional means to deal with the maladjustments of the agricultural economy during the preceding twenty-five years. Our people were scarcely ready for such an ambitious undertaking at that time. Nor were the departments and agencies of government that were involved. An evolutionary approach would have been better. Yet, as stated earlier, except for the intervention of the war, those involved in the program might well have learned enough about planning just by doing it to have kept the program in slow evolution over the years since. If this could have happened, our agricultural people and institutions would be doing a much better job than they are doing now with their newly conceived undertakings called by such names as "farm and home planning" and "rural development."

Three other terms also need to be clearly understood in this connection, *policies, plans,* and *programs.* Policies may be defined as objectives, ends, or goals. Plans represent the means for carrying out policies. Programs set forth the means to bring plans to fruition. Decisions have to be made about all three of these. After the decisions as to program comes operation, or the actual execution of the program, then, checking of performance and evaluation, and then re-planning, re-decision-making, and so forth.

A suitable term for all of these put together, the planning, the decision-making, the operation, the evaluation, and so on, is difficult to find for society in general. For private business, *entrepreneurship* is the term used. Probably *management* or *administration* are safer terms to use in the present context.

Our concern here, however, is with the planning only. This involves, as already explained, not only assembly and analysis of the facts and factors, or appraisal of the means, but also the developing of the alternative policies, the alternative plans, and the alternative programs, as a basis for the decisions with respect to each.

In order to avoid confusion in planning, *means* and *ends* must be clearly distinguished. The ends are results or objectives that one seeks to achieve; the means are the resources and ways of using them to attain the ends. Both involve both economic and noneconomic value judgments. Noneconomic value judgments derive from morals, ethics, politics, religious beliefs, and a wide array of intangible considerations. Economic value judgments may be either monetary or nonmonetary in nature. Often the different economic effects of alternative means have to be weighed and balanced against each other and evaluated. These also constitute economic value judgments. Economists, as economists, engaged in education (or planning) should present facts and information and propose alternative means and evaluate them only in terms of economic value judgments. They should make crystal clear that they recognize the existence and importance of noneconomic factors and even list and describe them, but they should scrupulously avoid any quantitative evaluation of them. The final choice of means rests with and represents the decisions of the people or their representatives and they will introduce the noneconomic factors into their value judgments.

If planning is carried on efficiently and effectively with due observance of recognized methods of research, teaching, and democratic procedures, the result will be the attainment of certain intermediate ends (which are, in essence, procedural means) such as (1) the *coordination* of institutional organization and administrative procedure, (2) the *integration* of policies, plans, and programs, and (3) the adaptation of national policies, plans and programs to local conditions. Thus the intermediate end of planning becomes an intermediate means resulting in or leading to the following more ultimate ends: (1) a more literate, objective, tolerant, and intelligent society, (2) a strengthening of the democratic system as a mode of social being, and (3) greater efficiency in the satisfaction of human wants.

These ends, in turn, constitute the means for attaining the ultimate ends which have to do with human satisfaction and the well-being of the individual.

PLANNING PROCEDURE

In the following will be spelled out point by point some of the details of the planning process that are significant for rural planning.

1. In the policy, plan, and program phases of the planning process, it is necessary not only to delineate the alternatives clearly, but also to appraise and estimate the probable outcome or results or effects of each. These results or effects should be stated in physical and economic terms, quantitatively so far as possible. Other associated effects can be stated only qualitatively at the best.

2. In each of these phases, it will be desirable to select the most likely set of alternatives to be considered by the decision-makers. The range of alternatives selected should be realistic and within the realm of possibilities as conditioned by (1) the relevant facts in the situation, (2) the ends, and (3) their adaptability to feasible plans and programs.

3. In the program phase of the planning, the statements of alternatives should go so far as to set forth what is to be done, who is to do it, when it is to be done, and in what order it is to be done.

4. Even though there exists a functional distinction between the four phases of management or administration — planning, decision-making, execution, and evaluation — these functions are integrated in the case of the small private firm. With all public and the larger private operational units these functions are likely to be separated — and wisely so.

5. As already stated, the more actively the decision-maker (or makers) can actually participate in the planning process, the better prepared he is to make sound decisions. It follows therefore that —

a. In the case of a small operating unit or firm, such as a farm, the entrepreneur first acquires the skill of planning his own business with the *aid* of a planning specialist rather than by having the planning specialist do the planning *for* him.

b. In the case of group units, the more nearly planning can be done by the people working *with the aid* of planning specialists rather than *by* planning specialists working *for* the people, the more nearly perfection is approached in observing and using democratic principles.

Budgetary procedure provides the tools of economic analysis to determine the use of resources for optimum economic returns. Hence, it is the recognized technique for making economic analyses within the social framework of planning procedure. It brings together and tests the knowledge and thinking from all fields of the arts and sciences, so that the individual firm or operating unit, be it a farm, or a community, or a region, or an industry, is considered as a unit.

6. The most feasible plans and programs for a group or area as a whole can be determined only by analyzing all or a sample of the individual operating units of an area by the budgetary or projection method to determine the adjustments most needed for optimum returns from the group or area as a whole.

7. The principles of planning analysis apply equally well to the management of the individual firm or to the group operational unit.

8. Since planning *is* essentially a learning process, recognized techniques for learning must be observed. These include techniques for stimulating, motivating, and deliberating (the development and adoption of alternative choices).

9. The teaching is consonant with democratic planning procedure in that the teacher stimulates the learner to do his own thinking — make his own decisions — rather than having the teacher decide himself what constitutes the truth, making the decisions himself and then giving the answers to the learner to memorize. (The latter is *authoritative* procedure.)

10. The *unity* teaching approach is consonant with democratic planning procedure. Here the learner considers the "whole" first (the budgetary approach) and then is better equipped to "go after what he wants" — the parts — and understand their relationship with each other. The opposite to this is the *morselization* approach whereby the learner considers the parts, associating them with past behavior and not in relationship with each other. This encourages static behavior.

11. Planning group leaders should help planning groups to:

a. organize themselves into groups;
b. decide and periodically re-decide the rules of their own conduct;
c. develop an atmosphere that is free, permissive, and encourages all to contribute;
d. develop an attitude of critical objectivity that will encourage discussion on a high quality level;
e. develop ways of continuous evaluation of both group product and group process.

12. Planning groups must be *representative* — that is, they should meet the rigorous requirements of geographical distribution, functional interests, and income classification.

13. Planning groups should recognize that they are created by the people, as *limited instruments* of group activity, and exist only by the *consent* of the *people* and are therefore *accountable and responsible* to the people. They must observe at all times the procedural means for preserving these democratic principles, namely, popular elections, petitions, initiatives, referendums, and recalls.

14. Every organization must have a *line organization* in order to execute decisions, to get things done. But knowledge and understanding (planning) must precede decision-making. This cannot be done by the *line*. It must be done by a *staff* or planning group. Staff planning services, whether formally organized or not, are bound to grow up in every organization. Their formal organization is necessary, however, if the most efficient forms of concerted human effort are to be achieved.

15. A staff planning service should be separate but should parallel the line organization. This provides the free interchange of knowledge and ideas horizontally at each level and vertically between levels.

16. The staff planning function must be regarded as continuous because of the dynamic nature of the society in which we live.

17. Free and unhampered communication is an extremely necessary phase of administration if it is to observe democratic principles. The administrator should:

a. secure appropriate clearance with all who are concerned before decisions are made: and
b. make the decisions known immediately to all who are involved.

An efficient staff organization facilitates free intercommunication.

ORGANIZATION FOR RURAL PLANNING

In this section, the authors are going to be so bold as to outline the structure and functioning of a potential nationwide rural planning organization.

A. The first major feature such an organization must have is an area-unit structure, and the area units should be political governmental operating units — the federal, state, county, and minor civil divisions. All space is included within their boundaries and all the area within a political unit is owned either privately or publicly.

The privately owned units are subject to the decision-making of their owners, which of course calls for planning in preparation for the decision-making. Owner decision-making is affected in part by the environment created by the policies, plans, and programs of the decision-makers of the overlapping governmental units of whose areas they are a part. The objective then is to create policies, plans, and programs which are unified and noncontradictory when they reach the owner decision-maker even though they come from various political jurisdictions and public agencies representing overlapping areas, levels, and functions.

Since the political divisions of government are all-inclusive spatially, and since they provide the basis for hierarchical organization at the varying necessary levels of administration, they then become the logical basis for organization in order to perform the planning function for the rural interests of the country. From this standpoint the *county* is the key unit in such a rural planning structure.

Comprehensive county rural planning includes the facilities for reconciling and consolidating the policies, plans, and programs of the smaller local political units into the larger units at state and national levels. It thus provides the means for re-combining smaller political units into various patterns to meet the special planning needs of such varied units as type-of-farming areas, watersheds, milksheds, drainage districts, reclamation districts, and the like.

But although comprehensive county rural planning as proposed herein would be very much worthwhile as a means of integrating and coordinating activities horizontally at the county level and vertically down to the community and neighborhood levels, it cannot discharge its full potential usefulness unless it is envisioned as a part of a nationwide system for comprehensive rural planning. This is so, for as indicated in Chapter 21, many of the rural public programs emanate from state and national levels.

B. The second major feature of such an area-structured organization must be a setup of rural planning committees at the town, county, state, and national levels with vertical communications up and down, and made up of members representing all appropriate agricultural and nonagricultural public agencies and all agricultural and nonagricultural organizations whose interests merit their inclusion on these committees. Their activities are concerned only with planning. They develop information, prepare suggested policies, plans, and programs and submit them, vertically or horizontally, to the appropriate decision-makers. These committees are the *staff* for the United States Department of Agriculture and all other agencies and organizations that are interested in rural affairs and seek collaboration with the planning setup. Their function is solely research and education (advisory).

C. The third major requirement of such an organization is that its planning committees must be assisted by planning service groups at each level. The personnel of these groups should consist of appropriate research and extension workers from the United States Department of Agriculture and the Land-Grant College system, working closely with personnel from other agencies. In some counties or other governmental units, the chairmanship of these planning service groups may be taken by local workers from other agencies within the Department of Agriculture that have strong programs under way. But, however chairmaned, any vertical communication should be with the planning service groups above and below and not through the line organization of other agencies.

The planning service at the top of the Secretary of Agriculture's office would be part of the Secretary's staff organization. It would be manned largely by personnel from the Federal Extension Service and the Agricultural Research Service. At the State level, a representative of the extension director would serve as executive secretary of the planning committee, and at the county level this function would be performed by the county agricultural agent. State experiment station personnel at these two levels would be drawn upon as needed. Extension and research personnel would not be voting members of the planning committees. This would be an entirely logical arrangement, since, as we have already seen, planning is a most effective educational technique. This would give the extension field agents another educational medium which would not only yield educational dividends but contribute to the coordination, integration, and adaptation of rural programs. And this would be done strictly within the province of research and education, for the planning committees would only develop the alternatives and pass them along as suggestions.

The personnel of the planning service groups at the different levels would need to be planning and research technicians especially qualified to render the kind of service needed, and in some measure specially trained for it. They would ordinarily be drawn from the extension and research branches of the U.S.D.A. and Land-Grant institutions, and in all cases included in these at the federal, state, and lower levels.

The farmer and other members of rural planning committees can contribute valuable information from their practical knowledge of conditions in their communities and counties and from their experience as farmers. Agency members can contribute basic information relative to their agencies and programs. However, the development of sound, wise rural plans requires that the data upon which planning committees base their plans be neither limited to the knowledge possessed by the farmers and agency committee members nor to the information available at the time a committee begins its analysis. The county rural planning committees need the professional services of research technicians to increase their fund of accurate, scientific knowledge of the problems confronting them. Although research workers may work closely with planning committees, they are not considered voting members of the committee.

It is apparent that the planning technician needs to be a wise, vigorous and alert person, with enthusiasm for planning, and one who can command the confidence of those with whom he works. He needs a knowledge and understanding of much more than the technological aspects of farming. He must have a sense for the economic and social problems confronting rural people. And he needs a special understanding of the interrelationships among the individuals, groups, and agencies involved. All this requires that he be, first, carefully selected; second, especially prepared for his job; and third, that he receive much on-the-job guidance in his first years.

D. Fourth is the matter of representation on the planning committees. County rural planning committees are built on the foundation of community or town committees (discussed in Chapter 20). These local committees are made up of representatives from appropriate groups within the community, including local government and democratically selected representatives from each of the natural neighborhoods within the town or community. Membership on the county committee in turn includes representatives selected in a democratic manner from each of the community committees.

Then, along with these representatives are those on the committee who represent groups, as follows:

Public Agencies — It is a part of the theory of county rural planning that farmers, equipped with practical experience and first-hand knowledge of their immediate problems, can assist administrators and agricultural technicians charged with the responsibility of operating administrative machinery devised to cope with rural problems. It is also part of the theory that administrators and trained agricultural technicians can assist farmers in analyzing the causes of their difficulties and in finding the proper type of remedial procedures to be followed by individuals, groups, or by government agencies. County rural planning committees, it is believed, can achieve a workable fusion between the expression of local needs and experience and the guidance of technical analysis and advice. Planning is done not by the experts alone and not by laymen alone but by representatives of both working together.

Farm Organizations — Farm organizations and groups of similar nature must be represented on the county rural planning committee. These organizations play an important part in our democracy by providing their members with another political avenue for exercising their rights and privileges of consent and control. They must be included in the planning process; otherwise they are denied one of their important democratic prerogatives. Although any representative of an organization brings to the committee the viewpoints of the group he represents, county rural planning committees need not fear domination by particularized interests, for the committee membership is diluted to the point where no one organization can dominate the thinking of the committee. Furthermore, an efficient committee observes the recognized principles of group dynamics in its conduct, and each individual in seeking common objectives becomes absorbed into the group and thus loses his identity as an individual.

Local Government — Obviously problems having to do with rural areas and the people in them cannot be separated from the nonrural interests. They are necessarily related to the more general and the specific problems that are of first-hand interest to the local governments. County rural planning committees immediately become involved in questions relating to land valuation, assessments, distribution of taxes, tax delinquency, local water control, roads, educational facilities, local health protection, recreation facilities, and so on.

Necessary adjustments in these fields may depend entirely upon local government action, or may require cooperation between local government agencies and state or federal agencies. Since one of the basic objectives of planning is to improve coordination and integration of local, state, and federal activities (vertically and horizontally), it is essential that local governmental agencies be represented on the county and community rural planning committees.

Urban Groups — County rural planning committees starting with problems of direct and immediate interest to rural people inevitably soon find themselves confronted with problems of more general interest. Rural planning by farmers alone would assume *that urban interests are insignificant* or that there is no relationship between rural and urban affairs; but such is not the case. The American farmer lives in an "urban" community. Hence, there should be systematic representation of nonagricultural interests on rural planning committees. Such representation may commonly include Chamber of Commerce representatives, bankers, businessmen (particularly those interested in processing or marketing farm products), lawyers, ministers, and newspaper editors.

TWO BASIC PROCEDURES

It is hardly safe to end our statement of rural planning without being somewhat more specific about two of its basic procedures, *area mapping* and *operating unit* planning.

Area Mapping — There is no need to explain what area mapping is — Chapters 9 to 17 have furnished abundant examples of it. What is needed is to clarify its objectives and its place in the planning process. Area mapping serves as a device for dealing with masses of facts and information in the same manner that statistical procedure serves the statistician in digesting, summarizing, and manipulating masses of data. It serves as a means for the systematic identification, sorting, grouping, simplification, summarization, and localization of heterogeneous factual information, opinions, conclusions, and recommendations. It enables committees to isolate by areas particular factors for purposes of comparison with similar factors in a broader geographic setting, thus comparing similarities and differences as they exist in different parts of the state, county, or community. It provides a means whereby planning discussions can be oriented and focused upon situations where they actually exist, thereby avoiding abstractions. In other words, it facilitates mutual understanding by avoiding confusion in the process of group planning.

The area mapping procedure is sometimes criticized as abstract and unrelated to situations familiar to the local people. It is said that planning must start at the place where people are in their thinking and experiences — that is, with pertinent questions or needs that are readily recognized and understood by rural people. But it is possible to gain the interest and understanding of lay planning committee members without sacrificing a scientific planning analysis approach.

This can be accomplished at the start by spending a limited amount of time on the needs, scope, and objectives of planning through properly stimulated discussion, whereby the members themselves develop the needs for planning and decide what should be accomplished. This is then followed immediately by having the committee discuss, identify, and list the opportunities (problems) for improvement. At this stage, each "problem" will tend to be identified and associated with certain areas. The causal factors will be identified for each in its area surroundings, and their interrelationships considered.

Rural planning areas are usually established on the basis of one of three criteria, namely, physical features, present land use, and existing land-use problems. The third of these, it will be apparent now, is the one that meets the needs of planning in its final stage.

Operating-Unit Planning — We first need to make sure that the difference between piecemeal planning and planning for the whole farm as a unit is fully understood. The first is limited to plans for a part of the farm organization or operation, perhaps to a single field at a time or to the farm woodlot, or to a single operation like purchasing and fattening feeder cattle. The second works out the effects of any proposed adjustment on the whole farm business, and commonly combines a set of related adjustments, such as improved pasture and forage production and keeping more livestock together with the needed equipment and buildings. Such whole-unit planning also frequently includes the setting up of full budgets of receipts, expenditures, and net incomes for possible alternative farm organizations. There is room for both piecemeal and whole-unit planning in our educational program. For example, the Soil Conservation Service program often needs to include preliminary widespread promotion of single practices, and can use conservation plans for single fields, pastures, or woodlots, along with its so-called "complete" farm plans as its final conservation objective for each farm. Its present three-stage procedure is essentially on this basis. Actually, no one of the Federal action agencies is in a position to do, unaided, a full job of whole-unit farm planning.

The nearest that any Federal agency comes to it is the Farmers' Home Administration with its plans for farms purchased by tenants or farms to be enlarged or developed to make them into economic units. The FHA, however, lacks two things needed to do such planning as well as could be, namely, much of the basic knowledge and understanding of farm organization and technology that is possessed by the staffs of the agricultural colleges and experiment stations, and the knowledge and skills needed for conservation planning and possessed by the S.C.S. technicians. The Agricultural Extension Service is likely to have more nearly all the knowledge and skills needed than any one of the federal agencies; but it lacks the resources and personnel required to furnish more than a very miner fraction of the planning guidance and assistance needed.

The simplest solution to this problem would seem to many extensioners to be simply to provide the extension services with the resources and personnel to do the whole job. But one might as well be realistic on this subject. It should be evident that Congress is going to continue the ACP payments for conservation practices. It is equally evident that it is going to continue the Soil Conservation district service to farmers. The direction in which we should be working is a harmonious coordination of the undertakings of the several federal agencies, and the surest way to achieve this is to have all of them contributing their parts to carrying out common whole-unit farm and other operating unit plans, and accompanying county land-use plans. On this basis all the resources and personnel needed will be available for good progress toward the goal of having a whole-unit plan for every farm and other operating unit in each county.

Local men and women trained in the use of budgetary procedure on individual farms will be useful members on rural planning committees in developing plans for other types of operating units which will eventually add up to plans for the county as a unit. Furthermore, valuable information on needed adjustments will come from individual operating unit planning that can be applied by the planning committees in developing alternative group proposals.

To supplement this work, the experiment station farm management research workers should carefully select a set of "model-type farms," that is, farms that are most nearly representative as to land, types of farming, size, and tenure for the farms of the county, and make a careful budgeting analysis of them. Since planning is a continuous process, they need also to estimate from year to year the probable effects of changing prices and cost-rates, changing acreage and marketing conditions, new developments in technology, and the like, on some at least of these farms, and to supply the results to the planning committees as well as to the farming public in general.

How much of an undertaking will such a rural planning program be? Organized and serviced as here outlined, with its county committees (including sub-committees) and community committees, it will ordinarily engage approximately 10 percent of the farm people in planning at any one time. Thus with a reasonable turnover in committees, all of each generation of rural people could have an opportunity to serve at some time on a planning committee. The community committees should hold at least one public meeting each year and thus through these community meetings potentially every rural family could be reached at least once a year. Hence, county rural planning potentially would provide many people (the decision-makers) with the opportunity to participate in the planning process and thus offer an effective and broad medium for conducting educational work, since each person who participated in some phase of the planning process would undergo an educational experience of the highest order.

As for the staff to service such committees, in a county such as Worcester, two planning technicians would be needed. One of these would work with the managers of individual operating units (farm and home planning). The other would service the planning committees in a manner here described.

Under present price levels such a staff would cost, say, $20,000 annually. This is less than 0.5 percent of the gross income from the agricultural industry of Worcester County. Obviously it would be unfair to charge this all to agriculture, for a large part of the income in rural areas comes from other occupations. Progressive corporate enterprises today maintain planning staffs that cost several times this $20,000. They are convinced that planning "pays." It could be that the rural interests of Worcester County, taken as a unit, have even greater opportunities for returns from a progressive, comprehensive, county rural planning committee organization.

Index